Harvey A. Bender

INTERNATIONAL SERIES OF MONOGRAPHS ON
PURE AND APPLIED BIOLOGY

Division: **ZOOLOGY**

GENERAL EDITORS: J. E. HARRIS AND E. W. YEMM

VOLUME 2

MORPHOGENESIS:
THE ANALYSIS OF
MOLLUSCAN DEVELOPMENT

MORPHOGENESIS:
THE ANALYSIS OF
MOLLUSCAN DEVELOPMENT

by

CHR. P. RAVEN

Professor of Zoology in the
University of Utrecht

PERGAMON PRESS

NEW YORK · LONDON
PARIS · LOS ANGELES
1958

PERGAMON PRESS INC.
122 East 55th Street, New York 22, N.Y.
10638 South Wilton Place, Los Angeles 47, California

PERGAMON PRESS LTD.
4 and 5 Fitzroy Square, London W.1

PERGAMON PRESS S.A.R.L.
24 Rue des Écoles, Paris V^e

Library of Congress Card Number 57–14446

PRINTED IN GREAT BRITAIN BY
ROBERT CUNNINGHAM AND SONS LTD., ALVA

Contents

Preface

THIS book has arisen from a series of lectures that the author gave in the years 1954-1956 for advanced biology students of the University of Utrecht. It soon became clear that the not inconsiderable amount of time and labour invested in collecting and working-through the relevant literature, might be made profitable to a wider circle.

The ever-rising flood of publications makes it a hard task for the expert to keep abreast of his own specialism; for the outsider in a certain field it has become impossible altogether. Science threatens to fall apart into innumerable super-specialisms. Under these circumstances, it appears that it is up to the specialist from time to time to draw up the balance-sheet of his own field of activity, in order to make clear to his fellow-scientists where we are standing, what has been accomplished up to the present, and which are the problems to be tackled in the immediate future.

A survey of the present state of affairs in the field of experimental embryology can be established in different ways. It may be centred around certain general problems, which are illustrated by drawing one's examples freely from all groups of the animal kingdom. In this way it is possible to draw in broad outline the general trends and laws of animal development, as far as present knowledge enables one to see them clearly.

This is the usual procedure, and it is a very valuable one, too. But it has some drawbacks, which make it desirable to approach the matter also in another way. There is the danger of unfounded generalization which is always imminent in this method of approach. Moreover, it is hardly possible to be exhaustive in this kind of survey, so that certain new data, the importance of which has not yet been generally recognized, may be easily overlooked. Finally, it is practically impossible to include an extensive survey of normal development which, however, must of necessity form the foundation on which all causal analysis must be based.

Therefore, it is important that such reviews of a comprehensive nature are supplemented with monographs restricting themselves to one branch of the animal kingdom only. Here the causal analysis of the experimental data can be preceded by a detailed description of the phenomena of normal development, so that the problems can be formulated with greater accuracy, and the peculiarities of the group can be taken into account. Examples of this kind are v. UBISCH's review papers on the development of the sea urchins and the Monascidia, respectively (*Verhandl. Kon. Ned. Akad. v. Wetensch. Amsterdam, Afd. Natuurk.* (II), **47**, 1950; (II) **49**, 1952). The present book also belongs to this category.

In writing it, I have tried to reflect as accurately as possible the present state of our knowledge with respect to molluscan development, whereby the literature up to about the middle of 1956 could be taken into account. I have not restricted myself to the mere facts, however, but wherever possible I have mentioned existing hypotheses or tried to frame new ones, in order, on the one hand, to explain the facts, and, on the other hand, to permit the formulation of new questions and the design of new experiments. I have often marshalled the facts in such a way that they might serve to illustrate the leading ideas. I realize that this lends a certain touch of subjectivity to the exposition. But in my opinion an author has a right to be subjective, as long as he does not strain the objectivity of the factual data.

Since my main interest is centred on the causal analysis of morphogenesis, the description of normal development has been subordinated to this purpose. Comparative embryological points of view have hardly been taken into consideration, but the cytological and cytochemical aspects of development have been especially emphasized. On the other hand, purely biochemical investigations, unless they had a direct bearing on morphogenesis, have also been left out.

It has not been my aim to give a complete bibliography of molluscan development. Papers of a descriptive nature have only been explicitly mentioned when necessary. But I have tried to include the literature on cytochemical and experimental embryological investigations of the last half century as completely as possible.

As regards taxonomy, as a rule only generic names have been mentioned, unless specific differences might be important in the context. The taxonomic names used by the authors have as a rule been taken over as such; no attempts have been made to bring them into harmony with the present state of nomenclature. Only in very obvious cases (*Lymnaeus* – *Lymnaea* – *Limnaea*; *Paludina* – *Vivipara* – *Viparus*; *Bythinia* – *Bithynia*) I have sometimes departed from this rule.

I am greatly indebted to many colleagues for their kind permission to make use of figures copied from their papers. To the Scientific Committee of the Zoological Society of London my thanks are due for the same reason.

CHR. P. RAVEN

Utrecht, December 1956

CHAPTER I

Oogenesis

1. The ripe egg

THE egg cells of most molluscs are spherical. The animal and vegetative sides are often clearly indicated. As a rule, the uncleaved egg is radially symmetrical around the main axis running through the animal and the vegetative pole.

This description holds also for some cephalopods (*Sepia*). In most cephalopods, however, the eggs are oblong, the long axis corresponding to the main axis of the egg cell. Moreover, e.g. in *Loligo*, the eggs are bilaterally symmetrical, one of the sides being flattened. Later, this flattened side becomes the hind-part of the embryo, the animal pole corresponding to its dorsal side.

The size of the ripe egg cells differs very much. To mention some examples: the egg diameter in *Mytilus edulis* is about 60μ; in *Paludina* 18μ, *Limnaea stagnalis* 120μ, *Littorina littorea* 130μ, *Litt. obtusata* and *rudis* 200μ, *Sycotypus canalliculatus* 1 mm, *Fulgur carica* 1·7 mm; *Argonauta* 1·3 mm, *Eledone* 8-15 mm, *Nautilus* 40-50 mm.

There is also a great diversity in yolk content. In general, the eggs of Lamellibranchiata, Polyplacophora and Solenoconcha are poor in yolk. In Gastropoda, yolk content differs much: little yolk e.g. in *Paludina*, much in *Nassa*, *Fulgur*, *Purpura*, *Buccinum*, *Murex*. The same holds for Cephalopoda, where yolk content increases according to the series *Argonauta<Octopus*, *Loligo<Sepia<Eledone<Nautilus*. In general, increase in egg size and in yolk content go hand in hand.

The superficial part of the egg cell is formed by a thin yolk-free ectoplasmic layer. Local thickenings of this layer may occur near the animal and vegetative poles, forming the so-called *pole plasms*. Animal pole plasms have been described, e.g. in *Cumingia*, *Dentalium*, *Crepidula*, *Fulgur*, *Physa*, *Planorbis*, *Limnaea* and *Limax*; vegetative pole plasms in *Cumingia*, *Dentalium* and *Limnaea*. It must be emphasized, however, that these pole plasms of different species differ greatly as to their size, composition and yolk content. It is not permissible, therefore, to consider them as homologous cytoplasmic differentiations without further proof; the term 'pole plasm' has only a descriptive meaning. In this sense, the 'germinal disc' of cytoplasm at the animal pole of the ripe cephalopod egg may also be called an animal pole plasm.

1

The egg cells may be surrounded by three kinds of membranes:

(1) *Primary egg membrane* or *vitelline membrane*. This is secreted in the ovary by the egg cell itself. In many cases (e.g. most Lamellibranchiata) it is the only egg membrane. Often it is very thin and hardly visible. There are many reports in literature of molluscan eggs being laid without a vitelline membrane (e.g. cephalopods); it is probable, however, that in these cases the extremely thin membrane has been overlooked. Moreover, in some cases the vitelline membrane is thrown off very soon after laying, e.g. *Mytilus, Dreissensia, Ostrea, Dentalium*. Often there is a small opening in the membrane; in Lamellibranchiata and Gastropoda this is always situated at the vegetative pole. It is called a *micropyle*. The use of this term does not imply, however, that it is used by the fertilizing sperm as a port of entrance; this is not the case, as a rule. Rather, this so-called micropyle represents a scar of the connecting stalk by which the egg cell has been attached to the ovary.

(2) *Secondary egg membrane* or *chorion*, formed in the ovary by the follicle cells surrounding the egg. It may be a thick and firm membrane, as in the Polyplacophora, where its outer side is covered with numerous warts or spines. In the cephalopods, the chorion is thickened at the animal pole, and pierced by a funnel-shaped hole, representing a true micropyle.

(3) *Tertiary egg membranes*, formed by the wall of the oviduct. They are highly variable in shape and composition. Horny egg-shells are found, e.g. in *Sepia*; calcareous shells in many land pulmonates (*Helix*); various kinds of egg masses, egg ribbons and cocoons, in which a certain number of egg cells, varying from a few to many thousands, are embedded in a common jelly-mass, are found in other gastropods.

2. Oogenesis

In molluscs various types of egg formation in the ovary occur.

In the Lamellibranchiata and Solenoconcha, egg formation is of the 'solitary' type, according to the classification by KORSCHELT and HEIDER (1902). We may describe as an example the process in *Cyclas*, as observed by STAUFFACHER (1894).

In *Cyclas*, the wall of the ovary consists of a regular columnar epithelium. Single cells of this *germinal epithelium* round off and change into *oogonia* with a large spherical nucleus with large nucleolus, and a thin layer of cytoplasm. Then they begin to grow, and protrude into the central cavity of the ovary; their connection with the basal membrane of the ovarian wall is narrowed to a slender stalk. On the surface of that part of the cell that projects freely into the cavity a vitelline membrane is formed, presumably as a reaction of the cell surface to the contact with the medium. In the stalk an accumulation of dark granules (mitochondria, according to Woods, 1932) appears, reaching towards the nucleus which lies at the base of the stalk. This may indicate the food stream entering the growing *oocyte* from the ovarian wall. The nucleolus shows signs of considerable activity, with formation of buds constricted off from the main nucleolus. The adjacent cells of the germinal epithelium lengthen and partly cover the stalk of the oocyte; presumably, they assist in transferring food substances to the latter. (According to Woods (1932) some of these cells are in *Sphaerium* wholly or partly incorporated into the substance of the growing oocyte.) Later, these cells withdraw from the stalk. The oocyte nucleus now moves towards the free end of the cell. Finally, the oocyte is set free into the ovarian cavity; a hole in the vitelline membrane (the so-called micropyle, cf. above p. 2) indicates the place of its last attachment.

The egg stalks, by which the growing oocytes are attached in the ovary, may become very long and slender in certain Lamellibranchiata (e.g. *Scrobicularia*).

In Polyplacophora and Gastropoda, less clearly also in Aplacophora, egg formation is of the 'follicular' type. Fahmy (1949) has described the process in the pulmonate *Eremina*. The undifferentiated germinal epithelium consists here of a continuous layer of flat cells with flat oval nuclei. Differentiation begins with the formation of male germ cells. Then some of the cells of the germinal epithelium differentiate into *nurse cells*. They extend on the inner side of the germinal epithelium, forming a second layer towards the lumen of the ovotestis. Finally the remaining cells of the germinal epithelium form oogonia, which begin their development, therefore, beneath a layer of nurse cells, and remain separated from the lumen by them during the whole period of oogenesis. When the oocyte begins to grow and protrudes into the cavity, the nurse cells form a *follicle* around it. This becomes thinner during growth of the oocyte, and finally disappears just before ovulation.

According to Ancel (1903), the follicle in *Helix* is not formed by the nurse cells, but by indifferent cells of the peripheral layer secondarily surrounding the oocyte. This author first advanced the idea that the differentiation of the germinal epithelium cells into either male or female germ cells is dependent on the absence or presence, respectively, of differentiated nurse cells at that time.

This idea was somewhat modified by Buresch (1911). Male and female germ cells develop in *Helix* side by side in the same acinus of the ovotestis, but the developing oocytes lie always near one or more nurse cells. Development in the male or female direction depends on the conditions of nutrition of the indifferent germ cell. The follicle is at first formed by the cytoplasm of the adjacent nurse cells; other cells from the germinal epithelium, also differentiating into nurse cells, may later be added.

In *Cavolinia*, different relationships were found by VITAGLIANO (1950). Here the germ cells develop as far as the pachytene stage in the region close to the protogonial zone of the gonad. From this stage onwards they may either remain adjacent to those nurse cells, highly charged with ribonucleic acid, lying in the male region of the gonad, in which case they develop into spermatocytes; or they migrate towards the centre of the gonad, where the nurse cells contain little RNA; in this case they become oocytes. Only during the last stage of their development (advanced vitellogenesis), do the oocytes pass into regions where the nurse cells are rich in RNA. Then meiosis continues. It is suggested that the sexual differentiation of the germ cells is determined by their spatial relationships to the two kinds of nurse cells, and that the process of meiosis is dependent on the intense production of RNA by the nurse cells.

In *Limnaea* (BRETSCHNEIDER and RAVEN, 1951) the egg cells develop likewise between the connective tissue capsule of the gonad and a layer of epithelium cells. They pass first through a period of amoeboid motility, during which they disperse over the acini. Then they become sedentary, begin to grow and a follicle forms around their protruding part in the same way as in *Eremina*, while the basal part of the oocyte remains in contact with the connective tissue layer (Fig. 6). The nucleus now takes an eccentric position in the apical half of the oocyte. After the growth period of the oocyte has come to an end, there is a rest phase of variable duration; then the follicle is autolysed and ovulation takes place.

The cytological changes taking place during oogenesis in the egg cells of the Polyplacophora have been described by GABE and PRENANT (1949). The primordial oocyte in the germinal epithelium has a big nucleus and a very thin layer of cytoplasm, which shows but little basophily. Later, a cap of basophil substance is formed against one side of the nucleus. It extends rapidly through the cell, and soon the whole cytoplasm is strongly basophil. With further growth the cytoplasm becomes heterogeneous; clear *areolae* appear, first in the neighbourhood of the stalk, and rapidly increase in number until the whole cytoplasm is filled with them. Then yolk formation begins in contact with the areolae; at the same time, the basophily of the cytoplasm decreases strongly. Finally the full-grown oocyte is completely filled with yolk.

Egg formation in cephalopods is also of the follicular type. In connection with the large size of the ripe egg, however, it exhibits the peculiarity that the follicle shows a temporary folding (Ussow, 1881; VIALLETON, 1888). The early oocytes are surrounded by one layer of flat follicle cells; later, these cells become columnar and form the *membrana granulosa*. This is surrounded by a second layer of connective tissue cells, the *theca*. In the meantime, the egg has protruded from the surface of the ovary, the theca forming a connecting stalk, in which blood vessels develop. Then the granulosa begins to fold inwards; both transverse and longitudinal folds are formed, together forming a reticulate pattern. Blood vessels lie in the folds. Yolk is secreted by the granulosa. It accumulates especially on the side of the stalk, pushing the cytoplasm with the germinal vesicle towards the free end of the cell, where the *germinal disc* is formed in this way. However, a very thin ectoplasmic lamella remains around the whole periphery of the yolk. When the oocyte has reached its final size, a chorion is formed beneath the granulosa. It is thickened at the free pole, where a lens-shaped thickening of the theca protruding into the granulosa prepares the formation of the micropyle. Then the folds of the granulosa disappear, and ovulation takes place through rupture of the follicle.

Presumably in all molluscs the side where the food stream reaches the growing oocyte becomes the vegetative side of the egg. Thus the polarity of the egg appears to be determined by its position in the ovary.

3. The behaviour of various cell components during oogenesis

a. THE NUCLEUS

In the nucleus of the developing egg cell one functional phase is followed by another. During the earlier part of oogenesis, the *generative* function of the nucleus predominates; during the later part, it is the *vegetative* function which especially attracts attention.

The first phase of *premeiotic phenomena* coincides with the very first stages of egg formation: oogonium and early oocyte. It is described by FAHMY (1949) for *Eremina*. The cells of the germinal epithelium have a nucleus containing irregular chromatin granules. At the beginning of female differentiation, a haploid number of double *prochromosomes* is formed by condensation of the chromatin. At the same time a nucleolus appears. The prochromosomes stretch to *leptotene threads*, each prochromosome leaving a globular remnant. The threads unite in pairs to *zygotene bivalents*, and then wind around each other into double *strepsitene spirals*, which are arranged radially around the central nucleolus (Fig. 2a). They shorten to *diplotene bivalents*, arranged peripherally be-

B

neath the nuclear membrane. Then they begin to disperse and lose their basophily.

From this time onwards, hence during the greater part of the growth phase of the oocyte, the nucleoplasm, apart from the nucleolus, is rather homogeneous, and the chromosomes are invisible. This is the vegetative phase, during which the nucleus plays an important part in the metabolic processes accompanying growth and vitellogenesis.

The size of the nucleus increases considerably during oogenesis. In *Limnaea*, from the earliest oocyte to the full-grown egg cell the volume of the nucleus increases 162 times (BRETSCHNEIDER and RAVEN, 1951). However, the growth of the nucleus does not keep pace with that of the egg cell as a whole; its relative volume decreases from 37 to 17 per cent of the egg volume (a similar decrease has been found in *Patella* by RANZOLI, 1953), and the nucleoplasmic ratio (in relation to the cytoplasm without the yolk) from 1 : 1·7 to 1 : 2·4. This latter decrease takes place mainly during the first part of oogenesis, which is followed by a long period of synchronic growth of nucleus and cytoplasm. However, during this phase apparently a periodic swelling and shrinking of the nucleus takes place. The nuclear membrane may be thrown into folds locally (Fig. 1); as a rule, the nucleolus is situated near this region, and an accumulation of Golgi substance is found in the neighbouring cytoplasm (GABE and PRENANT, 1949).

b. THE NUCLEOLUS

The growth of nucleolar substance during oogenesis shows no proportionality to that of the nucleus (e.g. BRETSCHNEIDER and HIRSCH, 1937). In *Patella*, nucleolar growth is at first more rapid than nuclear growth. At a middle phase of oogenesis, the nucleolar substance reaches a maximum. From this time no further increase takes place; towards the end of oogenesis the total nucleolar volume is even diminished. Consequently the nucleolar–nuclear and nucleolar–cytoplasmic ratios are highest in the middle of oogenesis (RANZOLI, 1953).

During the phase of vegetative function of the nucleus, the nucleolus shows signs of intense metabolic activity. This has already been observed by some of the older authors (STAUFFACHER, 1894; OBST, 1899), both in lamellibranchs and gastropods. They have shown that constrictions of the nucleoli and formation of nucleolar buds may occur, and that often the nucleolus exhibits a differentiation into parts with different staining properties (*amphinucleoli*). Similar observations have been made by later authors (e.g. LUDFORD, 1928); finally BRETSCHNEIDER has given a detailed account of these phenomena in *Limnaea* (cf. RAVEN, 1946a; BRETSCHNEIDER and RAVEN, 1951), while SERRA and QUEIROZ LOPES

(1945) independently arrived at similar conclusions with regard to the Helicidae.

The earliest oocyte in *Limnaea* has two nucleoli of unequal size, 4μ and 2μ in diameter, respectively. The smaller one soon disappears. The remaining nucleolus increases in size until about the middle of the

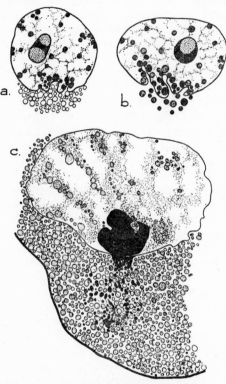

Fig. 1. Nucleolar activity during oogenesis in *Limnaea stagnalis*. Extrusion of formed substances through the nuclear membrane into the cytoplasm.

growth phase of the oocyte, reaching a maximum diameter of about 20μ; then it decreases again. Presumably, however, these changes are not regular, but show considerable fluctuations (similar fluctuations do also occur in *Patella*: RANZOLI, 1953). While the nucleoli of early oocytes are acidophil, during the greater part of the growth phase they have the character of amphinucleoli; finally, towards the end of oogenesis most nucleoli are homogeneously basophil. The metabolic activity of the nucleolus leads to the formation of nucleolar products, which takes place in two ways: (1) by the *intranucleolar* formation of vacuoles in the inner part of the nucleolus, which break through at its surface, and (2) by the appearance of *epinucleolar* buds in the cortical part of the nucleolus, which are then constricted off. While the intranucleolar secretion is probably polyphasic, the epinucleolar product formation, especially when it takes place simultaneously at two or more places of the circumference, leads apparently to irreversible changes of the nucleolus; it is only found towards the end of oogenesis. The formed products, which may be fluid, granular or highly viscous, first pass into the karyolymph, but may then be transferred to the cytoplasm through the nuclear membrane (Fig. 1).

Similar phenomena have been described in *Helix* and *Tachea* by SERRA and QUEIROZ LOPES (1945). The one to four nucleoli of the oogonia are restricted to one (seldom two in *Helix*) during the first part of the growth period, either by dissolution of the supernumerary ones or by fusion. The remaining single nucleolus is situated near the nuclear membrane. It then grows to 50–200 times its original volume. Nucleolar buds are formed on its surface, and nucleolar inclusions appear in its centre. Bud formation is cyclic; on an average, three cycles take place up to the end of oogenesis. The isolated nucleolar buds dissolve in the karyolymph. Their passage through the nuclear membrane into the cytoplasm was not observed.

This remarkable metabolic activity of the nucleolus during molluscan oogenesis has been confirmed by similar observations in Polyplacophora (GABE and PRENANT, 1949), *Dentalium* (ARVY, 1950a), Prosobranchia (FRANC, 1951), *Aeolis* (ARVY, 1950b) and in *Eremina* (FAHMY, 1949); apparently, it forms a common phenomenon in molluscs. FRANC distinguishes three types of nucleoli in Prosobranchia: (1) 'type à pustules' with small disc-like elevations forming on the nucleolar membrane; (2) 'type à vésicules', with one or two concentric vesicles in the nucleolus, and vacuolization of the intermediate layers, and (3) 'type à sphérules et corpuscules réfringents'. It is evident that the first two types show a close correspondence to those described by BRETSCHNEIDER in *Limnaea*.

In *Patella*, although the formation of an intranucleolar substance is indicated, no nucleolar buds occur, and no massive extrusion of nucleolar products into the karyolymph or the cytoplasm has been observed. This may be connected with the fact that the nucleolar substance is here divided among a great number (up to 100) of small nucleoli, which facilitates the exchange of substances by diffusion (RANZOLI, 1953).

c. The Golgi apparatus

The cycle of the Golgi apparatus during oogenesis appears to be very similar in all molluscs, as may be inferred from observations, e.g. in Polyplacophora (GABE and PRENANT, 1949), *Mytilus* (WORLEY, 1944), *Aplysia* (PARAT, 1928), *Planorbis* (BERTHIER, 1948), *Limnaea* (GATENBY, 1919; BRETSCHNEIDER and RAVEN, 1951), *Helix* (PARAT, 1928) and *Eremina* (FAHMY, 1949).

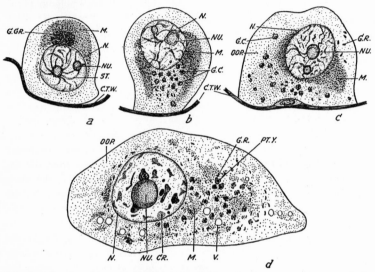

Fig. 2. Mitochondria and Golgi bodies during the first part of oogenesis in *Eremina desertorum*. *CR*, chromatin; *C.T.W.*, connective tissue wall of gonad; *G.C.*, Golgi complex; *G.GR.*, localized Golgi group; *G.R.*, Golgi rod; *M*, mitochondria; *N*, nucleus; *NU*, nucleolus; *OOP*, ooplasm; *PT.Y.*, proteid yolk; *ST*, strepsitene bivalent; *V*, vacuole. After FAHMY, 1949.

In the youngest stages (germinal epithelium cells, oogonia) a more or less spherical *Golgi zone* is found at one side against the nucleus. It consists of a central mass of basophil *archoplasm*, which probably represents the cytocentrum of the cell; this is surrounded by a circle of granular or rod-shaped osmiophil and argentophil bodies. Around the Golgi zone there may be a cloud of mitochondria (Fig. 2a). According to AVEL (1925), the Golgi zone of *Planorbis* can be isolated as a whole from crushed cells, the rods adhering to the archoplasm.

In the early oocyte the Golgi bodies begin to disperse through the cytoplasm, at first on one side of the nucleus, then all around it (Fig. 2, b-d). The number of osmiophil bodies increases, probably by division.

Soon a difference becomes visible between wholly impregnated bodies (*dictyoles*) and bodies with a chromophil cortex and a clear chromophobe centre (*dictyosomes*) (Fig. 4). In the latter, the osmiophil substance may become relatively more and more reduced, until only caps or curved rods, resting on a central chromophobe granulum remain. Finally in the full-grown oocyte the Golgi bodies are quite uniformly dispersed through the cytoplasm.

According to WORLEY, in *Mytilus* the Golgi bodies fuse to big irregular complex bodies during the latter part of the growth phase of the oocyte.

As regards the function of the Golgi apparatus during oogenesis, the following may be remarked. It is generally admitted that the chromophobe centre of the dictyosomes consists of proteins. The Golgi bodies may therefore play a part either in protein synthesis or in the accumulation of proteins synthesized elsewhere; the latter alternative appears the most probable one. In *Mytilus* these proteins are subsequently dissolved in the cytoplasm, according to WORLEY. In *Aplysia, Limnaea, Helix* and *Eremina*, however, it is evident that the Golgi bodies form the proteid yolk granules (Fig. 2, 4). In addition, they may contribute to the formation of fatty yolk: in *Mytilus* the single Golgi bodies during the earlier part of oogenesis accumulate proteins, whereas the complex Golgi bodies of later stages produce fat. In *Eremina*, after the proteid yolk has been formed, the osmiophil granules are set free again, accumulate in the peripheral part of the cytoplasm and become partly impregnated with fat.

d. THE MITOCHONDRIA

In early stages (germinal epithelium cells and oogonia) the mitochondria may either form a cloud at one side of the nucleus, mostly around the Golgi zone (e.g. *Aplysia, Limnaea, Helix, Eremina*) (Fig. 2a), or they may be arranged in an annular zone all around the nucleus (Polyplacophora, *Planorbis*; *Deroceras* and *Arion*: PELLUET and WATTS, 1951) (Fig. 3). Then a gradual dispersal through the cytoplasm takes place. At the same time the number of mitochondria increases; towards the end of the growth period, it may decrease again, however (GABE and PRENANT, 1949).

The mitochondria in the earliest oocytes of *Sphaerium* are at first concentrated in an annular zone about the nucleus. Later there is a great increase in their number, and they are accumulated in the region of the egg stalk, where materials are entering from the circulatory system. When the ovum is set free from the wall of the ovary, the mitochondrial cloud is slightly to one side of the micropyle which marks the point of previous attachment (WOODS, 1932).

In *Mytilus* the mitochondria begin to assemble in or just beneath the egg cortex towards the end of oogenesis; in the full-grown oocyte the rod-shaped mitochondria are lying here in a single layer, with their long axes perpendicular to the surface (WORLEY, 1944). Similar granules have been described in *Mactra* (KOSTANECKI, 1904, 1908), *Spisula* (ALLEN, 1953), and *Caecella* (MOTOMURA, 1954).*

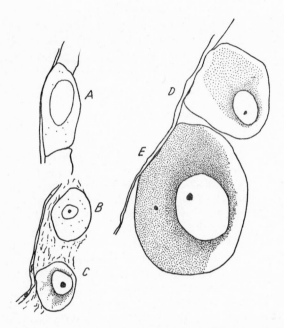

Fig. 3. Mitochondria in developing oocytes of *Deroceras laeve*.
(A) Germinal epithelial cell. (B-E) Growth stages of oocytes.
After PELLUET and WATTS, 1951.

The shape of the mitochondria is apparently very variable in different molluscs. They may be granular (*Planorbis*, *Eremina*) or rod-shaped (*Mytilus*), or both (*Aplysia*); at first there may be both granular and rod-shaped mitochondria whereas later the rods disappear (Polyplacophora); or there are at first only granular, which then transform into filiform mitochondria, but towards the end of oogenesis fall apart into granules (*Limnaea*).

* J. J. PASTEELS and J. MULNARD (*Arch. Biol.* **68**, 115, 1957) also observed cortical granules in *Barnea* and *Gryphaea*. Apparently, these granules form a typical component of the lamellibranchiate egg.

According to GATENBY (1919), in *Limnaea* part of the mitochondria grow very large and become impregnated with yellow pigment. It is evident, however, that he has confounded them with the proteid yolk granules. This error has for some time caused great confusion in the literature on vitellogenesis in molluscs.

4. Vitellogenesis

The yolk substances in molluscan eggs consist partly of proteins, partly they are of a fatty nature. We must distinguish, therefore, between *proteid yolk* and *fatty yolk*. Sometimes, the term 'yolk' is only applied to one of these substances. Many authors, when speaking of yolk, mean especially or exclusively the proteid yolk, in contradistinction to 'fat' or 'oil'. On the contrary, GATENBY and his followers (e.g. BRAMBELL, 1924) understand by 'yolk' only the fatty yolk in our terminology, while they call the proteid yolk 'mitochondria'.

a. PROTEID YOLK

In the eggs of some lamellibranchs (*Mytilus, Ostrea*) no formed proteid yolk is said to be present (WORLEY, 1944). It must be remarked, however, that CLELAND (1951) has isolated from the eggs of *Ostrea commercialis* a fraction of protein granules, which in the ripe egg are situated peripherally, and which contain no less than 39 per cent of the total protein (against 33 per cent in the ground cytoplasm). The amount of proteid yolk granules in other eggs differs greatly. In centrifuged *Limnaea* eggs, the proteid yolk occupies about 50 per cent of the egg volume (RAVEN, 1945; BRETSCHNEIDER and RAVEN, 1951) (Fig. 9, 10). In the eggs of nudibranchs, this amounts to 66–75 per cent (COSTELLO, 1939a); in *Crepidula*, it is more than 75 per cent (CONKLIN, 1917). These values have not been corrected for the hyaloplasm occupying the interstices between the granules.

It must be emphasized that these yolk granules are not always purely proteidic in nature; they may also contain a variable amount of lipids, as for example in *Aplysia* (PARAT, 1928).

The earliest oocyte does not yet contain any proteid yolk. The yolk granules are formed during the growth phase of the egg. This process is described in two different ways.

In gastropods (*Aplysia, Aeolis, Limnaea, Helix, Eremina*), the proteid yolk is formed by the Golgi bodies. The first yolk granules appear in the Golgi field. They are formed in the chromophobe internum of the dictyosomes. By their growth, the chromophil substance is more and more reduced to a peripheral ring or cap (Fig. 2).

In *Limnaea*, two kinds of proteid yolk granules may be distinguished.

Those of one type (so-called β–granules) are round. They first grow to a size of from 3 to 4 μ, then condensation takes place to a final diameter of 1·5μ. The other type (γ–granules) are bigger and oblong; they differ somewhat in their chemical composition from the β–granules (Fig. 4).

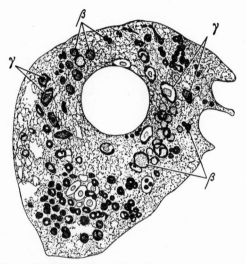

Fig. 4. Formation of proteid yolk (β- and γ-granules)
in growing oocyte of *Limnaea stagnalis*.

Electron microscopy of ultra-thin sections has shown that the β-granules contain numerous small particles, for the greater part arranged in a regular crystalline pattern. The particles, probably globular protein macromolecules, have a diameter of about 50 Å. The crystals are embedded in a homogeneous matrix of low electron density (ELBERS, 1957).

In *Loligo* (KONOPACKI, 1933), yolk formation in the early oocyte likewise takes place in vacuoles, which correspond to Golgi bodies. The acidophil spherules, of which this 'primitive yolk' consists, at later stages grow considerably and fuse. Moreover, acidophil substances from the follicle cells, probably representing simple proteins like histones and protamines, are added to the primitive yolk, together forming the definitive yolk of the ripe egg.

The description that is given for yolk formation in Polyplacophora (GABE and PRENANT, 1949) and *Dentalium* (ARVY, 1950a) differs from the above. In both cases, the yolk granules are formed in or near chromophobic islands (areolae) in the cytoplasm (cf. above, p. 4). It may be asked, however, whether these areolae are not a kind of 'Golgi negatives', in which case the two modes of yolk formation would be identical. The close connection of the mitochondria with the areolae suggests that the former may play some part in the processes leading to the formation of the yolk granules (ARVY, 1950a; cf. also PARAT, 1928).

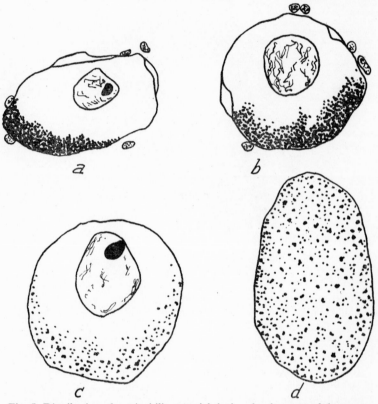

Fig. 5. Distribution of osmiophilic material during development of the oocyte of *Limnaea stagnalis appressa*. (a, b) Ovarian oocytes. (c) Oocyte at time of ovulation. (d) Oocyte in gonad lumen just after breakdown of germinal vesicle. After HARTUNG, 1947.

b. FATTY YOLK

While the eggs of lamellibranchs are poor in proteid yolk, they have a very high fat content. The eggs of *Pecten* have the highest iodine number known in all eggs (NEEDHAM, 1942).

The fat content, as determined by the centrifugation method, is about

5 per cent in *Limnaea* (RAVEN, 1945) (Fig. 9, 10), from 2 to 5 per cent in various nudibranchs, 10 per cent in *Cumingia* and 14 per cent in *Mytilus* (COSTELLO, 1939a); the values have not been corrected for hyaloplasm occupying the interstices between oil drops.

The fatty substances of the eggs occur in different forms:

(1) As free lipids, diffusely in the cytoplasm. Secondarily, they may be accumulated in certain cell structures, e.g. in mitochondria, which thereby transform into *lepidosomes* (*Helix*: PARAT, 1928); in Golgi bodies (*Eremina*: FAHMY, 1949); in or around proteid yolk granules (*Aplysia*: PARAT, 1928).

(2) As fatty yolk in the form of drops or globules, chiefly consisting of neutral fats. They may arise during oogenesis in two different ways: either in complex Golgi systems during later phases of oogenesis (*Mytilus*: WORLEY, 1944), or independently of visible cell structures in certain parts of the cytoplasm (PARAT, 1928; BRETSCHNEIDER and RAVEN, 1951).

According to HARTUNG (1947), in *Limnaea stagnalis appressa* and *Physa gracilis* the fat droplets appear first at the basal (= vegetative) side of the oocyte, forming a more or less dense cap. Later they disperse throughout the egg, moving at first especially in the subcortical region. This dispersal begins earlier in *Physa*, where a more or less uniform distribution of the fat droplets has been reached before the dissolution of the germinal vesicle. In *Limnaea stagnalis appressa* the dispersal of the fat globules does not begin until after ovulation, and a uniform distribution is only attained with the beginning of maturation (Fig. 5).

5. Cytochemistry of oogenesis

The following data on the chemical processes during oogenesis in molluscs have been established by cytochemical methods.

a. GLYCOGEN

In *Limnaea* (BRETSCHNEIDER and RAVEN, 1951) glycogen is not formed in connection with visible cell structures, but diffusely in the cytoplasm. Sometimes, however, an accumulation in vacuoles seems to take place, which then change into granules. The glycogen is more or less uniformly distributed throughout the egg.

b. DESOXYRIBONUCLEIC ACID

During the early premeiotic stages the chromosomes are Feulgen-positive. With the beginning of the oocyte growth the DNA reaction of the chromatin disappears, and remains negative till the end of oogenesis, when the tetrads become visible preceding maturation.

In some cases, the nucleolus is Feulgen-positive during certain stages (Polyplacophora: GABE and PRENANT, 1949; *Dentalium*: ARVY, 1950a; Prosobranchia: FRANC, 1951, BOLOGNARI, 1956; *Aplysia*: BOLOGNARI, 1954). Moreover, in some Prosobranchia the nucleoplasm is said to exhibit a positive DNA-reaction towards the end of vitellogenesis (FRANC, 1950). The same has been observed in early oocytes of *Anodonta* (BRACHET, 1929).

c. RIBONUCLEIC ACID

As a rule, the earliest oocytes have already a cytoplasm very rich in RNA. Only in the Polyplacophora, RNA does not appear before the beginning of the growth phase. During growth and vitellogenesis a considerable decrease in RNA content takes place; in some cases (Polyplacophora, *Dentalium*, Prosobranchia) this may even lead to a completely negative RNA reaction of the full-grown oocyte.

In *Patella* the RNA content of the cytoplasm is greatest when the relative amount of nucleolar substance is maximal. Increase and decrease of nucleolar volume and cytoplasmic RNA go hand in hand (RANZOLI, 1953).

The RNA may be found partly in diffuse form in the cytoplasm, partly it is bound to fine granules. In *Planorbis*, the latter arrange themselves in older oocytes around the proteid yolk granules (BERTHIER, 1948). A similar phenomenon may explain the fact that in *Limnaea* the β-granules, which are free from RNA in ovarial eggs, exhibit a strong RNA reaction after oviposition; apparently, during the passage of the eggs through the oviduct a fixation of RNA to the β-granules takes place.

The nucleolus is even in the youngest oocytes rich in RNA. Later only the basophil parts of the amphinucleoli contain RNA. The nucleolar buds in *Limnaea* and *Dentalium* are, according to ARVY (1949, 1950a), poor in RNA; however, in *Planorbis* also RNA-rich granules are formed by the nucleolus (BERTHIER). With the extrusion of the products the pyroninophily of the nucleolus diminishes strongly.

d. SULPHYDRYL COMPOUNDS

In *Limnaea*, glutathione is found in the cytoplasm and the nucleolus; in the latter, both the basophil and the acidophil parts contain the substance. Generally, the glutathione content decreases during oogenesis; the marked differences in content among oocytes of the same size indicate, however, that fluctuations due to a periodic synthesis and consumption occur. The observations point to an emission of glutathione by the nucleolus into the karyolymph, and its transmission through the nuclear membrane into the cytoplasm. In the eggs of *Aplysia* the amount of glutathione increases till the beginning of vitellogenesis, then it decreases strongly (BOLOGNARI, 1954).

Bound SH-compounds are found in *Helix* and *Tachea* especially in the karyolymph, somewhat less in the cytoplasm and the nucleolus. The nucleolar inclusions stain more weakly than the rest of the nucleolus (SERRA and QUEIROZ LOPES, 1945).

e. TYROSINE

As tyrosine is a general component of all proteins, and its content does not vary very much among various proteins, this reaction may be considered as a general protein test. In *Helix* and *Tachea* the oocyte nucleolus shows a positive reaction, which increases with growth. The intranucleolar inclusions stain more lightly (SERRA and QUEIROZ LOPES). According to ARVY (1949), the cytoplasm, nucleolus and nucleolar buds of *Limnaea* show the reaction; the nucleoplasm reacts negatively. In *Patella*, the cytoplasm and nucleoli contain a nearly constant amount of tyrosine during the whole of oogenesis. The reaction is somewhat stronger in the intranucleolar vacuoles, especially during the first phases of vitellogenesis (RANZOLI, 1953).

f. ARGININE

This reaction permits the detection of basic proteins, which are rich in arginine. In *Helix* and *Tachea* the nucleolus shows a strong reaction, especially during the periods of active nucleolar bud formation. The intranucleolar inclusions are poorer in basic proteins. In the cytoplasm the basic proteins are accumulated around the nuclear membrane. The 'yolk nucleus', which appears at the middle of the growth period after a phase of active nucleolar bud formation (and which probably represents the beginning of yolk formation in the Golgi field), shows a very strong reaction. After its appearance the amount of basic proteins in the cytoplasm shows a further increase (SERRA and QUEIROZ LOPES). In *Patella*, the reaction is positive in the cytoplasm of oocytes of all stages, but especially in the middle of oogenesis. During vitellogenesis the basic proteins are accumulated in the perinuclear cytoplasm. The intranucleolar vacuoles show a somewhat heavier staining than the rest of the nucleolar substance (RANZOLI).

g. TRYPTOPHANE

In *Helix* and *Tachea* the nucleolus gives a stronger reaction than the cytoplasm at all stages. The staining increases during growth. The intranucleolar inclusions stain more deeply than the rest of the nucleolus (SERRA and QUEIROZ LOPES).

h. Ascorbic acid (vitamin C)

This substance is found in the eggs of some molluscs (*Aplysia, Limnaea*) (Fig. 12), but not in others (*Pleurobranchaea*). It occurs either diffusely in the cytoplasm or bound to Golgi bodies (Bretschneider and Raven, 1951). Pelluet and Watts (1951) have followed its formation in *Deroceras* and *Arion*. The early oocytes are poor in ascorbic acid; later, a rapid increase occurs. In *Deroceras*, but not in *Arion*, the substance is also found in the nucleolus.

i. Alkaline phosphatase

This enzyme has been studied by Arvy (1949, 1950a). In *Limnaea* it is found in the cytoplasm, the nucleolus and nucleolar buds; in *Dentalium* in the nucleolus, but not in the cytoplasm. According to Pelluet and Watts, in *Deroceras* and *Arion* at first only a few granules are found near the oocyte nucleus; during oogenesis there is a rapid increase, so that the full-grown oocyte exhibits a strong activity in the cytoplasm; moreover, the nucleolus may show a diffuse reaction. Laviolette (1954) has made it probable, however, that this seemingly positive reaction in *Arion* is not due to alkaline phosphatase, but to the presence of calcium salts.

j. Benzidine peroxidase

The ripe eggs of *Aplysia* show a strong reaction of the whole egg (Ries, 1937). Centrifugation of the eggs shows that it is bound to the cytoplasm (Ries, 1938). Peroxidase granules have also been found in the egg cells of various Lamellibranchiata and Prosobranchia (Prenant, 1924). Sometimes, as in the oocytes of *Anomia*, they may be locally accumulated into a dense cloud. It is probable that they are mitochondria.

k. Indophenol oxidase

In *Aplysia* a positive indophenol oxidase reaction is given by uniformly distributed granules in the cytoplasm, which are accumulated in the fat zone upon centrifugation (Ries, 1937, 1938). Since, according to Mancuso (1954), fat droplets may react positively to the G-nadi oxidase reaction, it is probable that Ries' results do not concern the enzyme, but the fatty yolk.* In *Limnaea* (Bretschneider and Raven, 1951) in the early oocytes there is a small group of oxidase granules near the Golgi zone (Fig. 6). At later stages they are dispersed throughout the cytoplasm, and in the full-grown oocyte small groups of two to five granules line the periphery of the egg. This localization of the oxidase granules, and the fact that in centrifuged eggs the reaction is almost

* Cf. however p. 41 footnote.

restricted to the zone of mitochondria (RAVEN and BRETSCHNEIDER, 1942) (Fig. 13) prove that in this case the reaction is not due to fat droplets, and argue in favour of the assumption that the indophenol oxidase in *Limnaea* is bound to the mitochondria. This is confirmed by MANCUSO (1954) for the egg of *Physa*. The follicle cells of the growing oocytes of

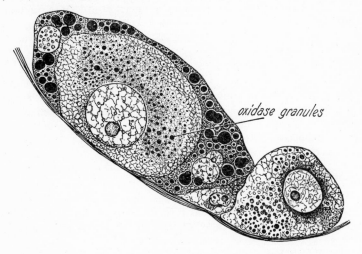

oxidase granules

Fig. 6. Indophenol oxidase reaction in early oocytes and follicle cells of *Limnaea stagnalis.*

Limnaea are extremely rich in substances giving a positive nadi-oxidase reaction, in the form of large drops in the cytoplasm; presumably, here we are dealing with fats accumulated by the follicle cells and serving as food substances for the growing egg (Fig. 6).

1. IRON

The changes in the content and localization of free ionic iron have been studied in *Planorbis* by BERTHIER (1948) and in *Limnaea* by BRETSCHNEIDER and RAVEN (1951). The results of these investigations show a complete agreement.

The cytoplasm of the earliest oocyte is iron-free. Later fine granules appear diffusely in the perinuclear cytoplasm. Still later, the iron is accumulated in the osmiophil parts of the Golgi bodies; like the latter, it forms ring- or cap-like structures upon the proteid yolk granules (cf. also ARENDSEN DE WOLFF-EXALTO, 1947). As the yolk granules increase in size, the coloration becomes weaker, so that it is nearly negative in the full-grown oocyte. However, during the passage of the eggs through the oviduct the reaction in the yolk granules suddenly becomes stronger again, so that it is very marked after oviposition. The variability of the reaction, even among oocytes of the same size, points to fluctuations, which are probably due to a ready transfer of iron from the free into the bound form and vice versa.

The basophil parts of the nucleolus also show a positive iron reaction. Finally, according to BERTHIER the follicle cells contain yolk granules with a high iron content, which are dissolved in the cytoplasm, whereupon the iron may pass into the oocyte.

m. PIGMENT

The eggs of *Mytilus* contain a carotenoid pigment which is partly bound to the yolk, but also diffusely in the cytoplasm (WORLEY, 1944). In *Limnaea* the early oocyte is still transparent; a yellow pigment appears during vitellogenesis. It is bound to the β-granules, and belongs to the melanins (RAVEN and BRETSCHNEIDER, 1942).

6. Conclusion

Although our present knowledge of the chemical processes going on in the egg cells during growth and vitellogenesis is still highly fragmentary, the observations of the last decade have thrown an interesting sidelight on the complexity of this intracellular chemical plant.

It has already become apparent that the nucleolus plays a controlling part in this fabric. Especially its basophil portions, rich in RNA, glutathione, tyrosine, alkaline phosphatase and iron, sometimes also containing DNA and ascorbic acid, appear as centres well equipped for the execution of synthesizing activities. Presumably, it receives single amino acids or lower polypeptides from the cytoplasm, together with ribonucleotides. These building materials may temporarily be stored in the intranucleolar vacuoles. Basic polypeptides rich in arginine, and other, non-basic polypeptides are synthesized. The basic proteins may partly be combined with the ribonucleotides into nucleoproteins. Part of the substances produced in this way are evidently passed on to the cytoplasm for further elaboration, either in a fluid form by way of the karyolymph, or as nucleolar buds, the substance of which seems partly to be passed out through the nuclear membrane in particulate form.

In the cytoplasm, quite a number of synthetic processes are evidently at work during oogenesis, by which the substances produced by the nucleolus, together with those taken up directly from the follicle cells, are further elaborated into the cell's own component parts. By analogy with what is known from other sources, we may assume that protein synthesis will chiefly take place in microsomes, in which a great part of the cytoplasmic RNA is accumulated. The decrease of RNA and gluta-thione during vitellogenesis is probably due to their being used up in this protein synthesis. The proteins formed at various places in the egg cell are for the greater part piled up in the internum of the Golgi bodies, which mould them into the form of the particulate yolk granules. The fact that the osmiophil parts of the Golgi bodies are rich in catalytically active substances such as ascorbic acid and iron indicates that further transformations of the absorbed proteins may take place here.

Further synthetic processes in the cytoplasm concern the neutral fats and other lipids, and the glycogen. The former may be further accumu-lated by the Golgi bodies in a similar way to the proteins; the free lipids may secondarily be absorbed by various cell structures.

Finally, the observations that the mitochondria contain indophenol oxidase; that they are found at early stages in the neighbourhood of the nucleus and the Golgi field; that they later disperse throughout the cell, but may exhibit a certain preference for the sites where vitello-genesis is going on; and that in at least some species a layer of mito-chondrial granules is formed in or immediately beneath the egg cortex, are in harmony with modern views, which ascribe to the mitochondria a predominant role in the generation and transmission of energy within the cell. Not only the oxidative breakdown of combustible substances, but also the phosphorylating mechanisms leading to the formation of high-energy phosphate compounds are supposed to be bound to these granules. It is easily understood, then, that they accumulate at those places in the cell where synthetic processes are at work.

As regards the causal factors controlling this intricate pattern of metabolic activities of the growing egg cell, nothing definite can be said. Evidently, there is here a wide field for future research into the physio-logy of oogenesis.

C

CHAPTER II

Maturation and Fertilization

A. DESCRIPTIVE PART

1. The time relations between maturation and fertilization

IN most molluscs, maturation of the egg may begin 'spontaneously' independent of fertilization, and continues till metaphase of the first maturation division. Unfertilized eggs are blocked at this stage; after the sperm has entered, maturation continues. Normally, fertilization takes place between the beginning of maturation and metaphase of the first maturation division. This holds e.g. for *Cumingia, Mytilus, Ostrea commercialis, Dentalium, Bulla, Crepidula, Physa, Limnaea, Limax, Helix* and *Eulota*.

In other cases (e.g. *Mactra, Ostrea gigas, Barnea, Pterotrachea, Arion*) the fertilizing sperm normally enters at the germinal vesicle stage. In at least some of these species, maturation does not begin spontaneously in unfertilized eggs under normal conditions.

2. Maturation

When maturation is approaching, the germinal vesicle of the full-grown oocyte may begin to shrink by extrusion of karyolymph. Then the *cytocentra* become visible near the nuclear membrane, often in an indentation of the latter. Sometimes there is at first a single cytocentrum, which then divides, the two daughter-centra moving apart (e.g. *Cumingia*: JORDAN, 1910; *Limnaea*: BRETSCHNEIDER, 1948). In other cases two centra become visible right from the beginning, lying against or at a short distance from the nuclear membrane (*Mactra*: KOSTANECKI, 1904; *Helix*: GARNAULT, 1888-89; *Arion*: LAMS, 1910).

Now the nuclear membrane begins to dissolve, first near the cytocentra. Small asters appear around the cytocentra, and the astral rays penetrate into the nuclear space. By a condensation of the chromatin the *tetrads* become visible. Sometimes the latter are surrounded by a somewhat denser substance, *paragenoplastin* (BRETSCHNEIDER, 1948). When the cytocentra have reached opposite sides of the shrunken germinal vesicle, the paragenoplastin with the tetrads begins to orient itself between them. In this way, the *first maturation spindle* is formed, while the nuclear membrane disappears altogether. The spindle may at first be bent, as it is already formed when the cytocentra have not yet reached diametrically opposite points of the circumference of the nucleus (GARNAULT, 1888-89; LILLIE, 1901); then it straightens afterwards.

The nucleolus begins to disappear at this stage. Sometimes, it may remain visible in the cytoplasm beside the maturation spindle for a considerable time (e.g. *Littorina*: DELSMAN, 1912; *Limax*: OBST, 1899). In all cases it is resorbed before the extrusion of the first polar body, however.

The first maturation spindle lies, except in the cephalopods, at first near the centre of the egg, and moves only secondarily towards the animal pole, where it places itself perpendicularly to the surface (Fig. 7a; Pl. III, A) (in some cases first somewhat obliquely: BLOCHMANN, 1882; VIALLETON, 1888). Its peripheral extremity comes into connection with the egg surface; at this point, a small indentation of the surface may temporarily be formed (e.g. *Physa*: KOSTANECKI and WIERZEJSKI, 1896; *Limnaea*: LINVILLE, 1900; RAVEN, 1945) (Fig. 7b; Pl. III, B).

The asters of the first maturation spindle sometimes exhibit a spiral arrangement of their rays (*Physa, Limnaea*: WEIGMANN, 1928; *Arion*: LAMS, 1910). According to WEIGMANN, these spirals may be clockwise or anti-clockwise without any regularity; presumably, they are not related to any hypothetical spiral structure of the cytoplasm, but are due to streaming movements in the latter.

Before entering upon a description of the structure of the maturation spindles, a few words may be said on the terminology employed. In the years around 1900, much attention has been paid to the structure of the 'achromatic apparatus' of the meiotic and mitotic divisions; it was described by the authors in every possible detail. Later investigations, especially by FRY, have shown, however, that the pictures obtained in microscopic preparations are greatly dependent upon the methods of fixation and staining used, and on the external circumstances at the moment of fixation. Although in my opinion FRY goes somewhat too far in his rejection of the reality of the 'central bodies', it is evident that many of the structures described by the earlier authors are artifacts. Moreover, a fatal confusion has arisen by the differences in terminology between various authors, especially the term 'centrosome', which is employed in a variety of ways and indicating quite different structures. We shall therefore avoid this term altogether.

From a survey of the literature, it appears evident that in most cells there is a privileged region of the cytoplasm, which plays a part in cell division, and has itself the capacity to multiply by division. We shall call this the *cytocentrum*. Under the influence of this centrum, during certain phases of cell life the surrounding cytoplasm acquires a radial arrangement of its submicroscopic structure, forming an *aster*. At first, at least in many cases this radial arrangement extends towards the middle, the astral 'rays' meeting in one point in the centre. In older asters, however, beginning in the centre and gradually extending outwards, the radial arrangement disappears and makes way for another, more disorderly structure. In this way, a more or less clear central area is formed in the middle of the aster, which may be called the *centrosphere*. In some cases, in or near the centre of the centrosphere a small dark granule may be visible, the *centriole*; in other species, however, such a centriole cannot be made visible even with special methods devised for this purpose.

Returning to the first maturation spindle of molluscan eggs, we may state that in all cases this spindle is provided with large asters at both ends, which at least in advanced stages have well-developed centrospheres (Fig. 7, a–b; Pl. II, A; Pl. III; Pl. V). In many cases there is a distinct centriole in these centrospheres. At a certain stage this centriole divides; this may occur during prophase (*Arion*: LAMS, 1910) or not until metaphase (*Zirphaea*: GRIFFIN, 1899) or anaphase (*Unio*: LILLIE, 1901; *Diaulula*: McFARLAND, 1897).

At the animal pole, where the outer extremity of the maturation spindle touches the surface, a cytoplasmic protrusion is formed. The outer half of the spindle projects into this protrusion (Fig. 7c; Pl. I, A; Pl. V, B). The aster at this end, which had earlier flattened itself against the surface, rapidly decreases in size. The whole spindle may shorten considerably. At anaphase, an equatorial thickening of the spindle fibres, the so-called *cell plate*, becomes visible. This comes to lie in line with the egg surface. The polar body is now constricted off by an annular furrow; thereby the cell plate is compressed to a *mid-body*, which, together with the spindle remnant, for some time connects the polar body with the egg surface (Fig. 15). The mid-body disappears towards the time when the second maturation spindle comes in contact with the surface.

In most cases the first polar body divides once; in *Loligo* even more than once (HOADLEY, 1930). In other species, however, the polar body never divides (e.g. *Limnaea*, *Bulinus*) or undergoes an incomplete constriction only (*Sepia*). As a rule, no resting nucleus is formed by the chromosomes in the polar body. The body may exhibit amoeboid movements shortly after its extrusion, e.g. in Opisthobranchiata (McFARLAND). Sometimes it collapses very soon (*Limax*).

At the end of anaphase of the first maturation division the *dyads* remaining in the egg reach the margin of the inner centrosphere of the spindle (Fig. 7c; Pl. I, A–B). At first they form a compact group, then they begin to move apart forming a more or less regular ring. At the

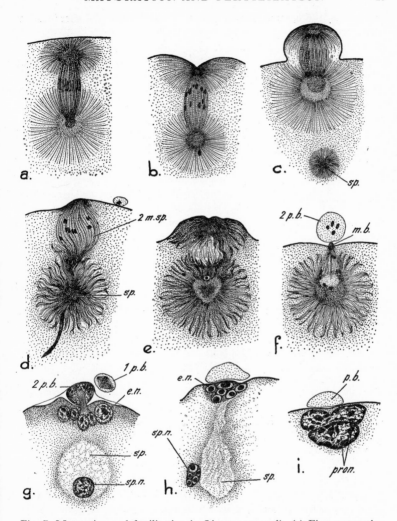

Fig. 7. Maturation and fertilization in *Limnaea stagnalis*. (a) First maturation spindle, early anaphase (cf. Pl. III A). (b) Late anaphase, spindle end in contact with egg cortex (cf. Pl. III B). (c) Telophase, formation of first polar body (cf. Pl. I A). Sperm aster (*sp.*) just formed. (d) Formation of second maturation spindle (*2.m.sp.*). Expansion of sperm aster (cf. Pl. I D). (e) Late anaphase of second maturation division (cf. Pl. I F). (f) Second polar body (*2.p.b.*) formed. Spindle remnant and mid-body (*m.b.*). (g) Karyomeres of egg nucleus (*e.n.*) in subcortical plasm. Sperm nucleus (*sp.n.*) in centrosphere of sperm aster (*sp.*). (h) This centrosphere in connection with animal pole (cf. Pl. IV A). (i) Copulation of pronuclei (*pron.*).

same time, the centrosphere begins to enlarge, while the surrounding astral rays shorten.

From a survey of the literature it appears that in all cases the second maturation spindle develops from this centrosphere. This holds e.g. for *Unio* (LILLIE, 1901), *Zirphaea* (GRIFFIN, 1899), *Crepidula* (CONKLIN, 1901), *Diaulula* (MCFARLAND, 1897), *Physa* (KOSTANECKI and WIERZEJSKI, 1896), *Limnaea* (RAVEN, 1949), *Helix* (GARNAULT, 1888-89), *Limax* (BYRNES, 1900; LINVILLE, 1900) and *Arion* (LAMS, 1910).

In those cases, where there are distinct centrioles (*Unio*, *Zirphaea*, *Diaulula*, *Physa*, *Limax*, *Agriolimax*, *Arion*) the daughter centrioles produced by division at an earlier stage move apart within the centrosphere. At the same time the latter becomes elliptical, with its long axis coinciding with the line connecting the centrioles. Between the latter, some connecting fibres may form the beginning of a *central spindle* (e.g. *Unio*, *Physa*, *Limax*, *Arion*). Then the centrosphere acquires a fibrillar structure, in this way transforming into the spindle (Pl. I, C).*

The developing second maturation spindle is at first more or less parallel to the surface or has an arbitrary direction. It then rotates into a radial position, and connects with the egg surface at the animal pole (Fig. 7d). In some cases, an indentation is once more formed at this place (*Physa*; *Bulinus*: DE LARAMBERGUE, 1939; *Limax flavus*: J. A. LEUSSINK, unpublished observations).

While the origin of the second maturation spindle is the same in different molluscs, less uniformity exists as regards its asters. Their formation takes place in one of the following ways:

(1) The asters of the second maturation spindle arise *de novo* from the cytoplasm at both ends outside the transforming centrosphere: e.g. *Unio* (LILLIE, 1901), *Diaulula* (MCFARLAND, 1897), *Limax flavus* (J. A. LEUSSINK, unpublished observations). In some cases, the rays of the old aster surrounding the centrosphere have not yet entirely disappeared at the moment the new asters begin to develop. It is a mere matter of words, however, to say that the new asters then develop *from* the old one. The essential thing is that the oriented condition of the cytoplasmic structure of which the aster is the visible expression, again begins to spread outwards from the poles of the developing spindle.

(2) When the centrioles are lying some distance inwards from the extremities of the centrosphere, aster formation begins within the

---

* Recent observations have shown that the centriole in *Limnaea stagnalis* remains undivided and moves as a whole to the outer pole of the developing second maturation spindle. This explains the further peculiarities in the development of this spindle mentioned below.

centrosphere area and extends only secondarily into the surrounding cytoplasm, e.g. *Limax agrestis* (BYRNES, 1900), *Agriolimax reticulatus* (Miss F. C. M. ESCHER, unpublished observations), *Arion* (LAMS, 1910). In this case also, the rays of the old aster may still be visible when the new astral radiations extend into the cytoplasm surrounding the centrosphere (*Agriolimax, Arion*).

(3) The aster at the outer pole of the second maturation spindle is formed *de novo* in the cytoplasm outside the centrosphere, whereas the inner aster arises from the sperm aster which fuses secondarily with the inner end of the spindle (cf. below): *Limnaea stagnalis* (RAVEN, 1949) (Pl. I, D–F).

While the inner centrosphere of the first maturation spindle transforms into the second maturation spindle, the dyads may for some time remain lying as a single group at one side, but then they continue their movement along the outer side of the centrosphere until they reach the equatorial plane of the spindle, where they arrange themselves into an equatorial plate (Pl. I, C; Pl. II, B). 'Mantle fibres' originating from the spindle poles and connecting with the chromosomes may assist in this movement.

In many cases the second maturation spindle is considerably shorter than the first e.g. *Bulinus, Limnaea*.

The formation of the second polar body closely resembles that of the first. A 'cell plate' and mid-body are also formed in this case (Fig. 7, e–f). The latter may remain visible for a considerable time, sometimes even till the beginning of cleavage (*Physa*).

The second polar body as a rule does not divide; exceptionally this may occur, however (e.g. *Amphorina, Loligo*). Sometimes it exhibits amoeboid motility (*Amphorina*). In other cases it soon swells and goes to pieces (*Limax*).

In *Helix, Limax* and *Arion* both polar bodies may be very large, in pathological cases even as large as the egg cell.

Immediately after the extrusion of the second polar body the chromosomes of the egg begin to swell into *karyomeres* (Fig. 7g). The latter then coalesce to form the *female pronucleus*, which, in consequence of its mode of formation, at first has a lobate contour, but later rounds off. In some cases a direct formation of a vesicular pronucleus from the egg chromosomes, skipping the karyomere stage, has been described (*Unio, Limax, Arion*); it seems probable, however, that in those cases the karyomeres have been overlooked.*

---

* A karyomere stage in the formation of the female pronucleus has recently been observed by us in *Limax flavus*.

Now a characteristic difference between gastropods and lamellibranchs becomes apparent. In the gastropods, the female pronucleus remains at the animal pole, where later the copulation of the two pronuclei takes place (Fig. 7i; Pl. II, C). In Lamellibranchiata, on the contrary, the female pronucleus moves to the centre of the egg, where it meets the male pronucleus.

The deep aster of the maturation spindle remaining in the egg after the extrusion of the second polar body may for some time grow considerably in size e.g. *Limnaea, Limax*. A spiral arrangement of its rays at this stage has been described in *Pleurophyllidia* (MCFARLAND, 1897), *Limax* (BYRNES, 1900) and *Limnaea* (WEIGMANN, 1928). Then this aster rapidly degenerates, the astral rays becoming blurred from the centre outwards, so that the centrosphere becomes very large (Fig. 7g). At the same time, the structure of the latter may become reticular or distinctly vacuolated e.g. *Unio, Crepidula, Limnaea, Limax*.

3. Fertilization

In the cephalopods, with their thick chorion, the sperm enters through the micropyle at the animal pole. In *Unio* (LILLIE, 1901), *Bulla* (SMALLWOOD) and *Crepidula* (CONKLIN, 1897) the sperm always enters the egg at the vegetative pole. In most lamellibranchs and gastropods, however, this may occur at any place of the egg surface.

Fertilization cones have been described in the pulmonate *Eulota* (IKEDA, 1930) and the limpet *Megathura* (KRAUSS, 1950). In *Eulota*, during dissolution of the germinal vesicle and formation of the first maturation spindle 10–20 conical hyaline protrusions are formed. At first, they consist of ectoplasm only; later the granular endoplasm also enters into them. The fertilizing sperm penetrates at the tip of one of these protrusions; then they are all withdrawn and the first polar body is formed. In *Megathura*, a fertilization cone appears only about five minutes after the fertilizing sperm has become attached to the egg surface. The sperm head is engulfed and soon the cone disappears.

According to MEVES (1915), in the fertilizing sperm of *Mytilus* the acrosome is suddenly dissolved on entering the egg.* In *Limnaea*, after penetration of the sperm the perforation hole in the egg cortex is

---

* According to J. C. DAN and S. K. WADA (*Biol. Bull.* **109**, 40, 1955) the *Mytilus* sperm reacts to the presence of unfertilized eggs by complete disappearance of the acrosome and extrusion of a slender filament. The acrosome consists of three parts: a basal part probably serving for the extrusion of the filament; a distal part containing the egg membrane lysin (cf. below p. 52); and an axial structure in the form of a tubular sheath, which perhaps contains a precursor of the filament. A similar acrosome reaction was observed in *Lithophaga, Spondylus, Crassostrea, Trapezium, Chama, Petricola, Mactra*, and *Zirphaea*.

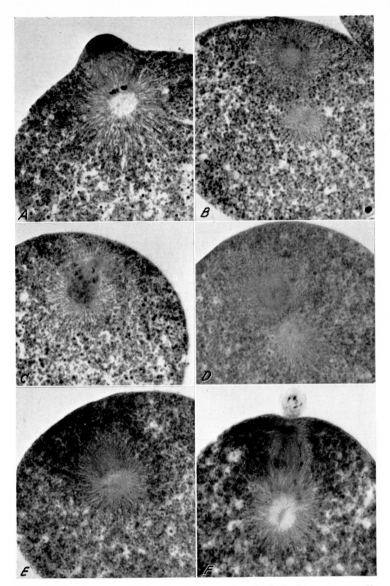

Plate I. The formation of the second maturation spindle in *Limnaea stagnalis*. (A) Telophase of first maturation division. Dyads have reached centrosphere of deep aster. (B) Dyads have moved somewhat apart, but are still capping centrosphere. Early sperm aster near centre of egg. Condensed sperm nucleus in subcortical position in lower right corner. (C) Transformation of centrosphere of first maturation aster into second maturation spindle. (D) Sperm aster has approached inner end of second maturation spindle. Dark granules in intermediate zone between the two structures. (E) Sperm aster has fused with inner end of spindle, forming its deep aster. (F) Meta- to anaphase of second maturation division.

[*Facing page* 28

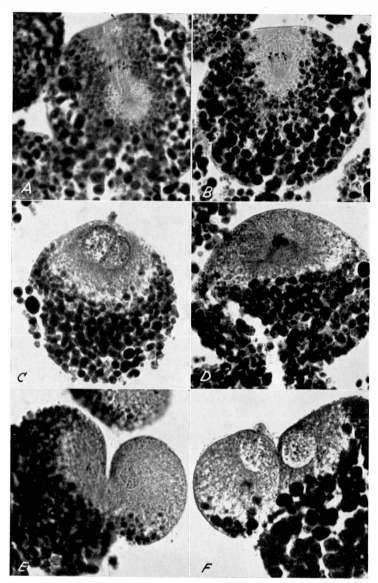

Plate II. Maturation, first cleavage and bipolar differentiation in *Aplysia lima-cina*. (A) First maturation spindle in early anaphase. Large inner aster. Fine (mainly fatty) yolk surrounding spindle and asters. Coarse (proteid) yolk peripherally. (B) Second maturation spindle in meta- to anaphase. (C) Copulation of pronuclei. Bipolar differentiation well advanced. (D) Formation of first cleavage spindle. Bipolar differentiation completed. (E) First cleavage. Blastomere AB at left, CD at right. Unequal distribution of egg substances. (F) Two-cell stage.

closed by a coagulum, sometimes forming a small protuberance (BRET-SCHNEIDER, 1948).

Nearly always the whole spermatozoon, including the tail, enters the egg. In *Bulla*, *Crepidula* and *Eulota*, however, the sperm tail is left behind outside the egg. The mitochondria lying in the middle piece of the *Mytilus* sperm are taken into the egg and soon become unrecognizable among the egg mitochondria (MEVES, 1915).

After the sperm has entered the egg, it moves, at least in the pulmonates, through the whole thickness of the egg cytoplasm, and finally comes to rest with its head somewhere immediately beneath the egg cortex. In *Unio* (LILLIE, 1901), on the other hand, the sperm, which has entered at the vegetative pole, immediately makes for the centre of the egg, where it comes to rest just above the egg equator. A path of alveolar protoplasm forms along its track.

Soon after the sperm has come to rest, the tail breaks away from the head. In some cases the head changes in shape, and rounds off (*Limnaea, Limax, Bulinus*). In *Mytilus* (MEVES, 1915), *Physa* (KOSTANECKI and WIERZEJSKI), *Limnaea* (LINVILLE, 1900; DE LARAMBERGUE, 1939) and *Limax* (LINVILLE) a rotation of the head has been described, by which it turns its basal side towards the egg centre.

The sperm tail is resorbed in the egg cytoplasm. The time at which this occurs seems to be more or less fixed, but differs in different species: either during the first maturation division (*Bulinus*) or between first and second maturation division (*Limnaea*, cf. RAVEN and HUPKENS VAN DER ELST, 1950), after the second division (*Physa, Helix, Limax*) or even as late as first cleavage (*Cymbulia, Tiedemannia, Arion*).

Polyspermy has been found in *Limnaea* (CRABB, 1927; BRETSCHNEIDER, 1948; HORSTMANN, 1955), *Helix* (GARNAULT, 1888-89) and *Bulinus* (DE LARAMBERGUE, 1939). Only one of the sperms forms a pronucleus, the supernumerary ones soon disintegrate.

Sooner or later a *sperm aster* becomes visible in the egg. Sometimes it originates in the immediate neighbourhood of the sperm nucleus, in other cases it first becomes visible at some distance from the latter. In a few instances its origin can be distinctly traced back to the middle piece of the sperm, e.g. in *Physa* (KOSTANECKI and WIERZEJSKI). The observation that the early sperm aster in *Limnaea* is often still connected with one end of the sperm tail (RAVEN, 1945) also argues in favour of this origin (Fig. 7d). Soon the sperm aster migrates to a deeper level. In this way it moves away from the sperm nucleus, which for some time remains behind beneath the egg surface (Pl. I, B). Initially the sperm aster is only small, and has no centrosphere, the astral rays meeting in one point (Fig. 7c; Pl. I, B). Later it increases in size, and a centrosphere appears (Fig. 7, d–e; Pl. I, E–F). In *Zirphaea, Unio, Mactra* and *Pleurophyllidia* a distinct centriole was observed in this centrosphere.

The time of appearance of the sperm aster differs much. It may become visible immediately after sperm entrance at pro-metaphase of the first maturation division (*Unio*), at anaphase of this division (*Limnaea*), or at meta- to anaphase of the second maturation division (*Mactra, Zirphaea, Crepidula, Pleurophyllidia, Physa, Bulinus*).

The further development of the sperm aster varies considerably. At least five possibilities may be distinguished:

(1) The sperm aster divides and forms an *amphiaster* with central spindle, which remains in existence until first cleavage and becomes the cleavage spindle. This has been described in *Physa* by KOSTANECKI and WIERZEJSKI (1896) and in *Mactra* by KOSTANECKI (1904) (cf. below, p. 31).

(2) A more or less distinct division of the sperm aster takes place, leading to the formation of a dicentric aster or of two loose asters without a central spindle, which disappear, however, before the prophase of first cleavage: *Pleurophyllidia* (MCFARLAND, 1897); sometimes in *Limnaea* (LINVILLE, 1900; DE LARAMBERGUE, 1939); sometimes in *Limax flavus* (J. A. LEUSSINK, unpublished observations).

(3) The sperm aster does not divide, but remains in existence with a very large centrosphere; this plays a part in the formation of the cleavage spindle: *Crepidula* (CONKLIN, 1901).

(4) The sperm aster remains undivided, and disappears after some time, at any rate before the prophase of first cleavage: *Barnea* (PASTEELS, 1930); mostly in *Limax flavus* (J. A. LEUSSINK); *Limax maximus* (LINVILLE, 1900); *Bulinus* (DE LARAMBERGUE, 1939).

(5) There is no sperm aster at all: *Cumingia* (JORDAN, 1910); *Limax agrestis* (BYRNES, 1900); *Agriolimax reticulatus* (Miss F. C. M. Escher, unpublished observations); *Arion* (LAMS, 1910).

Finally, there are two special cases which do not fit into any of these groups. The first one is that of *Unio* (LILLIE, 1901), where a comet-shaped sperm aster is formed immediately after sperm entrance. It has an apical centre, which soon divides, giving rise to a typical amphiaster. This goes ahead of the sperm nucleus in its migration to the egg centre. A short time before the metaphase of the first maturation division this amphiaster degenerates and disappears. Later, however, shortly after metaphase of the second maturation division, a new aster appears near the egg centre. It divides and gives rise to a small amphiaster, which disappears very soon, even before the extrusion of the second polar body is completed.

The second aberrant case is that of *Limnaea stagnalis* (RAVEN, 1945, 1949) (Fig. 7; Pl. I). The sperm aster appears immediately before the extrusion of the first polar body. During the formation of the second maturation spindle it grows rapidly in size, and a large centrosphere is formed in its centre. When the second maturation spindle has completed its rotation and is placed perpendicularly to the surface, the sperm aster fuses with its inner end and becomes the deep maturation aster (Fig. 7, d–e; Pl. I, E–F). In the region of fusion temporarily a somewhat darker zone, containing small vacuoles and granules, has been observed (W. M. HERREBOUT, unpublished observations) (Pl. I, D). This points to a certain cytochemical activity following upon the conjunction of the two structures. After the extrusion of the second polar body the aster becomes free again and moves a little into the depth. Its centrosphere becomes very large and vacuolated; the astral rays disappear from the centre outwards. Finally all remnants of the aster have disappeared before the prophase of first cleavage.

When the sperm has entered the egg, the sperm head at first retains its compact structure (Pl. I, B). It may increase a little in size shortly after insemination (*Unio, Spisula, Arion, Eulota*) or somewhat later (*Limax, Bulinus*), and a kind of vacuole may be formed around it (*Limnaea, Limax*). But its transformation into the male pronucleus does not begin until the second polar body has been extruded. At this moment, it begins to swell, synchronously with the egg chromosomes, and rapidly changes into a distinct pronucleus. In some cases, it may temporarily appear as a group of karyomeres (*Unio, Limnaea, Bulinus*), which later fuse to a lobate or polymorphic nucleus.

As soon as the sperm nucleus begins to swell, it also commences its migration towards the female pronucleus. In the gastropods, where the latter retains its position at the animal pole, the male pronucleus also moves to this pole. In the Lamellibranchiata, on the contrary, the two pronuclei start simultaneously with their migration, and meet one another in or near the centre of the egg. In *Sepia* (VIALLETON, 1888) the two pronuclei also migrate toward each other.

When the pronuclei meet (both have in the meantime become large, vesicular nuclei), they apply themselves closely against each other (Fig. 7i; Pl. II, C). Neither in gastropods nor in lamellibranchs does an actual fusion of the pronuclei take place, however. Only in *Sepia* do the pronuclei fuse with each other, according to VIALLETON (1888).

After the 'copulation' of the pronuclei has taken place, the *cleavage spindle* makes its appearance. According to KOSTANECKI and WIERZEJSKI (1896) and KOSTANECKI (1904), the sperm amphiaster directly becomes the cleavage spindle in *Physa* and *Mactra*. In my opinion, this statement cannot be accepted without some reserve. In the first place, the fact that the same author gives a similar description of the process in two rather unrelated species, whereas in all other molluscs a different mode of formation of the cleavage spindle obtains, must already engender some doubt. Moreover, KOSTANECKI and WIERZEJSKI mention that in *Physa*, after the pronuclei have met, the astral rays of the amphiaster decrease, and only with some difficulty may two centra be seen, which are considered to be identical with the original poles of the amphiaster. As regards *Mactra*, the figures given for this species in KOSTANECKI's paper are no more convincing.

Moreover, DAN, ITO and MAZIA (1952) did not observe any asters in association with the pronuclei in *Mactra* until just after the time when fusion begins. When the pronuclei flatten against each other, two asters are observed. The line connecting their centres runs through the plane of pronuclear contact.

It is probable, therefore, that the cleavage spindle in *Physa* and *Mactra* is formed in the same way as in other molluscs. Two new cytocentra appear against the two closely applied pronuclei. If they are derived from one of the cytocentra of the germ cells (and most authors are inclined to the view that they are descendants of the sperm cytocentrum), there is at least in most molluscs no clearly visible material continuity with the latter. According to CONKLIN (1901), in *Crepidula* the greatly enlarged centrospheres of maturation spindle and sperm aster coalesce near the pronuclei, and the new cytocentra arise in this area. In other molluscs, nothing of the kind has been found.

A central spindle is formed between the cytocentra, which lies against or between the pronuclei. From the centra 'mantle fibres' penetrate into the pronuclei. Their nuclear membranes are dissolved, the chromosomes become visible and are drawn into the spindle (Pl. II, D). As a rule, at first two clearly separated groups of chromosomes are present, which only unite with each other during metaphase.

4. Cytoplasmic activities

While the nuclear phenomena of maturation and fertilization are taking place, the cytoplasm of the eggs may show various activities.

In the first place, this may express itself in the occurrence of changes in shape of the whole egg. Such a change has been described in the egg of *Cumingia* at the moment of insemination (MORGAN and TYLER, 1930). About thirty seconds after the sperm has come in contact with the egg surface, the egg becomes ovoid, with the pointed end directed towards the sperm. This lasts thirty seconds or less, then the egg rounds off again.

Although occasionally a slight elevation of the vitelline membrane after insemination has been described in various molluscan eggs, no distinct fertilization membrane is formed in this group.

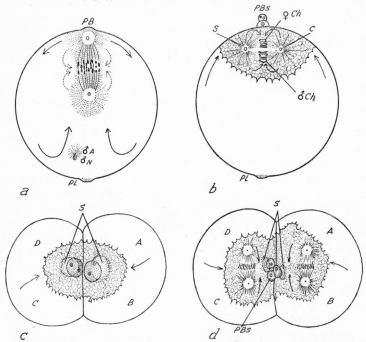

Fig. 8. Protoplasmic movements in the eggs of *Crepidula plana* during maturation and cleavage. (a, b) Viewed from one side, animal pole at top. (c, d) Viewed from the animal pole. (a) First maturation mitosis, the flow being up through the centre and down along the surface; the mitotic vortices are indicated by small arrows. (b) First cleavage mitosis, the protoplasm flowing up along the surface and down in the cleavage plane. (c) Telophase of first cleavage, showing final stage of first cleavage vortex, which was slightly dexiotropic in each cell. (d) Metaphase of second cleavage showing protoplasmic vortex slightly laeotropic. *A, B, C, D*, positions of future quadrants; ♂ *A*, sperm aster; *C*, cytocentrum; ♂ *Ch* and ♀ *Ch*, sperm and egg chromosomes; ♂ *N*, sperm nucleus; *PB*, polar body; *PL*, polar lobe; *S*, centrosphere. After CONKLIN, 1938.

Changes in shape may also occur in conjunction with maturation. The extrusion of each of the polar bodies may be accompanied by amoeboid movements of the egg, e.g. in *Dentalium* (WILSON, 1904), *Physa, Planorbis* and *Limnaea* (CONKLIN, 1910; CLEMENT, 1938; RAVEN, 1945), *Helix* (GARNAULT, 1888-89). As a rule, the amoeboid motility accompanying the first maturation division exactly coincides with the extrusion of the polar body, whereas at the second maturation division the amoeboid movements may be at their maximum some time after the extrusion of the polar body.

In *Dentalium* and *Physa* these amoeboid movements are strongest near the vegetative pole. In a way, these cases form a transition to those in which a so-called *polar lobe* is formed at the vegetative pole during both maturation divisions, e.g. *Pecten* (DREW, 1906), *Crepidula* (CONKLIN, 1938) and *Ilyanassa* (MORGAN, 1933, 1935a). The polar lobe of *Crepidula* is very small (Fig. 8a). In *Ilyanassa*, the lobe formed at first maturation is only small. The second lobe is larger and distinctly constricted off from the rest of the egg by a deep furrow; it reaches its maximum some time after the extrusion of the second polar body (Fig. 19).

According to CONKLIN (1938), in the eggs of *Crepidula* protoplasmic currents occur during maturation; in the axial part of the egg these currents are directed towards the animal pole, whereas a counter-current directed from the animal towards the vegetative side, occurs along the periphery of the egg (Fig. 8a). The movements of the maturation spindle, sperm aster and sperm nucleus are explained by these currents. The observations of MORGAN (1910), according to which in centrifuged eggs of *Cumingia* during the formation of the polar bodies protoplasmic currents occur, by which the accumulated fat and yolk substances are displaced towards the vegetative pole, agree with this view. Protoplasmic currents during maturation have also been observed in centrifuged eggs of *Limnaea* by RAVEN and BRETSCHNEIDER (1942) (Fig. 9).

These protoplasmic currents may, also in normal eggs, lead to considerable displacements of the granular inclusions of the egg. This is most pronounced in the eggs of those gastropods, where a concentration of all proteid yolk in the vegetative part of the egg occurs during or shortly after maturation, leaving at the animal pole an extensive area only consisting of hyaline protoplasm, or at most containing part of the fatty yolk. This phenomenon is most clearly expressed in the eggs of Opisthobranchiata, e.g. *Cymbulia* (FOL, 1875), *Aplysia* (RIES and GERSCH, 1936) (Plate II), *Navanax* (WORLEY and WORLEY, 1943). To a lesser extent it occurs also in some Prosobranchiata, e.g. *Neritina* (BLOCHMANN, 1881), *Columbella* (SPEK, 1934).

A related phenomenon is the formation of the *germinal disc* in cephalopods. In *Loligo*, when the sperm has entered the egg, clear cytoplasm streams from the central part of the egg towards the animal pole, where the germinal disc is formed (HOADLEY, 1930; SPEK, 1934). In *Sepia* granular cytoplasm accumulates during maturation and fertilization in the middle of the animal side, whereas peripheral parts of the blastoderm remain hyaline (VIALLETON, 1888).

A *vegetative pole plasm* is found in recently-laid eggs of *Dentalium* (WILSON, 1904a) and *Limnaea* (RAVEN, 1945). In *Dentalium* it is very dense and free of yolk granules. It is continuous with a very thin ecto-plasmic layer surrounding the whole egg, and with a thin layer around the germinal vesicle. In *Limnaea*, on the contrary, the vegetative pole plasm is rich in proteid yolk, containing a great part of the β-granules. When the egg leaves the gonad after ovulation, this pole plasm has not yet been formed; its accumulation at the vegetative pole takes place during the passage of the egg through the oviduct. At first, it occupies a

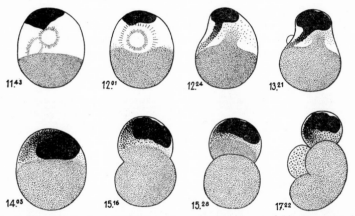

Fig. 9. The distribution of substances in a centrifuged egg of *Limnaea stagnalis* at various times after centrifugation. Redispersal of the accumulated fatty and proteid yolk, partly owing to protoplasmic currents during maturation.

well-defined sector of the egg at the vegetative pole, but during matura-tion it spreads beneath the egg cortex towards the animal side (Fig. 22, a–b; Pl. III). A gap in this layer remains at first at the animal pole, but after the extrusion of the second polar body it closes, and the substance of the vegetative pole plasm now forms a continuous layer of uniform thickness, the *subcortical protoplasm*.

Both *Dentalium* and *Limnaea* also possess an *animal pole plasm*. In *Dentalium* it originally forms a small disc of dense yolk-free protoplasm. After oviposition of the eggs in seawater it increases a little in size. After fertilization this pole plasm grows considerably, presumably by the addition of material from the rest of the egg. When the polar bodies have been formed, the animal pole plasm extends over the whole of the animal hemisphere.

In *Limnaea* there is no animal pole plasm during the first hours, but it appears about one hour after the extrusion of the second polar body (Pl. IV, A). It is very rich in α-granules (mitochondria). The viscosity of the animal pole plasm is rather low; when the eggs are centrifuged, it is not displaced as a whole, but split into its components which are arranged according to their specific gravities (RAVEN, 1946c).

5. The behaviour of various cytoplasmic inclusions during maturation and fertilization

a. PROTEID YOLK

As stated above, in the recently-laid egg of *Limnaea* (RAVEN, 1945) most β-granules are found in the vegetative pole plasm, whereas the majority of the γ-granules occupies the rest of the egg (Pl. III, A). The β-granules are shifted with the pole plasm substance, most of them later lying in the subcortical plasm. The γ-granules collect during the

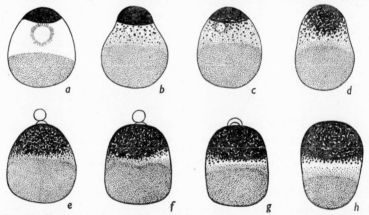

Fig. 10. Changes in the relative proportions of the layers in eggs of *Limnaea stagnalis*, centrifuged at different moments during the uncleaved stage. The centripetal zone increases, the centrifugal zone decreases in size owing to the swelling and consequent decrease in specific weight of the γ-granules.

maturation divisions around the asters and spindles (Pl. V, A). After the extrusion of the second polar body they are more or less uniformly distributed throughout the inner protoplasm of the egg. Beginning about ten minutes after the formation of the first polar body, vacuoles form around the γ-granules (Pl. I, B-F). They gradually increase in size, so that the cytoplasm, with the exception of the subcortical plasm and the animal pole plasm, has a highly vacuolar structure towards the end of the uncleaved stage, γ-granules lying in the vacuoles (Pl. IV, A).

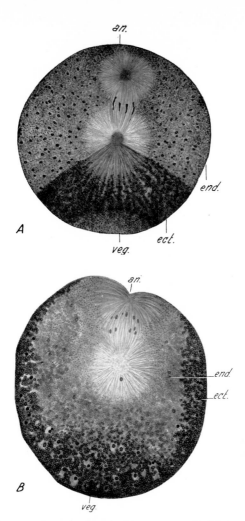

Plate III. The vegetative pole plasm in *Limnaea stagnalis*. (A) Egg immediately after laying. Early anaphase of first maturation division. Vegetative pole plasm (*ect.*) forms sector at vegetative pole (*veg.*) of egg. (B) Late anaphase of first maturation division. Outer end of spindle in contact with egg cortex at animal pole (*an.*); depression of egg surface. Vegetative pole plasm (*ect.*) has spread beneath egg cortex and surrounds inner plasm (*end.*), except at animal side. Beginning of formation of vacuoles around γ-granules.

[*Facing page* 36

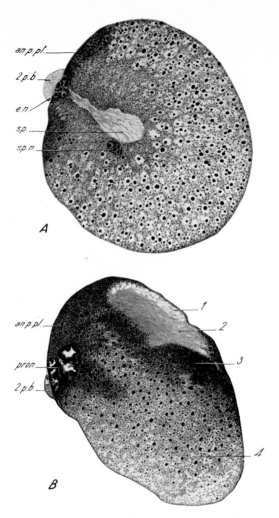

Plate IV. The animal pole plasm in *Limnaea stagnalis*. (A) Normal egg, about one hour prior to first cleavage. Animal pole plasm (*an.p.pl.*) at animal side beneath egg cortex. Rest of protoplasm strongly vacuolated, γ-granules in vacuoles. Karyomeres of egg nucleus (*e.n.*) at animal pole. Remnant of sperm aster (*sp.*) with clear area, reaching with neck-line projection to animal pole. Sperm nucleus (*sp.n.*) on its way to animal pole. (B) Egg, which had been centrifuged just after laying, and fixed $3\frac{1}{2}$ hours later. 1-4, layers of stratified egg substances; readjustment of substances not yet completed. Animal pole plasm (*an.p.pl.*) formed in neighbourhood of animal pole, where pronuclei (*pron.*) are also found.

While the compact γ-granules at the beginning of the uncleaved stage have a high specific gravity and therefore accumulate at the centrifugal end in centrifuged eggs, later the swollen γ-granules with their vacuoles are displaced centripetally at centrifuging (Fig. 10). From the changes in the relative volumes of the layers in centrifuged eggs, it can be calculated that the γ-granules absorb about three times their own volume of water during the uncleaved stage.

Similar relationships have been found in *Physa* by CLEMENT (1938). Vacuoles are formed also in this case from coarse yolk granules.

The vegetative concentration of the proteid yolk during maturation in opisthobranchs and some prosobranchs has been mentioned above (p. 34).

b. FATTY YOLK

In *Limnaea* (RAVEN, 1945) the oil droplets are rather uniformly distributed, but are absent from the maturation spindle and asters and the egg cortex. The concentration of oil drops is somewhat greater in the peripheral part of the vegetative hemisphere. The animal pole plasm, on the contrary, is very poor in fat.

In *Arion* (LAMS, 1910) the fat droplets are also preferentially located near the vegetative pole.

In *Physa* (MANCUSO, 1953) the fatty yolk shifts during maturation towards the vegetative pole. After the extrusion of the polar bodies fat droplets of various sizes are found in the vegetative three quarters of the egg, while the animal pole area is free of fat. The same holds for *Bithynia* (ATTARDO, 1955a).

On the other hand, in *Aplysia* (RIES and GERSCH, 1936) and *Navanax* (WORLEY and WORLEY, 1943) the concentration of the proteid yolk in the vegetative two thirds of the egg is accompanied by an accumulation of the fatty yolk granules in the animal part, where they occupy a layer between the proteid yolk and the clear hyaloplasm area at the animal pole (Fig. 11).

In *Ilyanassa* the lipid droplets, stainable with Sudan and with OsO_4, are likewise accumulated in the animal part of the egg, decreasing along a gradient towards the equator (CLEMENT and LEHMANN, 1956).

c. GOLGI

In *Limnaea* (RAVEN, 1945) dictyoles and dictyosomes are more or less uniformly distributed throughout the cytoplasm, but are absent from the spindles and asters. The same holds at first for the egg of *Navanax* (WORLEY and WORLEY, 1943), but after the vegetative accumulation of the proteid yolk the Golgi bodies lie chiefly, although not exclusively,

D

in the animal half. In *Tethys* they show a condensation around the nucleus. In *Aplysia* (RIES and GERSCH, 1936) the 'Speichergranula' (which, according to WORLEY and WORLEY, are presumably identical

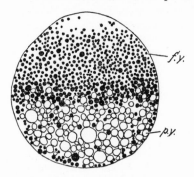

Fig. 11. Distribution of fatty yolk (*f.y.*) and proteid yolk (*p.y.*) in ripe egg of *Aplysia limacina* (cf. Pl. II C). After RIES and GERSCH, 1936.

with Golgi bodies) have at first mainly a peripheral location, but later they are concentrated in a narrow ring at the boundary between the proteid and fatty yolk zones (Fig. 12).

A transformation of dictyoles into dictyosomes takes place during maturation in *Mytilus* (WORLEY, 1944).

d. MITOCHONDRIA

In *Arion* (LAMS, 1910) and *Limnaea* (RAVEN, 1945) the mitochondria concentrate around the maturation spindles; often, they lie in rows between the astral rays (Pl. V, B). After the extrusion of the second polar body the mitochondria accumulate in both cases near the animal pole, where they lie in *Limnaea* in the animal pole plasm. In *Aplysia* (RIES and GERSCH, 1936) the mitochondria are at first peripherally located, but begin even before the dissolution of the germinal vesicle to accumulate at the animal pole. In *Ilyanassa* they are also mainly accumulated around the animal pole (CLEMENT and LEHMANN, 1956).

6. Cytochemistry

a. GLYCOGEN

In *Limnaea* (RAVEN, 1945) the glycogen is concentrated after the extrusion of the second polar body around the dwindling maturation aster. In centrifuged eggs it is heaped up in the zone of mitochondria (RAVEN and BRETSCHNEIDER, 1942) (Fig. 13e). Both observations might suggest that the glycogen granules are bound, at least at this stage, to mitochondria.

In *Physa* (MANCUSO, 1953) the glycogen shifts towards the vegetative side during maturation. After the extrusion of the first polar body it is restricted to the vegetative three quarters, after the extrusion of the second polar body even to the vegetative one third of the egg (Fig. 23a).

In the egg of *Helix* no glycogen at all has been found by quantitative biochemical methods (MAY and WEINLAND, 1953), but galactogen is present in considerable amount. Glycogen formation does not begin until the ninth or tenth day of development, when the heart and foot musculature are being differentiated.

b. MUCOPOLYSACCHARIDES

The granules of the proteid yolk in *Limnaea* exhibit a positive PAS-staining, whereby the γ-granules stain somewhat more strongly than the β-granules. The ground cytoplasm is weakly PAS-positive, especially in its denser parts, e.g. the animal pole plasm (H. VAN DER HEIDE, unpublished observations).*

c. DESOXYRIBONUCLEIC ACID

In *Barnea* and *Limnaea* DNA is found in the egg chromosomes and the sperm head, later in the pronuclei (BRACHET, 1929; RAVEN, 1945). According to ITO and LEUCHTENBERGER (1955), in *Spisula* the DNA in the sperm as well as in the egg pronucleus increase at the time of pronucleus formation from the haploid value up to approximately the diploid value.

d. RIBONUCLEIC ACID

In *Limnaea* RNA is found diffusely in the cytoplasm and in the β-granules (RAVEN, 1945). According to MINGANTI (1950), the chromosomes, beside DNA, also contain RNA.

CLELAND (1951) studied the nucleic acid content of various fractions of *Ostrea* eggs obtained by ultracentrifuging. This decreases in the series hyaloplasm > microsomes > mitochondria > proteid yolk.

e. SULPHYDRYL COMPOUNDS

In *Limnaea* glutathione in its reduced form is found around the nuclei and maturation spindles. In centrifuged eggs it is accumulated in the hyaloplasm zone (RAVEN and BRETSCHNEIDER, 1942) (Fig. 13d). Bound

---

* J. J. PASTEELS and J. MULNARD (*Arch. Biol.* **68**, 115, 1957) found mucopoly-saccharides in *Barnea* and *Gryphaea* in the cortical granules, the yolk, the mitochondria, and diffusely in the cytoplasm. The vegetative pole plasm of *Gryphaea* is free from polysaccharides.

sulphydryl compounds are found in the whole egg, but especially in its central part; the cortex is very rich in such compounds.

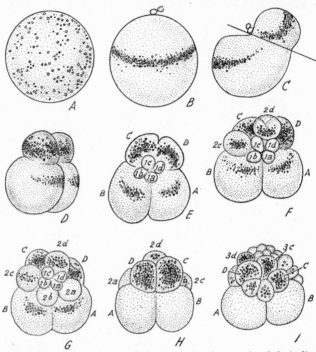

Fig. 12. Distribution of vitamin C during early cleavage in *Aplysia limacina*. (A) Immature egg shortly after laying. Vitamin C granules distributed in peripheral cytoplasm of whole egg. (B) Mature egg after completion of ooplasmic segregation, about three or four hours after oviposition. Annular arrangement of vitamin C granules. (C) Beginning first cleavage, viewed from one side. Plane of cleavage furrow indicated by line. (D) Four-cell stage, obliquely from one side. (E) In the next division the vitamin-free micromeres 1a-1d are formed. Viewed from the animal pole. (F) C and D have formed the second micromeres 2c and 2d, which contain somewhat less vitamin granules than their macromeres. (G) Twelve-cell stage, viewed from the animal pole. A and B have each formed a vitamin-free micromere 2a and 2b. (H) The same stage from the other side. (I) Somewhat further advanced cleavage stage in the same orientation as H. The cells C, D, 3c, and 3d, are especially rich in vitamin C. After RIES, 1937.

f. VITAMIN C

In *Aplysia* (RIES, 1937) vitamin C granules are at first uniformly distributed throughout the egg. During maturation they concentrate in a narrow peripheral supraequatorial ring, corresponding to the 'Speichergranula' (= Golgi bodies, cf. above p. 38) (Fig. 12).

g. BENZIDINE PEROXIDASE

In *Aplysia* (RIES, 1937) the whole egg at first gives the benzidine peroxidase reaction. With the beginning of maturation and the accompanying vegetative concentration of the proteid yolk, the reaction gradually becomes weaker in the animal cytoplasm, and stronger in the vegetative material. However, the enzyme is not bound to the yolk granules; in centrifuged eggs it is accumulated in the hyaloplasm along the boundary of the proteid yolk (RIES, 1938). In *Limnaea*, a similar localization of the benzidine peroxidase reaction has been found in centrifuged eggs (RAVEN and BRETSCHNEIDER, 1942); however, here it clearly corresponds to the zone of mitochondria (Fig. 13b).

h. INDOPHENOL OXIDASE

MANCUSO has shown (1954, 1955b) that a positive nadi-reaction may be given by two different enzymes: cytochrome oxidase and a stable M-nadi oxidase, as well as by some fatty substances. The latter circumstance may explain the findings of RIES (1937) in *Aplysia*, where a

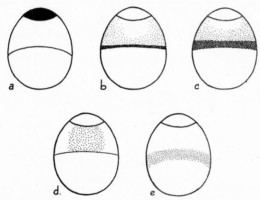

Fig. 13. Accumulation of cytochemical substances in centrifuged eggs of *Limnaea stagnalis*. (a) Fat. (b) Benzidine peroxidase. (c) Indophenol oxidase. (d) Glutathione. (e) Glycogen.

positive reaction is given by granules, which are uniformly distributed at first, but later concentrate in the zone of small fatty yolk granules in the animal half of the egg. Apparently, here it is the fatty yolk itself which gives the reaction.*

In *Limnaea* and *Physa*, the granules giving a positive indophenol

* RIES' results have recently been confirmed by ATTARDO (*Acta Embr. Morphol. exp.* **1**, 65, 1957), who has shown that the reaction in *Aplysia* is due to cytochrome oxidase bound to the mitochondria.

oxidase reaction are rather uniformly distributed, but are absent from the area of the maturation spindles. The reaction may also in this case be partly due to fatty yolk. However, observations on centrifuged eggs of *Limnaea* and *Physa* show that the mitochondria also exhibit a positive reaction (RAVEN and BRETSCHNEIDER, 1942; MANCUSO, 1954) (Fig. 13c), which is apparently due to the enzyme cytochrome oxidase, since it is inhibited by sodium azide (MANCUSO, 1955b). The same holds for *Bithynia*, where the cytochrome oxidase in normal eggs is restricted to the animal pole plasm (ATTARDO, 1955a) (Fig. 24).

i. LEUCOMETHYLENE BLUE OXIDOREDUCTASE

The oxidation of leucomethylene blue in *Aplysia* mainly takes place in the animal protoplasmic area (RIES, 1937). In centrifuged eggs, it is restricted to the zone of hyaloplasm (RIES, 1938).

j. VARIOUS OTHER ENZYMES

CLELAND (1951) studied the distribution of various enzymes in the fractions of *Ostrea* eggs obtained by ultra-centrifuging. Succinoxidase is found both in the proteid yolk and in the mitochondria, but its activity in the latter is about four times as strong. A similar localization is found with respect to various other enzymes of the tricarboxylic acid cycle; they are found in the proteid yolk granules and the mitochondria, but not in the microsomes and the ground cytoplasm. On the contrary, amylase occurs only in the ground cytoplasm, whereas lipase, apyrase and acid phosphatase are distributed about equally among ground cytoplasm and granules.

In the *Ilyanassa* egg, alanylglycine dipeptidase activity is probably contained in the hyaline protoplasm or its finer inclusions (COLLIER, 1954).

k. IRON

In the oviposited eggs of *Limnaea* ionic iron is bound to the β-granules; therefore, especially the subcortical plasm is rich in iron. No iron is found in the asters (ARENDSEN DE WOLFF-EXALTO, 1947).

7. Physicochemical properties of the egg system

a. pH

According to SPEK, in the eggs of various animals, treated with vital stains having the properties of pH-indicators (e.g. neutral red, nile blue hydrochloride, brilliant cresyl violet, etc.) colour differences between the animal and vegetative sides appear at the time of maturation or early cleavage. This he explained by assuming that this *bipolar differentiation* was due to a segregation of positively and negatively charged colloid particles, which were at first uniformly mixed throughout the cytoplasm, but later accumulated at opposite poles of the egg.

So, in *Loligo*, the egg is at first uniformly coloured in an intermediate tint. When the germinal disc is formed, this is stained with a tint corresponding to an alkaline reaction, whereas the rest of the egg shows an 'acid' colour. Similarly, in the egg of *Columbella*, after the 'bipolar differentiation' has taken place, the animal zone of clear cytoplasm stains with a purely 'alkaline' tint, then follows a zone with small granules showing a somewhat more 'acid' reaction, while the region of big yolk platelets in the vegetative half has a colour corresponding to a strong acid reaction (SPEK, 1934).

Similar differences of staining have been observed in *Aplysia* by RIES and GERSCH (1936). However, apart from the fact that they warned against a too ready conclusion on the existence of pH-differences from the results of vital staining experiments, their interpretation differs considerably from that of SPEK. According to them, rather than a segregation of colloid particles it is the concentration of the proteid yolk in the vegetative part of the egg which is responsible for the observed differences in staining.

This was confirmed by RAVEN (1938) by means of combined centrifugation and vital staining experiments, in which it was shown that e.g. in the eggs of *Aplysia* the proteid yolk accumulated by centrifuging stains with an 'acid' tint, while substances with 'alkaline' staining properties accumulated at first in the oil cap, and later diffused into the hyaloplasm zone. Moreover, in species in which no polar concentration of the yolk takes place, like *Limnaea*, no 'bipolar differentiation' becomes visible with vital staining (RAVEN, 1945).

b. rH

The oxidoreduction potential of the parts of the egg can be studied by means of basic dyes showing differences in colour between their reduced and oxidized forms (e.g. methylene blue, Janus green). In the eggs of *Aplysia*, after the bipolar differentiation (vegetative concentration of the proteid yolk) has taken place, the oxidation of leucomethylene blue occurs most rapidly in the animal zone of clear cytoplasm (RIES and GERSCH, 1936). On the other hand, the reduction of basic dyes (e.g. Janus green) begins in the vegetative material, and appears bound to the proteid yolk granules. The eggs of *Loripes*, *Ostrea* and *Cerithium* behave in a similar way (STRELIN, 1939). On the contrary, in *Chiton* (STRELIN) and *Navanax* (WORLEY and WORLEY, 1943) the reduction of methylene blue begins at the animal pole. No rH-differences can be demonstrated in this way in *Limnaea* (RAVEN, 1945).

c. OSMOTIC PROPERTIES

The osmotic relations of marine eggs with the surrounding medium in general raise no special difficulties. As a rule, the eggs are in osmotic equilibrium with seawater; they swell upon dilution of the medium, and shrink when it is made hypertonic.

In eggs laid in freshwater a great discrepancy must exist between the inner and outer osmotic pressure. We may expect, therefore, to find in such eggs special conditions serving to prevent an excessive swelling. *A priori*, three such conditions might be considered: (1) total impermeability of the egg surface to water; (2) a restricted water permeability, giving a slow swelling of the egg and embryo until a stage is reached where larval kidneys begin to function; (3) precocious development of a water-excreting mechanism. As we shall see, the two last-mentioned conditions are apparently found in freshwater molluscs.

CLEMENT (1938) and RAVEN (1945) have established that a slow swelling of the eggs occurs during the uncleaved stage in *Physa* and *Limnaea*, respectively. In both cases, the egg volume increases by about 40–50 per cent till first cleavage. The water taken up by the eggs is bound mainly to the swelling γ-granules (cf. p. 36). This swelling is an osmotic phenomenon; its rate is related to the osmotic pressure of the medium (RAVEN and KLOMP, 1946). The recently-laid *Limnaea* egg is in osmotic equilibrium with an 0·093 M non-electrolyte solution, having an osmotic pressure of about 2·1 atmospheres.

From the equilibrium volumes attained in solutions of different osmotic pressures, the *non-solvent volume* of the *Limnaea* egg has been calculated at 57 per cent of the original egg volume. This is an excessively high value, as compared with other eggs. The non-solvent volume of *Ostrea* eggs amounts to 44 per cent, according to LUCKÉ and RICCA (1941). This difference may be linked up with the above-mentioned special conditions of freshwater eggs.

This becomes much clearer with respect to the *permeability constants* for water. In *Limnaea*, this constant was found to lie in the neighbourhood of 2×10^{-7} (expressed in gram-molecules/sec/cm²/gram-molecule/ liter). In order to get an impression of the significance of this value, it is useful to realize that this means that only 6 grams of water permeate per hour through a surface of one square meter under a pressure difference of one atmosphere! From the figures given by LUCKÉ and RICCA (1941) it can be calculated that the permeability constant in the eggs of *Cumingia* is about four times, in those of *Ostrea* six times as large. Water

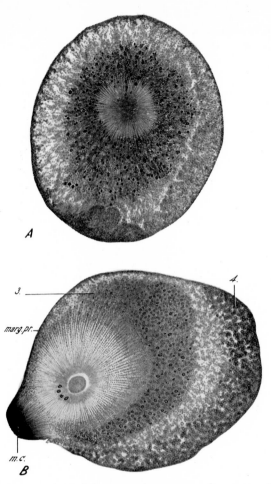

Plate V. Directive actions of the maturation asters on the movements of cytoplasmic components in *Limnaea stagnalis*. (A) Normal egg. Accumulation of α-granules (mitochondria) and γ-granules around deep aster of first maturation spindle. (B) Egg, which had been centrifuged just after laying and fixed one hour later, during formation of first polar body (*m. c.*). Derangement of layers by maturation aster. 3, Layer of α-granules (mitochondria). Granules penetrating in rows between astral rays. 4, Zone of proteid yolk (β) granules *Marg. pr.*, cortical layer.

[*Facing page* 44

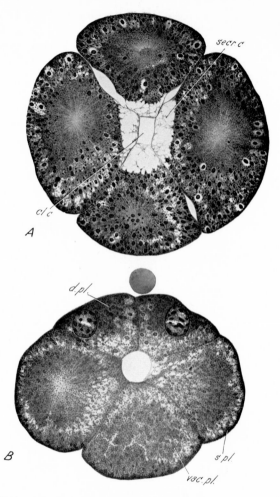

Plate VI. Early cleavage in *Limnaea stagnalis*. (A) Four-cell stage, equatorial section. Small central cleavage cavity (*cl.c.*). Secretion cones (*secr.c.*) on each of the four blastomeres. (B) Eight-cell stage, meridional section (somewhat oblique). Micromeres mostly consisting of dense protoplasm (*d. pl.*), macromeres of vacuolar protoplasm (*vac. pl.*). Narrow layer of subcortical plasm (*s. pl.*) left in macromeres.

permeability is therefore evidently restricted in the fresh-water snail in comparison with the marine forms.

In order to investigate whether there is also an active water excretion, *Limnaea* eggs were chilled to about 3°C, or treated with a 0·001 M KCN solution (RAVEN, BEZEM and GEELEN, 1953). The chilled eggs showed a significant volume increase of about 5 per cent immediately after the beginning of treatment, the eggs treated with cyanide a similar but not wholly significant swelling. These results point to the existence of an active water excretion mechanism, in agreement with ROBINSON's views on the maintenance of the osmotic equilibrium of cells as a steady state. As we shall see, such a mechanism becomes much more conspicuous at a slightly later stage (cf. below p. 75).

d. SPECIFIC GRAVITY

The water uptake by the uncleaved eggs of *Limnaea* is attended with a diminution of their specific gravity; they are at first heavier, then lighter than the surrounding egg capsule fluid (COMANDON and DE FONBRUNE, 1935; RAVEN, 1945).

e. VISCOSITY

The rate of stratification of the contents of eggs centrifuged at a certain combination of time and centrifugal force affords a measure of their *viscosity*. Strictly speaking, this term cannot be used here, since protoplasm is not a homogeneous fluid, but a system consisting of more solid and more fluid parts closely interspersed; apparently, *rigidity* is a better term. Moreover, different parts of the egg have not the same rigidity; in particular the superficial layer or egg cortex appears to have a much more solid consistency than the inner cytoplasm. However, we will follow here common usage and speak of the viscosity, with explicit reference to the inner cytoplasm.

The following observations may be mentioned here. Ovarial eggs of *Cumingia* have a higher viscosity than spawned eggs in seawater (MORGAN, 1910). Viscosity decreases with the breakdown of the germinal vesicle in *Ilyanassa* (CLEMENT, 1935) and *Aplysia* (RIES and GERSCH, 1936). In *Cumingia* there is then a rise in viscosity until a maximum is attained at telophase of the first maturation division, a fall to a low value between maturation divisions, a second maximum at telophase of the second maturation division, followed by a slight fall; a third rise when the pronuclei approach one another, followed by a sudden fall when they have come into contact, a pronounced minimum during prophase of first cleavage, then a rapid rise till anaphase-telophase (FRY and PARKS, 1934). Hence the fluctuations in viscosity reflect the mitotic cycles in the egg. In *Limnaea*, the maxima of viscosity during maturation divisions do not appear; viscosity begins to rise shortly before the extrusion of the second polar body, attains a maximum when the pronuclei meet, drops rapidly until prophase of first cleavage, and rises again when cleavage advances (RAVEN, 1945). A similar course of viscosity changes seems to obtain in *Aplysia*, according to PELTRERA (1940); however, in this case viscosity was not judged by the rate of stratification during centrifugation, but by the rate of redistribution of egg substances after the end of centrifugation, which may account for slight differences in the timing of viscosity changes.

The absolute 'viscosity' of the hyaloplasm of *Cumingia* eggs was determined with various methods by HEILBRUNN (1926) and COSTELLO (1934). All estimates lie below 0·06 (the viscosity of pure water being 0·01), hence indicating a highly fluid state of this component of the egg.

f. CORTICAL RIGIDITY

During centrifuging most eggs undergo a certain degree of elongation. The rate of this elongation under standard conditions provides a measure of the forces working in the egg surface. HARVEY pointed out that this is no pure interfacial tension, since the elastic strength of the cortex and vitelline membrane may come into play. Therefore, he uses the neutral term 'tension at the surface'. In view of recent experiments of MITCHISON and SWANN with sea urchin eggs it seems better to speak of 'cortical rigidity', however.

Its absolute value has been determined by HARVEY (1931), as the centrifugal force necessary to pull the egg in two parts. In *Cumingia* this is 0.54 dyne/cm, in *Ilyanassa* 1·1 dyne/cm.

Fluctuations in cortical rigidity occur during the uncleaved stage in *Limnaea* (RAVEN, 1945); it is low during the extrusion of the first polar body, shortly after the extrusion of the second polar body and immediately before cleavage, higher between these minima. The first two of these minima coincide with periods of amoeboid motility of the egg.

8. Some data on metabolism

Our knowledge of the metabolic processes taking place in the eggs during maturation and fertilization is only very fragmentary.

According to PASTEELS (1935), the breakdown of the germinal vesicle in *Barnea* is not inhibited by anaerobiosis, NaCN or mono-iodacetic acid.

The changes in respiratory activity of the egg occurring at the moment of fertilization vary in different species. In *Mactra lateralis*, respiration increases with fertilization by a factor 1·8, in *Ostrea virginica* by a factor 1·4 (BALLENTINE, 1940). In *Ostrea commercialis*, however, no change in respiratory rate takes place at fertilization (CLELAND, 1950). In *Cumingia* it decreases by a factor 0·45 (WHITAKER, 1933), and in *Spisula solidissima* there is also a decrease in oxygen consumption, the magnitude of which depends on the time that has elapsed between the egg's removal from the ovary and fertilization (SCLUFER, 1955). The respiratory quotient does not change at fertilization in *Ostrea commercialis* and *Spisula*. In *Ostrea* it is about 0·8 in unfertilized as well as recently-fertilized eggs, indicating a combustion of both carbohydrates and fat. In *Spisula* a value in the vicinity of 0·7 was found.

B. CAUSAL ANALYSIS

1. Maturation

As mentioned above (p. 22), in most mollusc eggs maturation begins spontaneously, e.g. after spawning in seawater. In some cases the breakdown of the germinal vesicle normally takes place after the sperm has entered the egg; but germinal vesicle breakdown can often also in these species be provoked in unfertilized eggs.

For example, in unfertilized *Ostrea gigas* eggs dissolution of the germinal vesicle takes place in seawater, but it is delayed in comparison with fertilized eggs; moreover, no normal maturation spindle is formed (INABA, 1936). In *Mactra*, maturation may be initiated in unfertilized eggs by treatment with seawater made hypertonic by evaporation or addition of KCl; one or two polar bodies may be extruded (KOSTANECKI, 1902). Hypertonic KCl-seawater also provokes maturation in unfertilized eggs of *Barnea*. No maturation takes place in isotonic solutions of NaCl, $MgCl_2$, $MgSO_4$ or $NaHCO_3$, nor in a mixture of these solutions. Addition of KCl or $CaCl_2$ to this inactive mixture gives a certain percentage of maturing eggs; addition of both these salts at certain concentrations may produce 100 per cent maturation (DALCQ, 1928). A certain percentage of maturations may also be provoked in *Barnea* eggs in seawater by irradiation with ultraviolet light (PASTEELS, 1931; TCHAKHOTINE, 1935); presumably, an increase in permeability for the ions of the medium is involved in this case.

A further analysis of these phenomena in *Barnea* has been carried out by PASTEELS (1938a, 1938b). Addition of KCl alone, in the absence of calcium ions, stimulates maturation only in those batches which also give a certain percentage of spontaneous maturations in the inactive salt mixture. When such eggs are pretreated with citrate, no maturations occur after addition of KCl. It is concluded that calcium ions give the actual stimulus for maturation; potassium has only a sensitizing action in those eggs, which had previously been impregnated with a certain amount of calcium in the ovary.

Similar results were obtained with the eggs of *Spisula* (ALLEN, 1953). Breakdown of the germinal vesicle may be initiated by ultraviolet irradiation, potassium, sodium, ammonia, hypertonicity and hypotonicity, and protamine. A minimum amount of calcium in the medium ($\pm 5 \times 10^{-4}$ *M*) is necessary. If irradiation of the eggs by ultraviolet light in the absence of calcium is followed by transfer of the eggs to normal seawater, germinal vesicle breakdown occurs, but the ability of the eggs to respond decreases with time. Monovalent cations increase, but divalent cations decrease the excitability of the egg. Maintenance of the egg in the germinal vesicle stage prior to fertilization is probably due to sodium-potassium antagonism. Release of calcium from protein binding in the cortex, followed by calcium activation of a proteolytic or lipolytic enzyme, is probably the direct cause of germinal vesicle breakdown.

SAWADA (1952, 1954 a and b) studied the question of what prevents maturation before spawning in *Mactra*. Germinal vesicle breakdown in seawater is inhibited by addition of body fluid of *Mactra* or *Meretrix*. The inhibitory substance is not removed by boiling or filtration with active carbon. Some inhibition was also obtained with heparin and tragant. A high percentage of germinal vesical breakdown could be provoked by periodate in the presence of calcium. It is concluded that the maturation divisions of the eggs in the ovary are prevented by the presence of certain polysaccharides in the body fluid and egg cortex. The removal of the inhibition evokes maturation, presumably through increased permeability to ions.

In those species, where maturation begins spontaneously, it usually stops at metaphase of the first maturation division in unfertilized eggs. According to HEILBRUNN (1920), this is caused in *Cumingia* by the tension of the stiff vitelline membrane. When this tension is removed, e.g. by softening the membrane through swelling, or its elevation or removal by shaking the eggs, the maturation divisions are continued and completed.

Mention may be made here of the classical experiments of DELAGE (1899) showing that fragments of *Dentalium* eggs, in which the germinal vesicle was intact at the moment of fragmentation, were unfertilizable, whereas non-nucleated fragments of eggs with ruptured germinal vesicle could be fertilized and developed as merogones. This shows that the properties of the egg change at the moment of germinal vesicle breakdown, presumably by the extrusion of the karyolymph into the cytoplasm.

When molluscan eggs are centrifuged some time before the extrusion of the polar bodies, the germinal vesicle or early maturation spindle is displaced; as a rule, it comes to lie in the zone of hyaloplasm. When maturation approaches, various things may occur. In some cases, the maturation spindle rises to the surface at some point, which bears no relation to the stratification of the egg, pushing aside the egg substances (e.g. oil, yolk) accumulated in this region, and the polar bodies are formed at this place (*Cumingia*: MORGAN, 1910; *Aplysia*: RAVEN, 1938). We may assume that in those cases the maturation spindle returns to the original animal pole, which has not been displaced by centrifuging. In other cases, the polar bodies are always extruded in the hyaline zone or immediately adjacent to it (*Physa* and *Limnaea*: CONKLIN, 1910; *Crepidula*: CONKLIN, 1917; Nudibranchia: COSTELLO, 1939b). Presumably, the return of the maturation spindle to the original animal pole has been hindered mechanically by the accumulated yolk substances, and the polar bodies now form at an arbitrary point of the surface. This does not mean, however, that the original polarity of the egg has been changed, as is shown by the further development of these eggs (cf. below p. 91). Some authors claim to have effected an actual change in polarity by strong centrifugal force (*Cumingia*: PEASE, 1940; *Aplysia*: PELTRERA, 1940). This needs further confirmation, however; in PELTRERA's case, the possibility of an orientation of the eggs in the centrifuge has not been taken into account.

We may conclude from these experiments that the original polarity of the eggs (which is related to their orientation in the ovary, cf. above p. 5) as a rule is not changed at least by moderate centrifuging. It must be bound to some component of the egg which is relatively immovable under the influence of centrifugal force. Presumably, this is the more or less solid egg cortex. The polar migration of the maturation spindle in normal development is controlled by factors residing in the cortex; when this migration is prevented, however, polar bodies may be formed at any point of the egg surface without interfering with the original polarity.

On the nature of the factors directing the movement of the maturation spindles nothing is known. One might think of electrostatic forces. However, attempts to change the course or direction of developmental processes in *Limnaea* by exposing the eggs to a strong electric field (RAVEN, 1948) had no effect; no abnormalities occurred as long as the egg cortex remained intact.

The next question concerns the cause of the inequality of the maturation divisions. The following observations have a bearing on this question. If *Crepidula* eggs are centrifuged after the maturation spindles have become affixed to the egg surface, the spindles are not displaced as a whole, but only stretched and distorted. When yolk is accumulated in the animal part of the egg, these stretched spindles may give rise to the formation of giant polar bodies, which may even be as large as the rest of the egg (CONKLIN, 1917). Similar results were obtained by CLEMENT (1935) in *Ilyanassa*, but in this case the second maturation spindles had

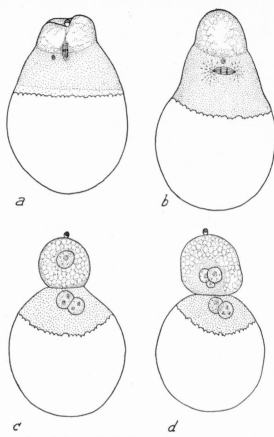

Fig. 14. Formation of giant polar bodies in centrifuged eggs of *Ilyanassa*. (a) Second maturation spindle forced away from animal pole, but remains connected by strands of cytoplasm. Condensed sperm nucleus at border of oil and cytoplasmic zones. (b) Second maturation spindle lying free in cytoplasmic zone. Sperm nucleus between spindle and oil zone. First polar body lost. (c, d) Giant polar bodies in eggs centrifuged before second maturation division. After CLEMENT, 1935.

been displaced as a whole towards the centre of the egg (Fig. 14). If the sperm nucleus came to lie in the giant polar body, the latter developed instead of the egg. A further analysis of this case was given by MORGAN

(1936, 1937). He showed that the division of the egg into two nearly equal parts at the time of the second maturation division only occurred, if the egg was elongated and constricted in the middle, and the displaced second maturation spindle was situated near the constriction. The cell division occurred at this place during anaphase of the second meiotic division, even when the two nuclei from this division passed into the same half. That part which contained the sperm nucleus cleaved, the other half did not. MORGAN points out that there is no reasonable ground for calling the cleaving half an egg, and the uncleaved half a giant polar body.

Anyhow, it appears that the inequality of the maturation divisions is not due to inherent properties of the maturation spindles, but to their eccentric position in the neighbourhood of the animal pole, which, as we have seen above, is controlled by cortical factors. Hence it follows that it must be possible to influence the course of the maturation divisions by exposing the eggs to external factors affecting the cortex. This is confirmed by the phenomena, summed up under the term *depolarization* by DALCQ.

Incidental observations on depolarization of the maturation spindles had already been made by KOSTANECKI (1904) in *Mactra*. PASTEELS (1930) then gave a full account of these phenomena in *Barnea*. Depolarization may be brought about by $CaCl_2$, to a less extent also by $MgCl_2$ or diluted seawater. In unfertilized eggs, the first maturation spindle is blocked in metaphase. The poles of the spindle may divide, so that pluripolar spindles are formed. In fertilized eggs, sometimes the first maturation division takes place below the surface; two second maturation spindles or one pluripolar spindle are formed following such a 'submerged' first division. In other cases, the second maturation spindle sinks into the depth and remains blocked in metaphase; a considerable enlargement of spindle and asters may then occur. In some cases giant polar bodies may be formed.

Depolarization of *Barnea* eggs may also occur following ultraviolet or X-ray irradiation (PASTEELS, 1931). Treatment with $CaCl_2$ only gives depolarization when it is suboptimal or supraoptimal; with optimal treatment of unfertilized eggs, normal polar body formation takes place as a rule (PASTEELS, 1938a).

In *Limnaea*, depolarization has been produced by treatment with weakly hypertonic solutions of $CaCl_2$ (RAVEN and MIGHORST, 1946) or LiCl (DE GROOT, 1948). The second maturation spindle may orient itself at right angles to the egg axis, and a 'submerged' second maturation division may ensue. In other cases, giant polar bodies are formed. Sometimes, the egg karyomeres appearing after extrusion of the second polar body are displaced towards the egg centre, and the migration of sperm aster and sperm nucleus is suppressed or delayed.

These experiments demonstrate that external factors affecting the egg cortex may indeed alter the course of the maturation divisions. This makes it probable, therefore, that these processes are controlled in normal development by cortical factors.

2. Fertilization

In many groups of animals, substances produced by the germ cells play an important part in fertilization. The existence of such substances has also been demonstrated in a number of molluscs.

The substances secreted by the eggs (*fertilizin* or *gynogamones*) act in various ways. In the first place, activation of the sperms by seawater containing egg secretions has been observed in *Megathura* (TYLER and FOX, 1939), *Haliotis* and *Fissurella* (V. MEDEM, 1942, 1945), and *Mactra* (METZ and DONOVAN, 1949). In *Chiton*, small clumps of 'dry' sperm, in which the sperms stick together by their tails, are transferred from the male to the female; under the influence of egg secretions, but also of various other substances, the sperms are released and become mobile (SOUTHWICK, 1939).

In the second place, sperm agglutination by egg secretion water occurs in *Chiton, Katharina, Ostrea, Solen, Pecten, Megathura* (TYLER, 1949a) and *Mactra* (METZ and DONOVAN, 1949). No such agglutination has been found in *Tapes, Venus, Patella, Fissurella* and *Haliotis* (V. MEDEM). Sperm agglutination in *Katharina, Mactra* and *Megathura* is not spontaneously reversible. In *Megathura*, the sperms are agglutinated by their tails (TYLER, 1940); in *Mactra* they agglutinate tail to tail, head to head, and probably head to tail. The agglutinin is probably a protein (TYLER and FOX, 1940).

Finally, in many molluscs (*Chiton*, oysters and mussels) spawning is induced by the presence of gametes of the other sex in the water. In the oyster, water containing egg secretions, but no eggs, suffices to induce this reaction in the male.

The substances found in sperm (*antifertilizin* or *androgamones*) also have various actions. Inactivation of own and foreign sperm has been found in various molluscs by V. MEDEM (1942, 1945), neutralization of the sperm agglutinins from eggs in *Megathura* by TYLER (1939).

Finally, *egg membrane lysins* have been demonstrated in sperm extracts of *Megathura, Haliotis, Fissurella* and *Mytilus* (TYLER, 1939; V. MEDEM, 1942, 1945; BERG, 1950; KRAUSS, 1950). The lysin of *Megathura* is probably a protein; electron-micrograms point to its localization in the acrosome of the sperm (TYLER, 1949b). In this connection, MEVES' observations on the dissolution of the acrosome at the moment of sperm penetration (p. 28) may be recalled.*

Immediately after the fertilizing sperm has made contact with the egg cortex, generally the eggs become refractory to the entrance of further sperms. Nothing is known in molluscs about the nature and course of this *cortical reaction*. According to TYLER and SCHEER (1937), in *Dentalium* the loss of fertilizability after fertilization is reversible. When the eggs are transferred soon after fertilization to acidified seawater (pH = 7·2), the development of the fertilizing sperm is blocked. The eggs can be fertilized a second time, after which they cleave normally; apparently, the first sperm has been eliminated or irreversibly blocked by the treatment. A similar reversal of fertilization reactions has been observed in *Spisula*, when the eggs were immersed during the first four or five minutes in calcium-free seawater, acidified seawater, or 0·3–0·5 per cent ether in seawater (ALLEN, 1953). These eggs could be reactivated by an artificial activating agent.

Observations by ITO and LEUCHTENBERGER (1955) indicate that normal fertilization in *Spisula* is dependent on a normal haploid amount of DNA in the sperm. Sperms with a subhaploid DNA value may penetrate into the eggs, but do not activate them.

3. Parthenogenesis

Natural parthenogenesis is found among molluscs in *Potamopyrgus jenkinsi* and *Campeloma rufum* (SANDERSON, 1940). In both cases there is only one maturation division, which is equational, so that we have to do with diploid parthenogenesis.

Experimental parthenogenesis has been induced in the Lamellibranchiata *Mactra* (KOSTANECKI, 1902, 1904, 1908), *Cumingia* (MORRIS, 1917; HEILBRUNN, 1925; HOLLINGSWORTH, 1941), *Ostrea* (INABA, 1936), *Barnea* (TCHAKHOTINE, 1935; PASTEELS, 1938a, 1938b), *Spisula* (ALLEN, 1953) and *Caecella* (MOTOMURA, 1954).

As usual, there is a great variety of activating agents: heat, ultraviolet irradiation, hypertonicity and hypotonicity, sodium, potassium and calcium chloride, sodium citrate, potassium permanganate, ammonia, butyric acid, ether, acetone, etc. According to HEILBRUNN (1925), activation is due to a coagulation of the cytoplasm. PASTEELS (1938) assumes that calcium is the actual activating agent, whereas the other treatments only have a sensitizing action, either by increasing the permeability of the egg cortex for the calcium ions of the outer medium, or by liberating

---

* S. K. WADA, J. R. COLLIER and J. C. DAN (*Exp. Cell Res.* **10**, 168, 1956) have shown that the egg membrane lysin of the *Mytilus* sperm is also contained in the acrosome, and is liberated by the breakdown of the latter on its contact with the vitelline membrane.

E

bound calcium in the cortex, which is then free to diffuse into the inner cytoplasm.

In *Mactra* eggs activated by hypertonic KC1-seawater, cleavage may take place, whether polar bodies have been extruded or not. When both polar bodies have been formed, first a kind of anastral spindle appears, and nuclear division takes place; the two nuclei formed by this division fuse, then in part of the cases a normal cleavage amphiaster is formed. When no polar bodies are extruded, abnormal mitotic divisions take place, which may result in the formation of a normal cleavage amphiaster. Under certain circumstances, however, activation leads to a kind of *differentiation without cleavage* (KOSTANECKI, 1908; also occasionally in *Cumingia*: MORRIS, 1917).

In *Cumingia, Ostrea, Caecella* and *Barnea* there is an inverse relation between polar body formation and cleavage: eggs which extrude both polar bodies do not cleave as a rule, those without polar bodies may cleave (MORRIS, HEILBRUNN, INABA, MOTOMURA, PASTEELS). If polar bodies are formed, as a rule a monaster cycle ensues. In *Ostrea* one monocentric division may be followed by normal dicentric cleavage, however (INABA). If polar body formation is suppressed, a 'submerged' first maturation division may occur; thereafter the two nuclei fuse and a cleavage spindle is formed (MORRIS).

These experiments do not give an unambiguous answer to the question as to the cause of bipolarity of the cleavage amphiaster. Neither do the following, contradictory, observations: Copulation of the pronuclei may be delayed by treatment of the eggs with abnormal seawater in *Crepidula* and *Barnea*. In *Crepidula* an amphiaster is then formed in conjunction with each pronucleus (CONKLIN, 1904); in *Barnea* the male pronucleus forms an amphiaster, the female one a monaster (PASTEELS, 1930).

PASTEELS (1950) observed in abnormal fertilized or activated *Mactra* eggs, in which a monaster cycle occurred, rhythmic movements of the vitelline membrane at the animal and vegetative poles. These are attributed to rhythmic changes in permeability of the egg cortex, leading to localized extrusions of substances from the egg.

The eggs of *Spisula* show slight changes of shape (wrinkling, indentations) following sperm penetration or activation. They are more pronounced after application of some activating agents (hypertonicity, hypotonicity, heat, cold, urea, sodium ions). Such changes in shape cannot be induced in the absence of calcium. Departure from spherical shape is associated with a decrease in volume of 6–8 per cent, and gelation of the cytoplasm, probably by expulsion of water. After four to five minutes there is a recovery of spherical shape, attended by liquefaction, probably through the uptake of water (ALLEN, 1953).

4. The normal sequence of the processes of maturation and fertilization

In normal development, the various processes taking place in the uncleaved egg, from the moment of laying to the beginning of first cleavage, within certain limits all have their fixed place, together forming a regular sequence of events. Not only do the various phases of the maturation divisions follow upon each other with regularity, but other, seemingly independent processes fit into this same sequence. For instance, the sperm aster in *Limnaea* always becomes first visible just before the extrusion of the first polar body. It fuses with the inner end of the second maturation spindle at the moment when this has completed its rotation. The sperm tail remains visible until anaphase of the second maturation division, when it is suddenly dissolved. The sperm nucleus begins to swell simultaneously with the egg chromosomes, immediately after the extrusion of the second polar body; simultaneously, it begins to migrate towards the egg nucleus.

RAVEN and HUPKENS VAN DER ELST (1950) studied the influence of hypertonic solutions on the *Limnaea* egg. In weakly hypertonic solutions, development as a whole was retarded, but the normal sequence was unchanged; apparently, all component processes were equally retarded. In stronger solutions, development was blocked at a certain stage, which was earlier, the more concentrated the solution. All processes normally occurring after this stage then dropped out too, so that e.g. in eggs blocked during the formation of the second maturation spindle, the sperm tail remained visible indefinitely in the cytoplasm. Apparently, therefore, all component processes are bound together in a common temporospatial pattern, either because the completion of each preceding process is a necessary prerequisite for the initiation of the next, or because all visible processes are controlled by an invisible basic process of a progressive nature. The following observations indicate that the latter explanation is the more probable one.

When *Limnaea* eggs are treated at early stages with lithium chloride, the egg chromosomes (dyads) may swell to karyomeres immediately after the extrusion of the *first* polar body (DE GROOT, 1948; RAVEN and ROBORGH, 1949) (Fig. 15). Then the sperm nucleus also swells to a male pronucleus, and migrates towards the animal pole. We may conclude from these observations that: (1) swelling of the egg chromosomes and of the sperm nucleus are coupled, both being probably due to a third factor, which may be a certain condition of the cytoplasm; (2) the swelling of the sperm nucleus and its migration are also coupled; either, it is only attracted by the egg nucleus when a certain degree of swelling has occurred, or it begins to swell only when it has migrated into a more suitable region of the cytoplasm. The latter has been shown to be the case in *Crepidula*, where the sperm nucleus, both in normal and centrifuged eggs, remains very small as long as it is in the yolk, but begins to grow rapidly when it emerges into a cytoplasmic region (CONKLIN, 1912).

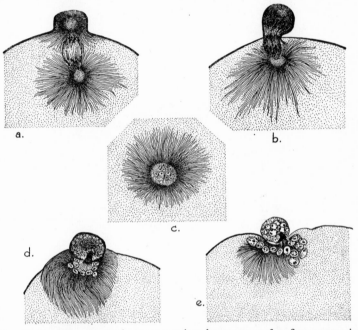

Fig. 15. Swelling of egg chromosomes into karyomeres after first maturation division in lithium-treated eggs of *Limnaea stagnalis*. (a) Late anaphase. (b) Telophase of first maturation division. (c) Swelling of chromosomes. (d, e) Karyomeres surrounding stalk ('mid-body') of first polar body.

In depolarized eggs of *Limnaea*, in which the egg karyomeres are displaced towards the centre, migration of the sperm nucleus appears to be delayed.

The following observation by RAVEN and ROBORGH also points to the significance of the state of the cytoplasm for the timing of the visible processes of maturation and fertilization. In Li-treated eggs, the amoeboid motility after the extrusion of the second polar body may be greatly exaggerated and prolonged, and the sperm aster may remain visible long after its normal time of disappearance, while its centre shows a strong vacuolization. There is a positive correlation between the two phenomena.

It appears probable, therefore, that the normal sequence of the processes of maturation and fertilization is due to a progressive change in the state of the cytoplasm, which successively switches on the various component processes, and provides the basic mechanism underlying their regular temporospatial order.

5. Ooplasmic segregation

Generally speaking, the various components of the egg cytoplasm of the ripe unfertilized mollusc egg are more or less evenly distributed throughout the egg. During the period from ovulation till first cleavage, however, while the nuclear processes of maturation and fertilization are taking place, a shifting of various egg substances occurs, through which they are accumulated or concentrated at certain places in the egg cell. Many examples of this have been mentioned above, e.g. the vegetative concentration of the proteid yolk in Opisthobranchia and Prosobranchia (p. 34), the polar concentration of the germinal cytoplasm in cephalopods (p. 34), the formation and displacement of the animal and vegetative pole plasms in *Limnaea* (p. 35), the differential distribution of fatty yolk (p. 37), Golgi bodies (p. 37), mitochondria (p. 38), glycogen (p. 38), vitamin C (p. 40), benzidine peroxidase (p. 41) and leucomethylene blue oxidoreductase (p. 42), in various eggs. All these processes together, which may be summarized under the term *ooplasmic segregation* (COSTELLO), bring about a situation, in which various parts of the egg differ more or less in their chemical composition: the mainly *intensive multiplicity* of the ripe oocyte begins to be transformed into an *extensive multiplicity* (cf. RAVEN, 1954).

It must be especially emphasized that all these processes of ooplasmic segregation take place in relation to the original animal-vegetative polarity of the egg cell. The egg substances accumulate at certain levels with respect to the main axis, either at the animal or vegetative pole of this axis or somewhere in between. At most, a certain localization with respect to the radial direction (from the surface inwards) may be involved too, as in the subcortical localization of the vegetative pole plasm material and the distribution of sulphydryl compounds in *Limnaea*. It is striking, however, that, apart from certain cephalopods, where the external shape of the egg is bilaterally symmetrical, no traces whatever of a bilateral symmetry occur during the uncleaved stage; so far as the visible localization of substances is concerned, all molluscan eggs are purely radially symmetrical till the beginning of cleavage. The only possible exception to this rule might be, as far as I know, the localization of the mitochondria in *Sphaerium* eggs, according to WOODS (1932; cf.

above p. 10). They are situated to one side of the micropyle, which is supposed, in most cases, to correspond to the vegetative pole of the egg. Since a rotation of the egg within the vitelline membrane would also account for this location of the mitochondria, this case provides no definite proof of a bilateral symmetry of the egg.*

We have mentioned above (p. 43) SPEK's hypothesis according to which a 'bipolar differentiation' occurs, in which electrically charged particles of opposite sign gather at opposite ends of the egg axis. This was supposed to be due to the establishment of an electric field by differential penetration of the ions of the outer medium through various parts of the egg cortex (*kataphoresis in the living cell*). A similar explanation has been given by COSTELLO (1945), who puts forward the possible role of diffusion potentials as a cause of ooplasmic segregation. There are, however, no direct observations supporting these views. *Limnaea* eggs exposed to a strong electric field showed no deviations of development, provided that the egg cortex remained intact; if, however, after some time the cortex was destroyed at the side of the anode, this was followed by a sudden stratification of the egg contents (RAVEN, 1948). As a matter of fact, this latter observation shows that the components of the cytoplasm are indeed electrically charged. It appears possible that an intracellular field is involved in their normal distribution, which is insulated from outward disturbance by the intact egg cortex.

Indirectly, the results of centrifuge experiments may contribute to our knowledge of the causes of ooplasmic segregation, as they show the manner in which a more or less typical localization of substances is reached from a quite atypical starting-point.

In the older investigations on centrifuged molluscan eggs, it was assumed that the substances displaced by centrifugal force remained for the greater part in their new positions, so that hardly any redistribution of substances took place (MORGAN, 1910; CONKLIN, 1910). Later it appeared, however, that in many cases the stratification brought about by centrifuging disappeared in a relatively short time, and a more or less normal distribution of substances was attained e.g. in *Ilyanassa* (MORGAN, 1933), *Aplysia* (PASTEELS, 1934; RAVEN, 1938; RIES, 1938) and *Limnaea* (RAVEN and BRETSCHNEIDER, 1942).

In this redistribution of substances, two phases must be distinguished:

* According to J. FAUTREZ (*Jour. Embr. exp. Morph.* 5, 300, 1957) the animal zone of hyaline protoplasm formed by the vegetative concentration of the yolk in *Aplysia punctata* does not coincide with the animal pole, but lies eccentrically on the side of the future blastomere D. In other species of *Aplysia* (*A. limacina*, *A. depilans*) such a phenomenon has not been observed; the polar bodies are situated as a rule in the centre of the clear hemisphere (cf. fig. 12B; pl. II, C). Only just before the beginning of cleavage does the asymmetrical position of the hyaline area become evident (fig. 12C; pl. II, E).

(1) the disappearance of the stratification and the recovery of a more homogeneous distribution of substances; (2) the occurrence of ooplasmatic segregations resembling those in normal development.

As regards the first point, it should be borne in mind that the separation and stratification of egg substances, as brought about by centrifugal force, becomes a very 'improbable' distribution, as soon as this force ceases to work. This means that there will be a tendency to the 'spontaneous' recovery of a more uniform distribution. Hence, the

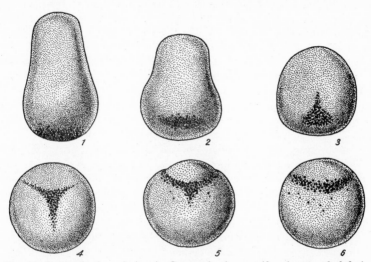

Fig. 16. Redistribution of vitamin C granules in centrifuged eggs of *Aplysia limacina*. (1) Immediately after centrifugation; granules accumulated at centrifugal pole. (2-4) Recovery of spherical shape. Granules migrate through centre of egg. (5-6) Granules returned to their normal position in the egg (cf. Fig. 12). After Peltrera, 1940.

thermal movements of molecules, expressing themselves as diffusion of dissolved substances and Brownian movements of granules, automatically lead to a disappearance of the sharp boundaries between substances. It has been observed in *Limnaea* that the substances demonstrable by cytochemical methods disperse through the egg even more rapidly than the particulate inclusions (Raven and Bretschneider).

On top of this, however, all displacements of substances due to other causes will in general only hasten the attainment of the state of equilibrium, which is given by the homogeneous distribution of substances. Such displacements are caused e.g. by the formation and movements of asters, spindles and nuclei during maturation and copulation of the pronuclei (Pl. V, B); by the cytoplasmic currents occurring during these processes (cf. above p. 34) (Fig. 9, 31a); and by the changes in shape of the egg (amoeboid movements, polar lobes) taking place at these stages (cf. above p. 32). Moreover, the elastic recovery of the spherical shape by the elongated egg after removal from the centrifuge may play an important part (Fig. 16); this has especially been emphasized by PEL-TRERA (1940). Finally, in some cases a viscous cytoplasmic network may be present, which is only stretched and distorted, but not broken during centrifuging, and which returns the egg components to their normal position after the end of centrifuging, e.g. in *Crepidula* (CONKLIN, 1917) and *Ilyanassa* (MORGAN, 1933) (Fig. 18).

The second phase distinguished above, the occurrence of ooplasmic segregations, in a way is quite the reverse of the first, as here a greater degree of heterogeneity arises from a more homogeneous distribution. This would represent the transition from a more to a less 'probable' state, unless special forces are admitted driving the system in this direction. In other words, from the observed segregation phenomena conclusions may be drawn about the existence of such forces.

As an example we may cite the case of *Aplysia*, where a bipolar differentiation takes place in centrifuged eggs irrespective of the direction of stratification (RAVEN, 1938). The behaviour of vitamin C granules (probably bound to Golgi bodies) has been especially studied by PEL-TRERA (1940). On centrifugation, these granules become heaped up at the centrifugal pole. After the end of centrifuging, however, they return within five to twenty minutes, depending on the circumstances, to their normal position, forming a supraequatorial ring as in normal eggs (Fig. 16). In eggs centrifuged early, before the beginning of maturation, the vitamin C granules do not attain this localization at once, but simultaneously with their segregation in uncentrifuged controls.

A second example is the animal pole plasm in *Limnaea*. In eggs centrifuged before maturation, this pole plasm forms at the normal time, about one hour after the second maturation division, near the original animal pole (RAVEN, 1945; RAVEN and BRUNNEKREEFT, 1951) (Pl. IV, B). This process takes time, however; a normal pole plasm is only formed when at least two hours have elapsed after centrifuging.

We may conclude from these observations that the factors controlling ooplasmic segregation, like those directing the nuclei and spindles, are bound to some component which is not displaced by moderate centrifuging, hence presumably to the egg cortex. We may assume e.g. in *Limnaea* that the cortex near the animal pole has special properties, as a result of which it begins at a certain stage to attract particular components of the cytoplasm. There are some indications that these special properties have only been obtained during maturation by an interaction between the cortex and the underlying plastin-rich cytoplasm of the spindle area. As a matter of fact, in eggs centrifuged early, a cytoplasmic

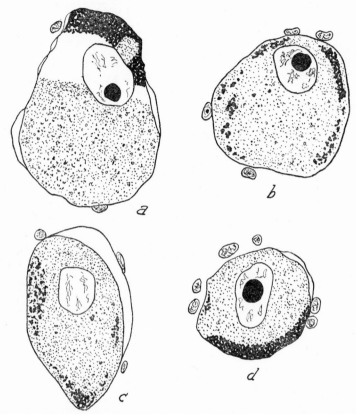

Fig. 17. Redistribution of fat in centrifuged oocytes of *Limnaea stagnalis appressa*. (a) Immediately after centrifugation, showing distinct stratification into an osmiophilic centripetal zone, clear central zone, and granular yolky zone. Granular area above germinal vesicle represents yolk 'trapped' at centripetal end of cell. (b) Oocyte fixed one-half hour following centrifugation; (c) fixed one hour after centrifugation; (d) oocyte fixed six hours after centrifugation. Cf. Fig. 5. After HARTUNG, 1947.

substance resembling the animal pole plasm, though somewhat less dense, accumulates at those places beneath the cortex where the hyaloplasm zone was situated immediately after centrifuging. Apparently, these parts of the cortex have properties resembling those of the animal

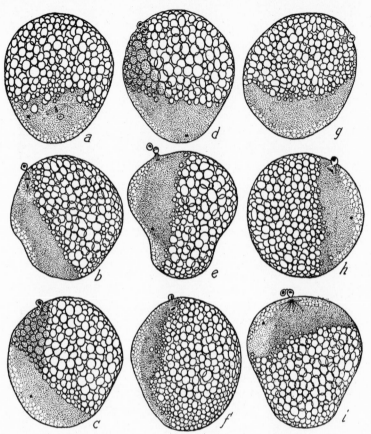

Fig. 18. The formation of the polar lobe in eggs of *Ilyanassa*, centrifuged in reverse orientation before the first polar body had been formed. The second polar lobe arose seventy minutes later. All nine eggs (except (a) and (i)) show partial return of the cytoplasm toward the animal pole. The polar bodies were given off before the spindle reached the pole. The lobe formed at or near its normal field. Even when as in (a) the spindle did not return to the animal pole, the lobe formed at the vegetative pole and contained only cytoplasm and oil. The egg drawn in (i) had probably not reversed or only partly so, and the polar bodies were given off at the animal pole. After MORGAN, 1933.

pole region. One might even surmise that in this way the alleged change in polarity by strong centrifuging (cf. above, p. 49) may be explained.

The view that ooplasmic segregation is controlled by cortical factors receives further support from those cases where this segregation is disturbed by external agencies affecting the egg cortex. For instance, in eggs of *Limnaea* treated with lithium chloride the normal distribution of the subcortical plasm may be disturbed, and the formation of the animal pole plasm entirely suppressed (DE GROOT, 1948).

The cortical factors responsible for the formation of the animal pole plasm in *Limnaea* apparently remain active for some time after the stage at which this pole plasm is formed in normal development. When the eggs are treated with lithium up to the stage of pole plasm formation, and then are transferred to tapwater, recovery may occur and a pole plasm is formed with some delay (VAN DEN BROEK and RAVEN, 1951). Moreover, in eggs centrifuged immediately before first cleavage, in which the mitochondria are heaped up in a middle zone of the egg, they are soon dispersed over the cells, and in the course of some hours accumulate near the animal pole as they do in normal eggs (RAVEN, 1946c).

It appears from HARTUNG's observations (1947) that similar directing cortical factors are already active during oogenesis. In centrifuged ovarial oocytes of *Limnaea* the fat droplets are accumulated centripetally, but they return within six hours to their original localization at the vegetative pole (cf. above, p. 15) (Fig. 17).

We come to the conclusion, therefore, that ooplasmic segregation is mainly controlled by cortical factors, which are not displaced by moderate centrifuging. MORGAN's experiments (1933, 1935a, 1935b) on the formation of the polar lobe in *Ilyanassa* also point to the importance of the egg cortex. If eggs are centrifuged in reverse orientation before maturation, the polar lobe forms at the time of second maturation in its normal position irrespective of the cytoplasmic substances it contains (Fig. 18). Therefore, the factors for polar lobe formation are apparently bound to the cortex. Presumably, this formation is due to a gelation and contraction of the cortex in the animal hemisphere in which the vegetative pole region does not take part.

CHAPTER III

Cleavage

A. DESCRIPTIVE PART

1. Spiral cleavage

In all molluscs, except the cephalopods, cleavage takes the form of *spiral cleavage*. Its general characteristics may be briefly outlined.

The first cleavage divides the egg meridionally into two cells AB and CD. At the second division, which is also meridional, AB divides into A and B, CD into C and D. A, B, C and D are further called the *quadrants* of the egg; in the majority of cases, they follow upon each other in this sequence in a clockwise direction, when the egg is viewed from the animal pole.

At the third division, in each quadrant an animal *micromere* is separated from a vegetative *macromere*; in this way, the *first quartette* of micromeres is formed (1a–1d), the macromeres being indicated by 1A–1D (Fig. 12, 23, 24, 28). The cleavage spindles have an oblique position with respect to the egg axis; as a rule, they are arranged according to a right-handed spiral (*dexiotropic*), so that each micromere is displaced toward the right (in a clockwise direction) with respect to its macromere, when viewed from the egg axis or from the animal side. In some species, however, the direction of cleavage is reversed, so that the third cleavage is anti-clockwise (*laeotropic*).

In each following division, the spindles become oriented approximately at right angles to those of the preceding division. Therefore, a regular succession of dexiotropic and laeotropic divisions occurs. This is the so-called *law of alternating spiral cleavage*. If one extrapolates this 'law' to the first two divisions of the egg, one might expect the first cleavage to be (as a rule) dexiotropic, the second laeotropic. As we shall see, in many cases there are indications that this is true.

At the fourth cleavage, which is laeotropic (apart from the cases of reversed cleavage mentioned above), a *second quartette* of micromeres (2a–2d) is formed from the macromeres, their remainder being denoted 2A–2D. The first micromeres divide, also laeotropically, into $1a^1$–$1d^1$ and $1a^2$–$1d^2$.

At the fifth cleavage a *third quartette* of micromeres (3a–3d) is formed, by a dexiotropic division, from the macromeres. The earlier formed micromeres may divide in the same direction, e.g. $1a^1$ into $1a^{11}$ and $1a^{12}$.

The sixth cleavage, which is again laeotropic, leads to the formation of a *fourth quartette* of micromeres, 4a–4d. The remaining macromeres are denoted as 4A–4D.

As a rule, about this time the regular character of spiral cleavage is lost; sooner or later, bilaterally symmetrical divisions take place, mostly beginning in the cells of the D-quadrant.

2. Variations in cleavage

This general pattern of cleavage may show many variations and modifications among the molluscs.

The first and second divisions of the egg may be equal, so that the four quadrants A, B, C and D are of the same size; this is e.g. the case in many gastropods (Fig. 20, 24). In other cases, however, the first and second cleavages are unequal. Usually CD is larger than AB, and D larger than C, so that at the 4-cell stage D is the largest quadrant, A, B and C often being of about the same size (e.g. most Lamellibranchiata) (Fig. 25, 26); at later cleavage, the second and fourth micromere of the D-quadrant (2d and 4d) are in this case often also larger than the corresponding cells in other quadrants. The reverse case, in which CD is smaller than AB, and D is smaller than the other three quadrants, is more rare; it is found in many Opisthobranchia (*Philine, Cavolinia, Cymbulia, Aplysia*; in the latter, however, C and D are as a rule of about the same size) (Fig. 12).

In many cases the inequality of the quadrants is connected with the occurrence of a *polar lobe* at early cleavages. Such a lobe constricts off from the vegetative pole at first cleavage; it rounds off considerably, so that it is only connected through a narrow stalk with the rest of the egg. The latter in the meantime has divided in two almost equal cells (so-called *trefoil-stage*). Then the polar lobe fuses with one of the cleavage cells, which thereby becomes CD; it now surpasses its sister cell AB in size by the volume of the polar lobe. At the second cleavage, a similar polar lobe forms at CD, which subsequently fuses with D (Fig. 19, 28). Finally, in some species (e.g. *Dentalium*) a polar lobe may appear once again at third cleavage, the substance of which is incorporated in the macromere 1D.

Polar lobes occur e.g. in *Pecten, Mytilus, Modiolaria, Ostrea, Dentalium, Bithynia, Nassa, Ilyanassa, Ocinebra, Urosalpinx* and *Fulgur*. There is no correlation between the yolk content of the eggs and the size of the polar lobes. For instance, the polar lobes of *Fulgur* are small, those of *Ilyanassa* large, although *Fulgur* eggs are much richer in yolk.

The characteristics of spiral cleavage may already become evident during the first two cleavages of the egg. In *Crepidula* (CONKLIN, 1897) after the completion of first cleavage the nuclei and asters of the two blastomeres are at first situated opposite one another on either side of the cleavage furrow. As soon as the blastomeres begin to flatten against

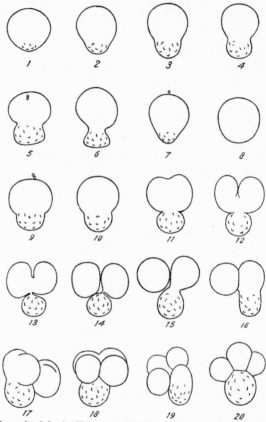

Fig. 19. The polar lobe in *Ilyanassa*. (1) First lobe, at first maturation division. (2-7) Second lobe, at second maturation division. (9-13) Third lobe, at first cleavage. (14-16) Fusion of third lobe with blastomere CD. (17-18) Fourth lobe, at second cleavage. (19-20) Fusion of fourth lobe with blastomere D. After MORGAN, 1935a.

each other, the nuclei are shifted in a clockwise direction, so that the line connecting them makes a sharp angle with the plane of first cleavage (Fig. 8c). The same has been observed in *Paludina* (DAUTERT, 1929).

Much more generally the spiral character becomes evident at second cleavage. In many cases, the spindles of this cleavage do not lie horizontally, but somewhat obliquely, their extremities corresponding to the future A– and C–quadrants lying nearer the animal side than the other ends. In consequence of this, the cleavage planes resulting from this division are not strictly meridional, but make a sharp angle with the egg axis. Therefore the cleavage furrows do not meet in one point at the animal pole, but the first and second furrow have a short stretch in common. In this so-called *cross-furrow* (better: *polar furrow*) two opposite blastomeres meet (Fig. 24c). At the vegetative side a similar situation obtains. The animal and vegetative polar furrows may either be parallel to each other, or they may cross each other at a nearly right angle. In the first case, two of the blastomeres (mostly B and D) have a rectangular or trapezoid plane of contact reaching from the animal to the vegetative side, while the other two are completely separated from each other. When the polar furrows are perpendicular to each other, two opposite blastomeres (as a rule A and C) have a triangular plane of contact in the animal half of the egg, whereas the other two have a similar plane of contact, but perpendicular to the former, in the vegetative half.

In some cases the second cleavage deviates from the so-called 'law of alternating cleavages'. For instance, in *Dreissensia* the second cleavage is dexiotropic, but is followed by a likewise dexiotropic third cleavage, after which cleavage follows its normal alternating course (MEISENHEIMER, 1901). In *Cumingia* there are two cleavage types, occurring in about equal numbers; in the one, the cells A, B, C and D follow one another in a clockwise, in the other type in an anti-clockwise direction (Fig. 25). Consequently, the second cleavage may be considered to be laeotropic or dexiotropic, respectively, although the spindles are horizontal. The third cleavage is dexiotropic, and all subsequent cleavages follow in their normal order (MORGAN and TYLER, 1930).

The number of micromere quartettes may be larger than four. In many cases (e.g. *Crepidula, Trochus, Littorina, Planorbis*) a fifth quartette is formed from the macromeres at a rather late stage of cleavage, immediately before or even during gastrulation.

The micromeres are not always smaller than the macromeres; in each division, however, the daughter cell lying nearer the animal pole is called a micromere irrespective of its size. In gastropods, as a rule, the cells of the first three quartettes are smaller than the macromeres; the fourth micromeres are, however, often bigger than the remaining macromeres. The difference in size between macromeres and micromeres increases with the yolk content of the eggs; it is small e.g. in *Patella, Fissurella, Trochus, Paludina*, and *Littorina*, but large in *Nassa, Bucci-*

num, Purpura, Fusus and *Fulgur.* In the Lamellibranchiata certain micromeres are often bigger than the macromeres; this holds especially for 2d, which is often bigger than 2D.

The appearance of bilateral symmetry as a rule is due to the fact that cleavage in the D–quadrant begins to differ from that in other quadrants. For instance, in *Ilyanassa*, where the D–quadrant is bigger than the other quadrants by fusion with the polar lobe (Fig. 19), nevertheless the first micromere 1d is smaller than the corresponding cells 1a, 1b and 1c; moreover, it divides later, and both its daughter cells $1d^1$ and $1d^2$ are also smaller than their correspondents in other quadrants. The 'tip cell' $2d^{11}$ is bigger than the corresponding cells $2a^{11}-2c^{11}$. Finally, the fourth micromere in the D–quadrant, 4d, is formed much earlier than 4a–4c (CLEMENT, 1952) (Fig. 27a, c).

There has been some controversy regarding the relationships between the first cleavage furrows and the axes of the future embryo. According to some authors, the first cleavage furrow corresponds to a frontal plane, AB being ventral and CD dorsal.* The second cleavage furrow would then coincide with the plane of bilateral symmetry. Others hold the view that the first furrow runs almost diagonally, AB being (in ordinary cleavage) ventral and to the left, CD dorsal and to the right. LILLIE (1895) pointed out that, in view of the mutual displacements of the blastomeres at later cleavage, the answer to this question depends on what is taken as point of reference. However, if one takes into account: (1) that the median plane is determined by the position of 2d and 4d, these two blastomeres indicating the dorsal side of the future embryo, and (2) that these blastomeres are formed by a laeotropic division from the D-quadrant, it is most obvious to consider a plane lying at a slight angle (e.g. of about 20°–30°) to the right (i.e. in a clockwise direction) of the second cleavage furrow, as the future median plane of the embryo (Fig. 25a). It follows that, in broad outline, the descendants of the second and fourth micromere quartettes are situated along the radii (A left, B ventral, C right, D dorsal), while those of the uneven quartettes and the macromeres lie interradially (A ventral left, B ventral right, C dorsal right, D dorsal left). Some qualification is needed with respect to the first quartette. The first division of this quartette, which is laeotropic, gives two quadruplets, $1a^1-1d^1$ and $1a^2-1d^2$, respectively.

---

* In molluscan embryology, as a rule the terms *anterior* and *posterior* are used here instead of *ventral* and *dorsal.* On morphological grounds, it seems better, however, to consider the second axis, running perpendicular to the main egg axis in the plane of bilateral symmetry, as dorsoventral. As a matter of fact, the animal pole corresponds to the *anterior* end of the trochophore. I have, therefore, consistently applied the latter terminology, even in those cases where the original authors do not.

The latter lie interradially, in conformity to the above-mentioned rule. The cells $1a^1-1d^1$, however, are pushed by the anti-clockwise division into a radial position, where they later link up with the second quartette cells (Fig. 24e).

These considerations all refer to the most common case, where the third cleavage is dexiotropic and the subsequent cleavages follow according to the rule of alternation. However, a few cases are known among gastropods, where cleavage is the mirror image of the ordinary pattern. This is linked up with the direction of coiling of the adult snails, as was first discovered by CRAMPTON (1894): those species where the shell is coiled according to a left-handed spiral have a *reversed cleavage* (e.g. *Ancylus rivularis, Physa heterostropha, Ph. fontinalis* and *Ph. hyponorum, Planorbis marginatus, Pl. carinatus* and *Pl. trivolvis*). Occasionally, in normally dextral snail species sporadic sinistral individuals or sinistral races may occur (the reverse is also true). It is not known, but highly probable, that also in these cases cleavage type is correlated with the direction of coiling.

Spiral cleavage does not always follow the regular pattern outlined above. For instance, in the Lamellibranchiata it is often much more irregular than in the gastropods, and differences in cleavage among the quadrants occur at an early stage. But also in some gastropods early deviations from the typical pattern may occur, as e.g. in *Philine*, where the macromeres in the lateral quadrants soon cease to divide.

Cleavage in cephalopods stands quite apart (*Sepia*: VIALLETON, 1888; *Loligo*: WATASE, 1891). Instead of a spiral cleavage, we have here a *meroblastic discoidal cleavage*, which has from the beginning a clearly expressed bilaterally-symmetrical character. The first cleavage furrow corresponds to the median plane of the germ disc. The second furrow, which is almost perpendicular to the first, divides each half into an anterior and a posterior cell. At the next cleavage the anterior cells are divided in two nearly equal halves by a radial furrow; the posterior cells, on the contrary, are, at least in the decapods, divided unequally by a furrow, which runs almost parallel to the first, into a smaller medial and a larger lateral cell. Until now, all blastomeres remain along the outer margin of the germ disc in open connection with the thin ectoplasmic layer surrounding the rest of the egg, which remains undivided. At the fourth cleavage, for the first time two or four cells appear, which are bounded on all sides by cleavage furrows (*blastomeres* according to VIALLETON, in contradistinction to the peripheral *blastocones*). At later cleavages, the number of these blastomeres in the central part of the germ disc increases. Sooner or later irregularities and deviations from a strict bilaterally symmetrical pattern appear. Cleavage results in a disc

F

of one layer of cells, resting on the uncleaved yolk, and of which the peripheral ones remain in open connection with the surrounding ecto-plasmic membrane and with the yolk.

3. Cell-lineage

In the years around the turn of the century, a large number of investigations were made on *cell-lineage* in molluscs. The following papers may be mentioned here: BLOCHMANN (1882: *Neritina*), HEYMONS (1893: *Umbrella*), LILLIE (1895: Unionidae), KOFOID (1895: *Limax*), MEISENHEIMER (1896: *Limax*; 1901a: *Dreissensia*), CONKLIN (1897: *Crepidula*; 1907: *Fulgur*), HEATH (1899: *Ischnochiton*), HOLMES (1900: *Planorbis*), ROBERT (1902: *Trochus*), CASTEEL (1904: *Fiona*), CARAZZI (1905: *Aplysia*), WIERZEJSKI (1905: *Physa*) and DELSMAN (1912: *Littorina*).

Generally the results are comparable in all species investigated, so that a number of general rules may be established.

The first three quartettes of micromeres produce the whole *ectoderm*. The *pretrochal part* of the ectoderm, which later develops into the head region of the adult animal, derives from the first quartette; the *posttrochal ectoderm* comes from the second and third quartettes. Among the ectomeres, the cell 2d takes a special position. It is the so-called *first somatoblast*, which forms the *somatic plate*, from which a great part of the dorsal and ventral ectoderm of the body, including the shell gland and the foot, is derived.

In addition to this, the second and third quartettes yield the *larval mesenchyme* (*ectomesoderm*).

The cell 4d is the *second somatoblast*. It forms, besides a number of endodermal elements, the whole *primary mesoderm*. The remaining part of the *endoderm* comes from the cells 4a–4c and the macromeres 4A–4D.

We have seen above (p. 68) that the cells $1a^2$–$1d^2$, formed at the first division of the first quartette cells, remain in an interradial position, occupying the four corners of a square surrounding the animal pole. These cells, the *primary trochoblasts*, at further cleavage divide only once or twice more. Their descendants form the greater part of the *prototroch*, but *secondary trochoblasts*, derived from the second quartette in the quadrants A, B and C, also take part in its formation. In *Ischnochiton* there are, in addition to this, *accessory trochoblasts* from the first quartette.

Between the trochoblasts the derivatives of $1a^1$–$1d^1$ extend in a radial direction. In this way, they form the four arms of the *molluscan cross*, together with the *tip cells*, $2a^{11}$–$2d^{11}$. The arms of the cross therefore have a radial position (ventral, dorsal, left and right), in contradistinction to the annelid cross, where the arms are placed interradially. The arms may consist for a considerable time of one row of cells (e.g. *Crepidula, Neritina, Littorina, Planorbis*), or they may soon be split into several cell rows by transverse divisions (*Trochus, Umbrella*). In the latter case the cross is not very distinctly visible. The centre of the cross is occupied by the *rosette*, the derivatives of the cells $1a^{11}$–$1d^{11}$ (Fig. 27c). The latter divide into the *apical rosette cells*, $1a^{111}$–$1d^{111}$, which surround the animal pole, and the *peripheral rosettes*, $1a^{112}$–$1d^{112}$, occupying the angles between the arms of the cross.

Generally the cross is most distinct in Gastropoda and Polyplacophora; in Lamellibranchiata no distinct cross is formed.

The first somatoblast 2d is in general not very prominent in gastropods; as a rule, it is of the same size as the corresponding cells in the other quadrants. In lamellibranchs and scaphopods, on the other hand, 2d is very large, often larger than its sister cell 2D; it may be the largest blastomere of all. In this case it often divides symmetrically.

The larval mesenchyme has not always the same origin. Sometimes all three micromere quartettes contribute to its formation e.g. in *Cyclas, Pisidium, Pholas, Teredo, Dreissensia* and *Patella*. As a rule, however, it is derived from cells of the second and third quartettes, situated in the quadrants A, B and C. In some cases its origin could be traced back more accurately to certain blastomeres, e.g. in *Crepidula* to descendants of 2a, 2b and 2c; in *Littorina, Fiona* and *Physa* to the cells $3a^{2111}$, $3a^{2211}$, $3b^{2111}$ and $3b^{2211}$; finally, in *Unio* it is solely derived from $2a^2$. It must be remarked that in a number of species no larval mesenchyme has been found at all: *Dentalium, Siphonaria, Aplysia, Limax*.

In some cases the origin of the *stomodaeum* could be traced back to certain cells of the second and third quartettes. For instance, in *Ischnochiton* these *stomatoblasts* are the cells $2a^{222}$–$2d^{222}$ and $3a^2$–$3d^2$.

At an early stage of cleavage, after the third quartette of micromeres has been formed, the macromere 3D partly withdraws from the surface and bulges with the greater part of its mass into the cleavage cavity. Often this occurs at the 24-cell stage (e.g. in *Crepidula, Littorina, Fiona, Umbrella, Planorbis, Physa, Limax*), but sometimes earlier (20-cell stage in *Trochus*) or later (56-cell stage in *Patella*). At the next division of this cell, which occurs either immediately afterwards or much later (64-cell stage in *Trochus*), the larger interior part of the cell is constricted off as second somatoblast 4d. Consequently, this lies from the beginning with a great part of its substance in the egg interior. An exception to this rule is formed by *Paludina*, where 4d with its descendants remains at the surface of the blastula (DAUTERT, 1929). At further development, the second somatoblast divides almost bilaterally in two equal *mesendoblasts*; on further division the latter may first produce one or more *enteroblasts*, while their remaining parts form the *teloblasts* giving rise to the left and right *mesoderm bands* (Fig. 27a).

It has recently been claimed by SMITH (1935), CROFTS (1938) and CREEK (1951) that the mesoderm in *Patella, Haliotis* and *Pomatias* is not derived from 4d, but from the macromere 4D. Since neither of these authors has followed the cell lineage in detail, this contention can hardly be accepted without further confirmation.

4. Changes in shape of the cleavage cells

At each division the cleavage furrows cut deeply into the egg (provided that this is not too rich in yolk, as e.g. in the cephalopods). The two daughter cells separated by the furrow round off considerably, tending to become spherical; therefore, their surface of contact is reduced more and more, until they seem to touch one another in one point only. Immediately afterwards, the reverse process sets in; the cells begin to flatten against each other, the cleavage furrow is more and more reduced, and is replaced by a flat partition-wall between the adjacent cells. This process repeats itself at each division (Fig. 20).

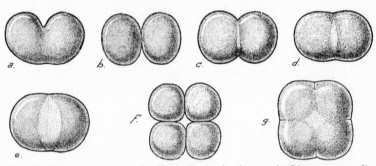

Fig. 20. Changes in shape of cells during early cleavage in *Limnaea stagnalis*. (a-c) First cleavage. (d-e) Formation of first cleavage cavity. (f) Second cleavage. (g) Flattening of cells and reappearance of cleavage cavity.

In some cases, a forthcoming unequal division may already be anticipated in the shape of the cell. For instance, in *Dreissensia* the formation of 1d is preceded by a protruding cytoplasmic lobe at the animal side of D, into which the cleavage spindle only subsequently enters (MEISENHEIMER, 1901a).

A peculiar phenomenon is found in *Physa* (WIERZEJSKI, 1905) and *Limnaea* (RAVEN, 1946b) at the 24-cell stage. At this stage, all cells extend with conical protrusions towards the centre of the egg, where they meet. Here a central cytoplasmic area, free from yolk granules or mitochondria, is formed in the tips of the cells, especially of the micro-meres. In *Physa* this area becomes vacuolated, according to WIERZEJSKI. We shall return to these phenomena below (p. 80).

5. The cleavage cavity

In eggs of marine molluscs (e.g. *Trochus*) little lens-shaped cavities may occur between the blastomeres already at early stages of cleavage. However, in general these cavities remain small and isolated from each other; a wide cleavage cavity, if any, is only formed at later cleavage stages.

On the contrary, in many fresh-water molluscs and land pulmonates there is, from the 2-cell stage on, a wide cleavage cavity, which opens periodically to the exterior.

This *recurrent cleavage cavity* has first been described in detail by KOFOID (1895) in *Limax*. Similar observations have been made by MEISENHEIMER (1896) in *Limax*, HOLMES (1900) in *Planorbis*, MEISEN-HEIMER (1901a) in *Dreissensia*, WIERZEJSKI (1905) in *Physa*, COMANDON and DE FONBRUNE (1935) in various gastropods (*Bithynia tentaculata, Limnaea limosa, auricularis* and *stagnalis, Physa acuta, Planorbis* sp., *Ancylus lacustris, Succinea putris, Agriolimax agrestis*), CARRICK (1939) in *Agriolimax*, and RAVEN (1946b) in *Limnaea stagnalis*. A similar cleavage cavity has also been found in *Anodonta, Cyclas* and *Amnicola*.

After the first two blastomeres have flattened against each other, small lens-shaped clefts appear in the partition wall between the cells. These clefts coalesce into a single cavity extending through the greater part of the interblastomeric wall (Fig. 20, d–e).

In *Limnaea*, the subcortical protoplasm (cf. above p. 35) moves in-wards with the cleavage furrow (Fig. 21a). Therefore, a layer of this protoplasm covers the two sides of the interblastomeric wall (Fig. 21b). When the cleavage cavity has appeared, a strong vacuolization occurs in this region, which leads to the formation of conical prominences on the inner surface of the cells, bulging into the cleavage cavity, from which they are separated by a fine protoplasmic lamella (Fig. 21c). Apparently, a rapid secretion of water into the cleavage cavity takes place in these *secretion cones*, as evidenced by the rapid enlargement of the cavity (Fig. 21d). This may go so far that the blastomeres are stretched to crescent-shaped segments bounding a nearly spherical cavity. Finally, the latter breaks through to the exterior; its contents are suddenly expelled, either at the animal or the vegetative pole, and the egg shrinks to about its original size. The opening connecting the cleavage cavity with the exterior soon closes, and the whole process may repeat itself once or twice, before the second cleavage begins. At the 4-cell stage the same cycle of events occurs; after the blastomeres have flattened against each other, a cleavage cavity appears by the coalescence of clefts in the cell walls (Fig. 20g), and secretion cones are formed on all four blastomeres (Pl. VI, A). The wide cleavage cavity as a rule breaks through some time before the third cleavage, and is reformed a second time. During further cleavage this regular succession of slow swelling and rapid contraction continues until gastrulation. Secretion cones may again be observed in *Limnaea* at the 8– and 16–cell stages, both on the macromeres and micromeres, but not at later stages. At the 24-cell stage in *Physa* and

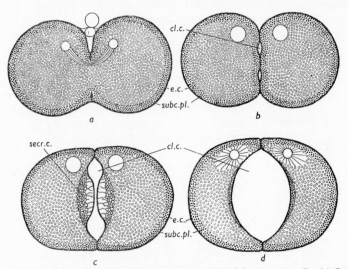

Fig. 21. The formation of the first cleavage cavity in *Limnaea stagnalis*. (a) Constriction of first cleavage furrow. (b) Appearance of lenticular clefts in interblastomeric wall. (c) Cleavage cavity (*cl.c.*) formed by coalescence of clefts. Secretion cones (*secr.c.*) on inner surface of blastomeres. (d) Wide cleavage cavity. *e.c.*, egg cortex; *subc. pl.*, subcortical plasm.

Limnaea the cleavage cavity for some time disappears entirely; later, it reappears, but its shape and size are very irregular and variable (Pl. VII, A). Besides a central cavity, situated somewhat eccentrically towards the animal side, lenticular clefts between adjacent cells may be present, which fuse secondarily with the central cavity. Finally in *Limnaea limosa*, according to COMANDON and DE FONBRUNE, the contractions take place at regular intervals, about every twenty minutes.

As to the functional significance of these phenomena, KOFOID has expressed the opinion that we have to do here with an excretory and possibly respiratory mechanism, comparable to the contractile vacuole of Protozoa. By means of this mechanism the cells would get rid of their metabolic waste products. Although it is possible that this is true, in my opinion the excretion of water is still more important. We have seen above (p. 44) that one of the properties of the eggs of freshwater animals which may enable them to survive in a strongly hypotonic medium, may consist in the precocious development of a water-excreting mechanism. The 'recurrent' cleavage cavity represents just such a mechanism.

The following observations argue in favour of the view that this cleavage cavity serves as a mechanism of osmotic regulation. KOFOID observed that in eggs of *Physa* and *Amnicola*, raised in salt solutions, the cleavage cavity appeared later and remained smaller than in eggs in water. In *Limnaea*, the vacuolization of the egg by the swelling of γ-granules (cf. above p. 36) does not markedly increase after the cleavage cavity has appeared; at later cleavage stages, there is even a strong decrease in the size of these vacuoles, which finally disappear almost entirely. When the eggs are kept in distilled water, however, in which no cleavage cavity is formed (cf. below p. 104), the vacuolization becomes much stronger, and the eggs cytolyse at the 4-cell stage under the symptoms of a vacuolar degeneration (RAVEN and KLOMP, 1946; RAVEN and VAN ZEIST, 1950).

Finally, the fact that in the eggs of *Paludina*, which develop *in utero*, no similar cleavage cavity is formed, also argues in favour of the above-mentioned view.

6. Nuclear phenomena

Generally, the early cleavage spindles are provided with large asters. The first cleavage spindle lies at first horizontally near or above the centre of the egg, and its two asters are the same size, even in those cases where first cleavage is unequal. In the latter cases, the spindle is shifted at the stage of metaphase towards one side until one of the asters comes in touch with the egg cortex; then this aster becomes smaller than the other one, and the resulting cleavage divides the egg into two cells of different size (e.g. *Unio*: LILLIE, 1901; *Barnea*: PASTEELS, 1931).

Equatorial thickenings of the spindle fibres appear at anaphase. The first cleavage furrow cutting through the egg from the animal side pushes the equatorial part of the spindle in a vegetative direction. Since the spindle ends with the chromosomes retain their position near the animal pole, the spindle may be bent in the middle at this stage (WIERZEJSKI, 1905; RAVEN, 1946b) (Fig. 21a). A mid-body and spindle remnant may remain visible for a considerable time.

In the meantime, the asters have begun to disappear. The centro-spheres may enlarge considerably; sometimes, they elongate in the direction in which the spindles of next cleavage will be formed (LILLIE, 1901). The chromosomes swell into karyomeres, which fuse to a resting nucleus; the latter is at first irregular in shape, but then rounds off and becomes vesicular. The nuclei, which have moved apart at the division, later approach one another and come to lie opposite each other on either side of the cell wall (MEISENHEIMER, 1896). In those cases where a wide cleavage cavity is formed, the nuclei are often situated in the immediate neighbourhood of this cavity, only separated from it by a thin protoplasmic lamella.

The prophase nuclei of the next division exhibit in *Limnaea* a distinct unilateral accumulation of the chromatin at the side facing the egg surface. New cytocentra appear on either side of each nucleus. The nuclear membrane is indented, then dissolved at these places, and the spindles of second cleavage are formed.

At the next few cleavages the course of events is similar to that at first cleavage. However, at later stages of cleavage the behaviour of the nuclei and spindle apparatus changes in some respects. At telophase no distinct karyomeres are formed any more, the chromosomes fusing at once to a vesicular nucleus; this occurs in *Limnaea* from the 16-cell stage on. The asters decrease in importance as the cells become smaller; in *Limnaea* at a stage of about 40 cells only the primary mesomeres still have distinct asters, whereas the other mitoses appear more or less anastral. The one-sided accumulation of the chromatin in prophase nuclei does not occur in *Limnaea* after the 24-cell stage. Finally, distinct nucleoli are formed in the resting nuclei of later cleavage stages. In *Limax* even the nuclei of the 2-cell stage have big nucleoli, according to MEISENHEIMER. In *Limnaea*, on the contrary, the nuclei of early cleavage stages have only scattered nucleolar granules. At the 24-cell stage, each nucleus possesses two or three nucleoli; at later stages, their number is reduced to one or two. The size of the nucleoli increases considerably at later stages (Pl. VII, A). They are amphinucleoli, possessing an inner vacuole which stains differently from the rest of the nucleolus; apparently, the nucleoli play a part in cell metabolism, just as during oogenesis. From a stage with about 120 cells, it seems that occasionally whole nucleoli break through the nuclear membrane and fall apart in the cytoplasm.

The position of the nuclei in later cleavage stages in *Limnaea* is very characteristic; they are situated on the boundary between the ecto- and endoplasm (Pl. VII, A).

As regards the size of the nuclei, it may be said that in general larger blastomeres have larger nuclei; nuclear size is roughly proportional to cell size (LILLIE, 1895). On the other hand, nuclear size is dependent on the length of the preceding resting period (CONKLIN, 1907, 1912).

In yolk-rich eggs (e.g. *Fulgur*), at later stages in some macromeres nuclear division may continue, whereas cell division stops. In a way, these cases form a transition to meroblastic cleavage, as found in the cephalopods.

7. Segregation of cytoplasmic substances

The ooplasmic segregation, which began in the uncleaved egg, and led to a more or less unequal distribution of substances throughout the egg, continues during cleavage, although the process is complicated here more and more by the formation of the cell walls.

This affects in the first place the distribution of the yolk. In most cases the proteid yolk is concentrated to a greater or lesser extent in the vegetative parts of the egg, so that it later passes mainly into the endomeres. This is even the case in those eggs where during the uncleaved stage no distinct segregation of the yolk had taken place, as e.g. in *Paludina* (DAUTERT, 1929). But also in those cases, where vegetative concentration of the proteid yolk had already begun before the beginning of cleavage, the process is continued during cleavage, a similar polar segregation taking place in each blastomere; this leads then to a still sharper separation of egg substances. Such a progressive segregation of the proteid yolk has, for instance, been observed in *Fulgur* (CONKLIN, 1907), *Crepidula* (CONKLIN, 1917) and *Aplysia* (RIES and GERSCH, 1936). In general, it leads to a distribution, in which the cells of the first quartette of micromeres contain hardly any proteid yolk, those of the second quartette somewhat more, and so on, so that yolk content increases in an animal-vegetative direction along a gradient.

A similar progressive segregation taking place in cephalopods leads to a regular increase in the area of yolk-free cytoplasm at the animal pole of the egg, from which the blastoderm develops (VIALLETON, 1888).

In *Limnaea* the relationships are somewhat more complicated (RAVEN, 1946b). At first and second cleavage, the cytoplasmic substances are distributed about equally among the blastomeres. Prior to third cleavage, however, the subcortical plasm concentrates towards the animal side, and fuses with the animal pole plasm and the perinuclear plasms into a common mass of dense cytoplasm, rich in mitochondria and β-granules of the proteid yolk. At the third cleavage, most of this plasm passes into the micromeres, which consequently consist for the greater part of this dense cytoplasm, and have only a thin zone of vacuolar cytoplasm along the cleavage cavity (Pl. VI, B; Fig. 22d). On the contrary, in the macromeres the dense plasm is restricted to the animal side and the circumference of the nuclei, while their greater part consists of strongly vacuolated cytoplasm with γ-granules. At subsequent cleavages a similar un-equal distribution of substances takes place, so that the relative amount of dense cytoplasm in the cells decreases at later cleavage stages in an animal-vegetative direction. In all cells, this substance lies at the outer side, forming the *ectoplasm*, whereas the vacuolar cytoplasm forms the *endoplasmic* part of the cells. Therefore, at later cleavage stages the most

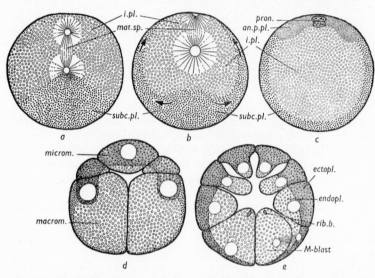

Fig. 22. Diagrammatic representation of ooplasmic segregation during early stages in *Limnaea stagnalis*. (a) Vegetative pole plasm (*subc.pl.*) in egg immediately after laying (cf. Pl. III A). (b) Extension of vegetative pole plasm (cf. Pl. III B). (c) Formation of animal pole plasm (*an.p.pl.*) at stage of pronuclei (*pron.*) (cf. Pl. IV A). (d) Eight-cell stage. Micromeres (*microm.*) mostly consisting of dense plasm, formed by fusion of animal pole plasm with greater part of sub-cortical plasm (cf. Pl. VI B). (e) Blastula. Differential distribution of dense ectoplasm (*ectopl.*) and vacuolar endoplasm (*endopl.*) (cf. Pl. VII A). For-mation of primary mesoblast (*M-blast*) by oblique division. *i.pl.*, vacuolated inner plasm; *macrom.*, macromeres; *mat.sp.*, maturation spindle; *rib.b.*, 'ecto-somes'.

animal micromeres consist mainly of ectoplasm; the supraequatorial micromeres have more endoplasm, while in the blastomeres of the vegetative half the endoplasm largely exceeds the ectoplasm in amount (Pl. VII, A; Fig. 22e).

Still more complicated relationships are found in those cases where there is a polar lobe. For instance, in the uncleaved egg of *Dentalium* (WILSON, 1904a) there is an unpigmented area of protoplasm at the animal pole, a similar unpigmented area at the vegetative pole, while the remaining part of the egg is pigmented. At the first and second cleavage the animal white area is equally distributed over the quadrants A, B, C and D. At third cleavage the micromeres 1a–1d consist exclusively of the unpigmented material; a small part of the latter passes into the macromeres. By progressive segregation the amount of this unpigmented area in the macromeres increases subsequently, so that the second micromeres in the quadrants A, B and C consist almost entirely, the third micromeres still to a large extent, of this unpigmented protoplasm.

The substance of the vegetative white area is included in the polar lobe at first cleavage, and passes as a whole into CD; in the same way, it is transferred to D at the second cleavage. At the next division, a polar lobe is formed once more, the material of which passes into the macromere 1D. Then the polar lobe substance leaves the vegetative pole and is shifted in the animal direction, where it fuses with the animal white substance remaining in 1D. The micromere 2d, which forms at the next cleavage, is larger than the corresponding cells 2a–2c, and consists for the greater part of the united polar plasm substance. The following micromeres of the D-quadrant, 3d and 4d, consist also of unpigmented material only.

It may be concluded that, while the animal unpigmented substance is distributed more or less equally among the cells of the first three micromere quartettes, the material of the vegetative pole plasm passes mainly into 2d and 4d, possibly also 3d.

Displacements of cytoplasmic substances during cleavage may occur through protoplasmic currents. CONKLIN (1938) describes vortical movements occurring in *Crepidula* during early cleavage. Such currents occur around the poles of the amphiasters. At the animal side they are stronger than in the vegetative part of the egg. Their direction is clockwise at the first cleavage, counter-clockwise at the second one, and so on (Fig. 8). CONKLIN supposes that the place and direction of cleavage spindles and cleavage planes, and the segregation of cytoplasmic substances during cleavage, are controlled by such currents.

The constriction by the cleavage furrows may also lead to displacement of substances. Ussow (1881) already observed in the eggs of cephalopods streaming movements of the protoplasm in the direction in which the cleavage furrows were cutting through; cytoplasmic granules were drawn along by these currents. In *Limnaea* (RAVEN, 1946b) the subcortical plasm moves inwards with the cleavage furrows. When the blastomeres flatten against each other, it forms a layer on either side of the partition wall, in which subsequently the 'secretion cones' are formed (cf. p.73) (Fig. 21). A similar streaming inwards of superficial protoplasm along the cleavage furrows has been described in *Crepidula* by CONKLIN.

In some instances processes of localization of discrete substances have been observed. In *Neritina* (BLOCHMANN, 1882) particular granules are found in the uncleaved egg, which are localized during cleavage in two cells of the second quartette situated at left and right; according to CONKLIN they are the cells $2a^1$ and $2c^1$.

In *Physa* WIERZEJSKI (1905) observed during second cleavage a special kind of granules in the cytoplasm, which come to lie at third cleavage in the vegetative asters of the cleavage spindles. They are then displaced towards the vegetative pole, where they accumulate near the vegetative polar furrow. At the 24-cell stage these *ectosomes* are shifted centrally along the cell walls to the central extremities of the macromeres. Soon afterwards they disappear.

Similar 'ectosomes' have been observed in *Limnaea* (RAVEN, 1946b; MINGANTI, 1950). They first become visible at the 8- to 16-cell stage as dark granules in the vegetative part of the macromeres. These granules fuse to a few dark bodies, which are very rich in RNA, and are surrounded by a zone of basophil cytoplasm. At the 24-cell stage they are situated at the central ends of the macromeres 3A–3D; at the next division of these blastomeres they pass into the cells of the fourth quartette (Pl. VII, A). They are still visible at a 64-cell stage; then they gradually disappear, but even at a 124–cell stage basophil particles are found in this region.

Presumably, the contact between macromeres and micromeres in the centre of the eggs of *Physa* and *Limnaea* at the 24–cell stage, and their connection at later stages by protoplasmic bridges, is of special importance. Probably an exchange of substances between the cells occurs at these places (WIERZEJSKI, 1905; MINGANTI, 1950).

The second somatoblast 4d, which is constricted off from its mothercell towards the egg interior by an oblique division (cf. above, p. 71), differs from the beginning from all other cells by being almost entirely devoid of ectoplasm (Fig. 22e). In *Limnaea*, at a 60–cell stage the vegetative extremities of the two mesendoblasts contain a special dense and darkly-staining plasm. At later stages all mesomeres consist of dark cytoplasm with many γ–granules.

At later cleavage stages all superficial cells of the eggs of *Limax* (MEISENHEIMER, 1896), *Planorbis* (HOLMES, 1900) and *Limnaea* (RAVEN, 1946b) ingest 'albumen' from the surrounding egg-capsule fluid, which is laid down in the ectoplasmic part of the cells in special *albumen vacuoles*. These vacuoles appear in *Limax* already at the 16–cell stage, in *Limnaea* not before a stage with about 40 cells. At first, they occur only in the animal cells (Pl. VII, A), somewhat later also at the vegetative side. At later stages they grow in size, and coalesce partly to larger vacuoles. When the eggs are treated with basic vital dyes, the latter are accumulated in the albumen vacuoles. Presumably, these vacuoles may be considered as a *vacuome* in the sense of PARAT (1928).

In *Limnaea*, at a 40–cell stage certain cells, presumably belonging to the second quartette, bear conical prominences on their outer surface (Pl. VII, A). At a 60–cell stage they have developed to dark 'ringlets'. About 40 to 60 of these ringlets are present at a 120-cell stage. Nothing can as yet be said about their significance or function.

8. The behaviour of various cytoplasmic inclusions during cleavage

a. PROTEID YOLK

Something has already been said about the distribution of the proteid yolk among the cells, and the progressive segregation of yolk and cyto-plasm taking place in many eggs (cf. above, p. 77).

In some cases, a very unequal distribution of the yolk among the cells takes place, already at the first cleavages, e.g. in thecosome pteropods (*Cymbulia, Cavolinia*), where nearly all the yolk is found at the 4-cell stage in A, B and C, whereas D consists almost exclusively of hyalo-plasm (FOL, 1875).

In *Limnaea* the β–granules are at first mainly distributed with the subcortical plasm, so that these granules later occupy the ectoplasmic parts of the cells. On the contrary, the γ–granules, mostly surrounded by watery vacuoles, mainly come to lie in the endoplasm (Pl. VII, A). At later cleavage stages the vacuolization of the endoplasm diminishes strongly. At the same time, presumably a transformation of the proteid yolk takes place (RAVEN, 1946b; 1946c). This is very clear in eggs centrifuged a short time before cleavage, in which at a certain moment protein granules appear in regions which were initially free of yolk, thus indicating that a mobilization of the proteid yolk has begun (Pl. VII, B). In normal eggs of this stage (about 40 cells) the number of β–granules diminishes strongly, while at the same time the (more baso-phil) γ–granules become more numerous. It is probable that the nuclei, which are situated at the boundary of ecto- and endoplasm and exhibit a strong nucleolar activity, and the Golgi bodies play a part in this transformation of the proteid yolk.

In some cases the amount of proteid yolk shows a distinct decrease during cleavage, e.g. in *Crepidula* (CONKLIN, 1912) and in *Navanax* (WORLEY and WORLEY, 1943).

b. Fatty yolk

The behaviour of the fatty yolk is very different. In *Aplysia* (RIES and GERSCH, 1936) and *Navanax* (WORLEY and WORLEY, 1943), where the fatty yolk is accumulated already at the uncleaved stage in the animal part of the egg, it passes mainly into the micromeres. In *Navanax* a gradual reduction in the amount of fatty yolk during cleavage is evident.

In *Ilyanassa* the lipid droplets, lying in the animal part of the egg, arrange themselves at the 4–cell stage in each quadrant into a narrow zone at the boundary between the clear animal cytoplasm and the proteid yolk. At further cleavage very few droplets pass into the cells of the first micromere quartette, somewhat more into the second, while the cells of the third quartette receive numerous fat droplets and some proteid yolk. At the formation of 4d, this obtains nearly all the rest of the fatty yolk left in 3D. At the division of 3A, 3B and 3C, on the contrary, a rather uniform distribution of the lipid droplets among the daughter cells takes place (CLEMENT and LEHMANN, 1956).

In *Physa* and *Bithynia*, where the fat droplets are restricted to the vegetative three quarters of the egg (MANCUSO, 1953; ATTARDO, 1955a), the first micromeres receive no, the second micromeres only little, fatty yolk. In *Limnaea* the fat droplets are mainly distributed with the vacuolar protoplasm, so that they later lie in the endoplasm. Therefore, the micromeres have only few fat droplets, mainly situated along the cleavage cavity; most of the fat passes into the macromeres.

c. Golgi

No localization of the Golgi bodies takes place during cleavage in *Mytilus* (WORLEY, 1944) and *Limnaea* (HIRSCHLER, 1918; GATENBY, 1919; RAVEN, 1946b). The Golgi bodies, which are more or less uniformly distributed throughout the egg, are divided passively among the cleavage cells.

On the contrary, the 'Speichergranula' of *Aplysia*, which were accumulated in a supraequatorial ring at the uncleaved stage (RIES and GERSCH, 1936), pass into special cells at cleavage. The first micromeres 1a–1d and the second micromeres 2a and 2b receive none of these bodies. Part of them come to lie in 2c and 2d and in the macromeres 3A and 3B. But the greater part of these granules are later found in the cells 3C, 3D, 3c and 3d. At later cleavages they are also passed on to particular cells (Fig. 12).

In *Navanax* a similar concentration of the Golgi bodies in a narrow ring at the boundary of the animal plasm and the proteid yolk takes place, but only at the 4–cell stage (WORLEY and WORLEY, 1943). Since the cleavage furrow of third cleavage cuts through the cells just in this region, the Golgi bodies are divided almost equally among micromeres and macromeres.

In *Mytilus* and *Navanax* the Golgi bodies increase during early cleavage in size, but not in number. According to HIRSCHLER and GATENBY, they remain entirely inactive during cleavage in *Limnaea*. However, later observations have shown that they probably take a part in the transformation of the proteid yolk, new yolk granules being formed in the Golgi internum. At later cleavage stages these Golgi bodies have disappeared as such; presumably, they have been used up in yolk transformation. But in the meantime a new generation of Golgi bodies has been formed. Already at the 24–cell stage a new Golgi field, surrounded by fine dictyoles, has appeared against the inner side of the nuclei. Later these Golgi granules begin to spread through the cytoplasm (RAVEN, 1946b).

d. MITOCHONDRIA

In *Mytilus* (WORLEY, 1944) the mitochondria remain passive during cleavage, and do not increase in number. Most of them remain concentrated in a single layer beneath the surface.*

In *Limnaea* the mitochondria, which are at first accumulated in the animal pole plasm, mainly come to lie in the ectoplasm of the cells. Partly, they collect in small groups of about five to six granules together; these groups are especially found along the cell boundaries. Their number increases during early cleavage (Miss H. E. VAN HEYNINGEN; W. G. VAN DER LEE, unpublished observations).

In *Ilyanassa* the mitochondria, lying in the animal part of the egg, are concentrated after the second cleavage, in each of the four cells A, B, C, and D, in a narrow sickle-shaped zone between the clear animal cytoplasm and the proteid yolk. The cells of the three first quartettes of micromeres all obtain a rich supply of mitochondria; in the macromeres during this period the zonal arrangement of the mitochondria remains. At the sixth cleavage most of this zone appears to pass into the fourth

* Peculiar phenomena have been observed by PASTEELS and MULNARD (*Arch. Biol.* **68**, 115, 1957) in eggs of *Barnea* and *Gryphaea*, stained with toluidine blue. In the uncleaved egg numerous small granules (a-granules) show a metachromatic staining. With the appearance of the sperm aster, and during early cleavage, larger β-granules are formed in the neighbourhood of the nuclei and asters. The strong metachromatic staining of these granules arises at the expense of the a-granules; apparently, a substance which has bound the dye in its metachromatic form, is transferred from the a- to the β-granules. The two kinds of granules (not to be confounded with those denoted similarly in the *Limnaea* egg!) are thought to belong to the mitochondria. They both contain mucopolysaccharides and show a strong activity of acid phosphatase. The β-granules are distributed unequally during cleavage, CD receiving more of them than AB, and D more than C.

micromeres 4a–4d, whereas the cells 4A–4D only receive few mito-chondria (CLEMENT and LEHMANN, 1956).*

A distinct segregation of mitochondria also takes place in *Sphaerium* (WOODS, 1932). A mitochondrial cloud in the uncleaved egg passes at first cleavage as a whole into CD, then into D, 1D, 2D and 3D. Finally, most of it passes into 4d, and at the next division is divided equally among the two mesodermal teloblasts.

9. Cytochemistry

a. GLYCOGEN

In *Physa* (MANCUSO, 1953) the glycogen is restricted at the 2– and 4–cell stages to a vegetative calotte of the cells. The first micromeres have no, the second micromeres little glycogen; most of it passes into the macromeres (Fig. 23).

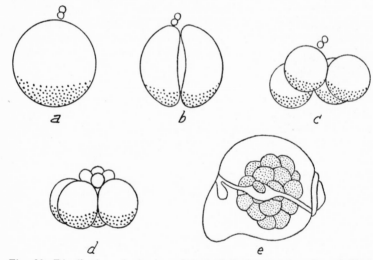

Fig. 23. Distribution of glycogen (stippled) during development of *Physa rivularis*. After MANCUSO, 1953.

In *Limnaea* (RAVEN, 1946b) an accumulation of glycogen occurs at the 24–cell stage in the central protoplasm, where all cells meet. At a 70–cell stage, the cells 4a, 4b and 4c (but not 4d) are rich in glycogen.

* In *Aplysia*, according to ATTARDO (*Acta Embr. Morph. exp.* **1**, 65, 1957) the mitochondria are found in the animal part of the blastomeres at the 2- and 4-cell stages. At later cleavage they pass mainly into the first micromeres 1a – 1d and the cells 2a, 2b, 3a and 3b. At the 24-cell stage the trochoblasts $1c^2$ and $1d^2$ are very rich in mitochondria.

b. Mucopolysaccharides

Besides the staining of cytoplasm and proteid yolk granules, in *Limnaea* a weak positive PAS-staining of the nucleoli of cleavage nuclei was observed. When the cells begin to ingest 'albumen', the albumen vacuoles in the ectoplasmic parts of the cells are heavily stained. The same results were obtained with 2–4–dinitrophenylhydrazine (H. van der Heide, unpublished observation).

c. Lipids

Fauré Fremiet and Mugard (1948) observed in the egg of *Teredo* a cortical argyrophily, probably due to the presence of lipids or lipoproteids. At first it is uniformly distributed over the surface of the uncleaved egg; at the 2-cell stage it is stronger in CD than in AB, at the 4–cell stage stronger in D than in either A, B or C. At the 8-cell stage the first micromeres remain colourless. At the next stages 2d has a strong argyrophily, 2D a much weaker one; 3d remains colourless, but 4d is strongly argyrophil, whereas 4D is colourless. Hence, the substance in question passes mainly into the first and second somatoblast; probably, however, 2a, from which the larval mesenchyme takes its origin, also gets part of it. At later stages the shell gland and mesoderm are argyrophil.

d. Desoxyribonucleic acid

In *Limnaea* DNA can at early stages be demonstrated only in the chromosomes at mitosis; the resting nuclei and prophase stages are Feulgen-negative. At later cleavage stages also the prophase nuclei react positively. According to Minganti (1950) from a stage with 24–32 cells a weak positive Feulgen reaction may also appear in the resting nuclei.

e. Ribonucleic acid

In *Limnaea* (Raven, 1946b; Minganti, 1950) RNA is found especially in the β-granules, to a lesser extent in the cytoplasm. Therefore, the subcortical plasm, and later the ectoplasm, are more deeply stained than the endoplasm. The perinuclear plasm is likewise more basophil than the rest of the cytoplasm. The nucleoli, including their internum, are rich in RNA. Finally the 'ectosomes' are very rich in RNA. Minganti supposes that a transfer of RNA from the inner ends of the vegetative blastomeres into the animal micromeres, by way of connecting protoplasmic bridges, takes place.

f. Sulphydryl compounds

At early cleavage stages glutathione is found in *Limnaea* in the perinuclear plasm. No difference between animal and vegetal cells in this

G

respect is visible. In *Pleurobranchaea* no selective localization of gluta-thione takes place either (RIES, 1937).

The ectoplasm of *Limnaea* is richer in bound sulphydryl compounds than the endoplasm. The nucleoli also show a strong reaction.

g. VITAMIN C

In the egg of *Aplysia* (RIES, 1937) the vitamin C, which is bound to the Golgi bodies ('Speichergranula') shows the same distribution as these bodies (cf. above p. 82) (Fig. 12).

h. BENZIDINE PEROXIDASE

The enzyme shows no segregation in *Limnaea*. In *Aplysia* (RIES, 1937) its distribution parallels that of the proteid yolk. The enzyme is not bound to the yolk platelets, however, but to special granules.

i. INDOPHENOL OXIDASE

In *Aplysia*, where a selective localization of the reaction has been described by RIES (1937), it is apparently due to the fatty yolk.* In *Physa* the cytochrome oxidase, localized in small granules (probably mito-chondria), is more abundant in the animal hemisphere (micromeres)

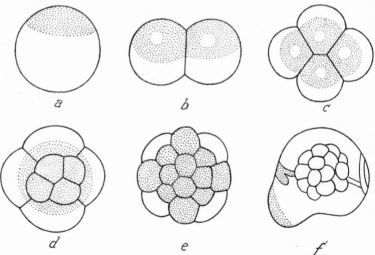

Fig. 24. Distribution of cytochrome oxidase (stippled) during development of *Bithynia codiella*. After ATTARDO, 1955a.

than in the vegetative part (MANCUSO, 1955b). In *Bithynia* it is con-centrated near the animal pole at the 2– and 4–cell stages, then passes

* Cf. however p. 41, footnote.

entirely into the first and second micromeres. In the blastula the whole animal calotte contains the enzyme (ATTARDO, 1955a) (Fig. 24).

j. LEUCOMETHYLENE BLUE OXIDOREDUCTASE

The oxidation of leucomethylene blue in *Aplysia* is restricted at the 2–cell stage to CD. The reaction then preferentially takes place in C; finally, especially the micromeres of the C–quadrant give the reaction (RIES and GERSCH, 1936).

k. IRON

Since free ionic iron in *Limnaea* is especially found in the β–granules, it is mainly the ectoplasm which gives the reaction. For the same reason, the animal cells react more strongly than the vegetative ones. The nucleoli are weakly coloured (ARENDSEN DE WOLFF-EXALTO, 1947).

10. Physicochemical properties

a. pH

According to SPEK (1934), the cells of the germinal disc in *Loligo* are stained by vital dyes with a tint corresponding to an alkaline reaction, in contradistinction to the yolk which shows an 'acid' colour. In *Columbella* the animal micromeres have an alkaline protoplasm; then follows a layer of cells with an intermediate colour, whereas the vegetative part of the egg exhibits an acid reaction.

RIES and GERSCH (1936) have shown that the colour differences in *Aplysia* are connected with the distribution of the proteid yolk. The latter shows an acid reaction, whereas the yolk-free protoplasm of the micromeres stains in an 'alkaline' tint.

b. rH

The reduction of Janus green takes place most rapidly in the vegetative cells of *Aplysia*, which contain the proteid yolk (RIES and GERSCH, 1936). As regards the oxidation of leucomethylene blue, cf. above.

The macromere of the D-quadrant in *Nassa*, and the cells D and 2d in *Anodonta*, exhibit a less rapid reduction of basic dyes than the other cells (STRELIN, 1939).

In *Limnaea* and *Planorbis* no differential dye reduction takes place.

c. OSMOTIC PROPERTIES

We have seen above (p. 75) that the formation of a 'recurrent' cleavage cavity in freshwater molluscs may be considered as an adaptation of these eggs to their hypotonic environment by the precocious development of a water-excreting mechanism. It appears, however, that this mechanism at early cleavage stages is not yet able fully to counterbalance the osmotic uptake of water through the cell surface. Observations by RAVEN, BEZEM and ISINGS (1952) have shown that the swelling of the eggs of *Limnaea* continues after the onset of cleavage. The sum total of the cell volumes at the 8–cell stage amounts to about 270 per cent of the initial egg volume. Apparently, the rate of swelling has greatly increased in comparison with the uncleaved eggs: the volume increase from the beginning of cleavage to the early 8–cell stage is 125 per cent in less than four hours, as against 45 per cent in about four hours during the uncleaved state. If we further take into account that in the meantime a certain amount of water has been extruded by way of the cleavage cavity, it may be safely assumed that the average rate of water intake through the egg surface during early cleavage is at least five times as large as in the uncleaved egg. This cannot be fully explained by the increase in surface area. As a matter of fact, it can be calculated that the total cell surface at an early 8–cell stage with spherical blastomeres is about 3·6 times as large as the initial egg surface; at all earlier stages it is less. Moreover, it appears improbable that the increase in swelling rate is due to a rise in osmotic pressure of the cells. Hardly any further swelling occurred in eggs transferred at the 4–cell stage to a 0·1 per cent LiCl solution; this indicates that the osmotic value of the cleavage cells is lower than that of the recently-laid egg. It is likely, therefore, that the increased rate of swelling after the beginning of cleavage must be ascribed to an increase in the permeability of the egg surface to water.

The decrease in the vacuolization of the cytoplasm at later cleavage stages in *Limnaea* suggests that at these stages the water excretion through the cleavage cavity matches or even exceeds the osmotic water uptake.

d. SPECIFIC GRAVITY

This is further supported by observations on the specific gravity of the eggs, which fluctuates inversely with their water content. In *Limnaea limosa* the specific gravity is at a minimum prior to the first extrusion of water from the cleavage cavity at the 2–cell stage. It then shows a gradual increase at later stages, with rhythmic fluctuations in conjunction with those of the cleavage cavity (COMANDON and DE FONBRUNE, 1935). The same holds for other species investigated by these authors.

e. VISCOSITY

The viscosity changes during the first three cleavages in *Limnaea* were studied by HEIKENS (1947). Viscosity is low just prior to each division, begins to rise at the moment at which the cleavage furrow appears, and reaches a maximum ten to fifteen minutes later, after which there is a gradual decrease. The rise in viscosity corresponds to late anaphase or early telophase, the maximum to late telophase, and the decrease to the reconstitution of a resting nucleus.

11. Differential susceptibility

A differential susceptibility with respect to various noxious agents has been observed during cleavage in various molluscs. In general, it is expressed in the fact that cleavage in certain parts of the egg is delayed or blocked. With greater injury cytolysis occurs, which may be restricted to certain blastomeres.

In some cases it appears that small cells are generally more susceptible than larger ones, as e.g. in *Barnea* (PASTEELS, 1930).

Sometimes, susceptibility is maximum at a certain stage of development. For instance development in *Limnaea* is easily blocked at the 4-cell stage by distilled water and lithium chloride (RAVEN and VAN ZEIST, 1950), urea (RAVEN and KLOMP, 1946) and thiourea (SOBELS, 1948). Presumably, susceptibility is highest a short time before third cleavage. This may be connected with the important processes of cytoplasmic segregation taking place at this moment.

Finally, certain blastomeres may be more susceptible than others. In *Teredo*, susceptibility is greater in CD than in AB (FAURÉ FREMIET and THAUREAUX, 1949). The trochoblasts of *Limnaea* are more resistant than other cells. The macromeres in *Nassa*, *Cerithium*, *Limnaea*, *Physa* and *Planorbis*, on the other hand, are relatively susceptible. In *Nassa*, especially the polar lobe, and later the macromeres of the D-quadrant, are highly susceptible. In *Anodonta*, the blastomeres D, 1D and 2d are more susceptible than the other blastomeres (STRELIN, 1939a, 1939b). Apparently, susceptibility of the cells is related to their morphogenetic significance. The data are too fragmentary, however, to permit any general conclusion.

12. Some data on metabolism

Our knowledge is also in this case very scanty.

CLELAND (1950) studied the respiration of developing *Ostrea* eggs. Respiration begins to rise with the onset of cleavage. It exhibits rhythmic fluctuations with the cleavage cycles, the rate of respiration being high from prophase to metaphase or perhaps anaphase, and low during telophase and interphase. The rise in respiratory rate continues until about $3\frac{1}{2}$ hours after fertilization, when there is a plateau coinciding with the division of the somatoblast, a further rise till from four to five hours, and a new plateau during hatching. The plateaux coincide with periods of diminished rate of division. If the nuclear divisions are suppressed with colchicine, respiration drops to a certain value. This 'residual respiration' is higher, the more cells are present. Carbon dioxide causes a depression of respiration. The respiratory quotient remains constant during cleavage at a value of about 0·8. Presumably, a mixture of carbohydrate and fat is combusted during cleavage.

An R.Q. of ±0·8–0·85 has also been found during cleavage in *Aplysia* (BUGLIA, 1908). MEYERHOF (1911), studying the calorific quotients in addition to the respiratory exchanges, concluded that fat is the principal fuel throughout development in this species.

On the contrary, the mean value of the R.Q. during early stages of development of *Limnaea* was found to be 1·05 by BALDWIN (1935). This suggests that fat is being synthesized at the expense of carbohydrate. This was confirmed by extraction of the ether-soluble substances at the beginning and the end of embryonic development.

The oxygen consumption rate of the egg of *Spisula* increases gradually during development, up to the swimming blastula stage. The R.Q. value, which is about 0·7 immediately after fertilization, shows a gradual increase towards unity (SCLUFER, 1955).

BERG and KUTSKY (1951) studied the respiration of isolated blastomeres in *Mytilus*. The oxygen consumption is higher in CD than in AB, but when it is calculated per unit of volume, it is 13 per cent lower in CD. The isolated polar lobe has an oxygen consumption per unit volume which is 25 per cent less than that of the whole egg. Normal embryos exhibit a gradual rise in oxygen consumption, followed by a fall just prior to hatching. Embryos from isolated AB–blastomeres also show this fall, but CD–embryos do not. Cell division in AB–embryos decreases gradually, and stops at the time when the oxygen consumption diminishes; on the contrary, in CD-embryos cell division continues. The oxygen consumption of the isolated polar lobe remains more or less constant; no fluctuations could be observed in relation to the periods of amoeboid activity.

No significant difference of alanylglycine and leucylglycine peptidase activity between AB and CD was found in *Mytilus* (BERG, 1954a).

Recent information on the uptake of radioactive phosphorus in the form of phosphate in *Mytilus* (BERG, 1954b) conforms to the data on oxidative metabolism. Allowing for differences in amount of cytoplasm, AB blastomeres incorporate P^{32} from the surrounding solution at a much faster rate than either CD blastomeres or polar lobes. A further segregation of incorporation rates occurs at the cleavage of the CD cell: isolated C blastomeres take up P^{32} more rapidly than do the D cells. Partial fractionation of the compounds into which the P^{32} enters shows that about 95 per cent is incorporated into the labile (acid soluble) compounds. Differences in uptake of P^{32} are found between blastomeres, however, even if only the remaining 5 per cent non-labile compounds are considered. No increase in uptake rate of P^{32} occurs at cleavage, although there is a change in surface-volume ratio.

B. CAUSAL ANALYSIS

1. Polarity and symmetry in cleavage

In the determination of the direction of cleavage planes, the original animal-vegetative polarity of the egg, which is presumably bound to the cortex, is first involved. In eggs centrifuged before first cleavage, the displaced pronuclei or cleavage spindles return to the animal pole (CONKLIN, 1917: *Crepidula*). The first two cleavage furrows nearly always pass through the original animal pole, irrespective of stratification, even when cleavage takes place in the centrifuge (MORGAN, 1910: *Cumingia*; CONKLIN, 1910: *Physa* and *Limnaea*). Consequently their place of intersection does not necessarily correspond to the point where the polar bodies are lying, if the latter have been formed at an abnormal place (cf. above, p. 49). In eggs which are moderately compressed, the first cleavage furrow also tends to pass through the animal pole (*Cumingia*: BROWNE, 1910; TYLER, 1930). However, if the eggs are compressed perpendicularly to the egg axis, this furrow is often oblique or equatorial.

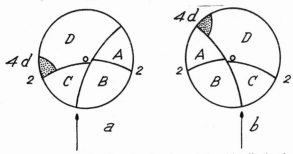

Fig. 25. Diagrams indicating the location of the 4d-cells in the two types of cleavage occurring in *Cumingia*. After MORGAN and TYLER, 1930.

The original egg polarity may possibly be altered by very strong centrifugal forces. COSTELLO (1939b) submitted eggs of Nudibranchia to centrifugal forces up to 277,000 times gravity. When the eggs were centrifuged during the second maturation division, and the second polar body was formed at some distance from the first, the first and second cleavage furrow usually intersected at the point where the second polar body lay. At third cleavage, micromeres were formed in the normal way. Since the two polar bodies were drawn together in the process, it was not possible to decide whether the micromere pole corresponded to the first or the second polar body. PEASE (1940) centrifuged *Cumingia* eggs with forces up to 123,000*g*. The direction of the first cleavage plane was related to the stratification; in most cases it bisected the oil cap. The polar bodies were mostly extruded in the hyaline zone; the first and second cleavage furrow intersected at this point. Further cleavage was normal; the prospective significance of the blastomeres was not changed. PEASE concludes from his experiments that a new cleavage polarity had appeared under the influence of stratification, and that this was retained during further development.

The second axis to which cleavage is related, is the dorsoventral axis (cf. p. 68, footnote). This does not become visible until cleavage. As we have seen above (p. 57), in the uncleaved eggs no trace of a second axis has in general been found in the visible egg structure. The question therefore arises whether the dorsoventral axis, which, together with the original main egg axis, defines the plane of bilateral symmetry, is formed *de novo* during or immediately before cleavage by an epigenetic process, or was already preformed in an invisible way in the uncleaved egg.

The observations of MORGAN and TYLER (1930, 1938) on the egg of *Cumingia* have a bearing on this question. They showed that the first cleavage plane in this species in 78 per cent of the cases goes exactly through the sperm entrance point, whereas it passes at only a slight distance from this point in the remaining cases. As first cleavage is unequal, the first cleavage furrow does not run through the animal pole, but it deviates either to the right or to the left. Therefore, the smaller blastomere AB lies either to the right or to the left of the sperm entrance point in nearly equal proportions. At the second cleavage CD divides unequally; the large blastomere D is always situated opposite the sperm entrance point (Fig. 25). In consequence of this, the blastomeres A, B, C and D follow each other either in a clockwise or an anti-clockwise direction. As further cleavage is of the normal type, the blastomere 2d is formed in all cases by a laeotropic division from 1D. Therefore the plane of symmetry of the embryo nearly coincides either with the first or with the second cleavage plane. MORGAN and TYLER, in their discussion of these facts, consider two possibilities: either the sperm entrance point determines the position of D, and thereby (but apparently in combination with a second factor) the plane of symmetry, or the preformed bilateral symmetry of the egg permits the sperm to penetrate most easily at a certain point of the circumference. They do not decide between these alternatives. It must be said, however, that there are no factual data in favour of the second one.

In those eggs where first cleavage is unequal, in most cases the cleavage spindle shifts to one side, as mentioned above (p. 75). In many instances an unequal first cleavage may be made equal through certain interventions, e.g. by compression (*Cumingia*: BROWNE, 1910; TYLER, 1930) (Fig. 26b), ultraviolet irradiation (*Barnea*: PASTEELS, 1931; *Teredo*: FAURÉ FREMIET and THAUREAUX, 1949), abnormal ionic composition of the medium (*Barnea*: PASTEELS, 1930), $MgCl_2$ solution (PASTEELS, 1931),

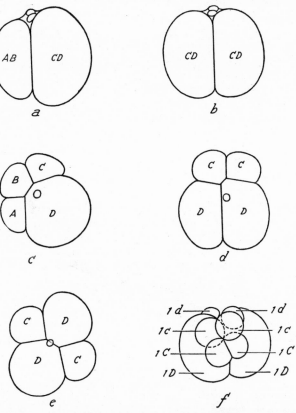

Fig. 26. Cleavage of normal and equally divided *Cumingia* eggs. (a) Normal two-cell stage. (b) Equally cleaved egg. (c) Normal four-cell stage. (d, e) Two types of four-cell stage from equally cleaved eggs. (f) Eight-cell stage from the type of equally cleaved egg shown in (d). After TYLER, 1930.

excess of KCl or anionic detergents (*Teredo*: FAURÉ FREMIET and MUGARD, 1948; FAURÉ FREMIET and THAUREAUX, 1949). After an equalized first cleavage the second cleavage is often unequal in both blastomeres; two types of 4–cell stages are produced, according as the smaller cells are formed towards the same side or at opposite sides (Fig.

26, d–e). At the next cleavage the formation of micromeres takes place. Each of the half-blastomeres formed by an equal first cleavage therefore behaves as a CD–cell.

Apart from the effect of compression, which may perhaps be explained by a purely mechanical interference with the normal displacement of the cleavage spindle, all other treatments mentioned above point to an influence on the egg cortex (cf. above, p. 51). Presumably, the inequality of first cleavage is due to local cortical factors influencing the orientation of the cleavage spindle. The further behaviour of the cells after equalized first cleavage might be explained by the assumption that there is a special substance in the egg which normally passes as a whole into the larger blastomere, but when equally divided among the blastomeres impresses on both the character of a CD–cell.

A special case is provided by such eggs as *Aplysia*. Here the first cleavage spindle remains in a symmetrical position near the animal pole. The cleavage furrow cuts at first symmetrically through the egg, but then deviates to one side, and separates the small blastomere CD from the large AB–cell (Pl. II, E–F; Fig. 12). PASTEELS (1934) admits that in this case the deviation of the cleavage furrow is due to the presence of a substance in the vegetative half of the egg, which is analogous to the polar plasm in other eggs, but which has a more diffuse localization. The observation that the cleavage may also in this case be equalized by ultraviolet irradiation, rather points to a cortical than an endoplasmic localization of the responsible factors, however.

Particular relationships are found in those species where a polar lobe appears during cleavage. Here the first cleavage begins as an equal division with a cleavage spindle in the symmetrical position. The polar lobe rounds off, and is for some time connected with the rest of the egg only by a slender stalk; it then fuses secondarily with one of the blastomeres, which at further cleavage proves to be CD. This may be repeated at the second cleavage, the polar lobe now fusing with D (Fig. 19).

If the polar lobe is removed at first cleavage, the rest of the egg shows an equal cleavage, all blastomeres at the 4–cell stage being of the same size (*Dentalium*: WILSON, 1904a; *Ilyanassa*: CRAMPTON, 1896). If the polar lobe substance is removed only partly, the polar lobes at the next cleavages are smaller, and the CD– and D–blastomeres are smaller than normally.

If unfertilized eggs are cut into two nearly equal parts, which are then fertilized, animal fragments show as a rule an equal cleavage without polar lobe. Vegetative fragments cleave as a normal egg, with appearance of a polar lobe at early cleavages. The same cleavage type is shown by meridional fragments.

Likewise, animal fragments of fertilized eggs show equal cleavage without polar lobe, but vegetative fragments, which lack a nucleus, do not cleave in this case. The same holds for animal and vegetative fragments of fertilized *Ilyanassa* eggs fragmented by strong centrifugation (MORGAN, 1935a, 1935b, 1936).

By certain treatments of the eggs, the formation of a polar lobe can be suppressed, with ensuing equal cleavage; e.g. by cold treatment (*Ilyanassa*: CRAMPTON, 1896; *Ostrea*: YASUGI, 1938), heat, centrifugation, salt mixtures, nicotine, chloroform (YASUGI) or alcohol (*Nassa*: STRELIN, 1939). In those *Ostrea* eggs where a polar lobe appears, cleavage is never equal. On the other hand, in some eggs where polar lobe formation is suppressed, unequal cleavage nevertheless takes place (YASUGI).

If the first polar lobe is suppressed and this cleavage is equal, at second cleavage as a rule both blastomeres form a polar lobe and cleave unequally, like CD; two types occur also in this case, according as the C–blastomeres lie at the same or at opposite sides.

CRAMPTON isolated the half-blastomeres of *Ilyanassa* after enforced equal cleavage from one another; both cleaved, although more or less irregularly, in a manner resembling that of a whole egg.

In some cases it was observed that a polar lobe was formed at first cleavage, but this was divided more or less equally among the two cells, e.g. in *Ilyanassa* eggs cleaving under compression or after cold treatment (TYLER, 1930; MORGAN, 1936). Both after complete or incomplete division of the polar lobe, the two cells then behave as CD-cells: they divide unequally, and then form micromeres at the next cleavage.

It is evident from these experiments that the agent of unequal cleavage lies in the polar lobe in these eggs. Again the question may be posed whether the polar lobe fuses in an arbitrary way with one of the half blastomeres, which thereby becomes CD, or always moves to one side in consequence of a preformed dorsiventrality of the egg.

The first view was advocated by SCHLEIP (1925) on account of his experiments with dispermic *Dentalium* eggs. Such eggs show a simultaneous division into three or four cells. In triaster eggs, all cleavage furrows are meridional; a polar lobe is formed, which fuses with one, two or three of the blastomeres or remains isolated from the rest of the egg. In tetraster eggs, various cases may be distinguished. Either all cleavage furrows are meridional, so that the four cells are arranged in one layer around the egg axis; the polar lobe may then fuse with one, two or four of these cells. Or the four blastomeres show a tetrahedral arrangement, with either one or three cells at the vegetative pole; the polar lobe substance is then divided among one, two or three cells, according to the circumstances. In any case those blastomeres, which have received all or a part of the polar lobe substance, behave at further cleavage like CD–cells, although often more or less irregularly. SCHLEIP concludes from these observations that the polar lobe fuses in an arbitrary way with any blastomere with which it happens to come into contact, and which thereby becomes a CD–cell. The dorsoventral axis of the embryo would therefore be determined epigenetically at early cleavage.

The objection may be raised against this conclusion that cleavage in these dispermic eggs proceeds abnormally from the start, and that it therefore sheds no light on the course of normal development. MORGAN (1936) therefore tends to the other view that dorsiventrality is preformed in the uncleaved egg. Unfortunately, the *experimentum crucis* attempted by this investigator—the removal of one of the blastomeres at the trefoil stage in *Ilyanassa*—did not give the expected decision. As a rule the other blastomere also cytolysed. Only six eggs out of a large number survived; in four of them the polar lobe fused with the remaining cell, in two it did not. The problem of whether there is preformation of dorsiventrality, or its epigenetic origin during early cleavage, remains unsolved, therefore. It must be stressed once more, however, that there are no visible signs of a bilateral symmetry in the uncleaved eggs (apart from cephalopods). Moreover, in my opinion the following observations argue strongly against a preformed bilaterality of the egg.

When the first polar lobe in *Dentalium* is removed, cleavage of the remaining part of the egg is equal, as mentioned above. This does not only hold for the first two cleavages, but also at later cleavage; no signs of a bilateral symmetry appear. As in a normal egg, four quartettes of micromeres are formed. But, while in normal development the micromeres 2d and 3d are much bigger than the corresponding cells in the other quadrants, in lobeless eggs all four quadrants are alike, so that cleavage is radially symmetrical with respect to the quadrants (WILSON, 1904a).

The same holds for *Ilyanassa*. In normal development, cleavage in the D–quadrant differs in the following points from the other quadrants: D is bigger than A, B and C; but 1d and its derivatives $1d^1$ and $1d^2$ are smaller than their correspondents. Moreover, 1d divides later than 1a–1c. The tip-cell $2d^{11}$ is bigger than $2a^{11}$–$2c^{11}$. Finally, 4d is formed much earlier than the other fourth micromeres and consists of clear protoplasm instead of containing much yolk like the latter. In lobeless eggs all these differences have disappeared; the D–quadrant cannot be distinguished from the other ones, and cleavage is radially symmetrical with respect to the quadrants (CLEMENT, 1952) (Fig. 27).

If, therefore, there is indeed a preformed bilateral symmetry, no trace of it becomes apparent in these eggs in the absence of the polar lobe.

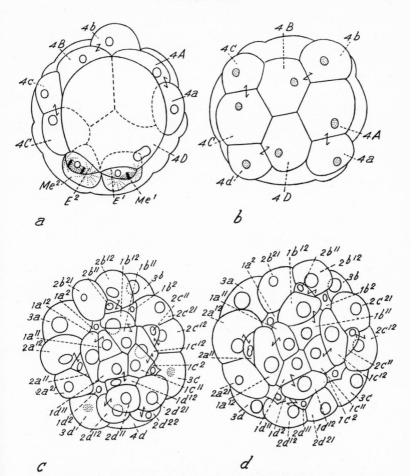

Fig. 27. Cleavage of normal and lobeless eggs of *Ilyanassa obsoleta*. (a) Normal egg. Vegetal pole towards the observer. 4a, 4b and 4c have just been formed; 4d has already given rise to the four cells E^1, E^2, Me^1, and Me^2. The latter are dividing and will produce the mesoblast cells m^1 and m^2. (b) Comparable stage of lobeless egg. 4d is indistinguishable from the other members of the fourth quartette. (c) Normal egg, animal view. Macromeres omitted. The cell $1d^{12}$, the basal cell of the cross, is smaller than the corresponding cell in the other quadrants; $2d^{11}$, the tip cell of the cross, is larger than the corresponding cell in the other quadrants. (d) Comparable stage of lobeless egg. Both $1d^{12}$ and $2d^{11}$ are of the same size as the corresponding cells in the other quadrants. A mesendoblast cell 4d, present in the control, is absent in the lobeless egg. After CLEMENT, 1952.

2. The determination of cleavage pattern

The direction of cleavage planes and the mutual sizes of blastomeres are dependent, (1) on the direction and place of the cleavage spindles, (2) on local activities of the egg cortex directly influencing the course of the cleavage furrows. These are related in their turn to the polarity and symmetry of the egg as a whole, and to the number of preceding divisions.

The orientation of the cleavage spindles may be altered by mechanical, physical or chemical treatment of the egg. A mechanical intervention in cleavage is shown by the experiments on cleavage of compressed eggs (*Cumingia*: BROWNE, 1910; TYLER, 1930; *Crepidula*: CONKLIN, 1912; *Ilyanassa*: TYLER, 1930; MORGAN, 1936). In such eggs, cleavage spindles place themselves preferentially according to the longest diameter of the cells, hence parallel to the compressing surfaces. Therefore, the cleavage planes have a tendency to be perpendicular to the compressing surfaces.

A similar mechanical interference with cleavage may be brought about by centrifuging (e.g. *Crepidula*: CONKLIN, 1917; *Cumingia*: PEASE, 1940). The primary cause in this case is probably the local accumulation of the yolk substances, by which the spindles are displaced mechanically.

Abnormal positions of cleavage spindles may also occur after cold treatment (*Crepidula*: CONKLIN, 1938). This is ascribed to the disappearance or modification of protoplasmic currents, which orient the spindles in normal development.

Finally deviations in direction of the cleavage spindles may be brought about by factors influencing the egg cortex: abnormal ionic composition of the medium (*Barnea*: PASTEELS, 1930), lithium chloride (*Limnaea*: RAVEN and ROBORGH, 1949), thiourea and saccharose (*Limnaea*: SOBELS, 1948; FABER, 1950), ultraviolet radiation (*Barnea*: PASTEELS, 1931).

If eggs of *Crepidula* are centrifuged during early cleavage, in some cases the first or second division is equatorial instead of meridional, or unequal instead of equal. Nevertheless, each of the four resulting cells behaves as a quadrant, begins at the right moment with the formation of micromeres, and forms three ectomeres at its most animal side (CONKLIN, 1917).

The same holds if the first two cleavages are abnormal in eggs under compression (MORGAN, 1936) or in salt mixtures (PASTEELS, 1930). If the second cleavage spindles are vertical in compressed *Ilyanassa* eggs, the ensuing equatorial cleavage is nearly equal (apart from the polar lobe), so that no precocious micromere formation can be induced in this way (TYLER, 1930) (FIG. 28).

In *Ilyanassa* eggs in sugar solution, cell division may be blocked, while nuclear division goes on. After return to seawater, simultaneous division into four cells on a common vegetative base occurs; one hour later each of these cells forms a micromere (MORGAN, 1936).

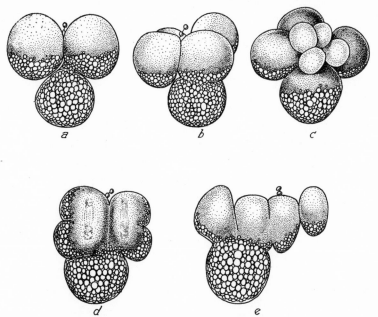

Fig. 28. Cleavage of normal and compressed *Ilyanassa* eggs. (a, b, c) Normal two-, four- and eight-cell stages. (d) Second cleavage of an egg compressed from the late two-cell stage to the four-cell stage. (e) Second cleavage of an egg compressed from the early two-cell stage (shown in (a)) to the four-cell stage. After TYLER, 1930.

These experiments seem to show that the beginning of micromere formation is not dependent on a normal course of the preceding cell divisions, but occurs at a certain moment in the mitotic cycle of the egg. However, there are other observations which are not compatible with such a view.

If *Crepidula* eggs at the 2–cell stage are cooled for six hours, often the second cleavage is omitted; after return to room temperature the eggs immediately begin with micromere formation, and three pairs (instead of quartettes) of micromeres are formed, after which one of the macromeres even forms a typical second somatoblast 4d (CONKLIN, 1938) (Fig. 29). In other eggs only one nuclear division occurs in the cold, but no cell divisions; the single binucleated 'macromere' then again forms three pairs of micromeres. Apparently, it is not necessary for two mitotic divisions to have been completed in a normal way for the egg to begin micromere formation. The latter is obviously dependent on some fundamental process which goes on during cold treatment, although perhaps at a reduced rate. According to CONKLIN, the cytoplasmic currents controlling the position and direction of cleavage spindles are of special importance in this connection.

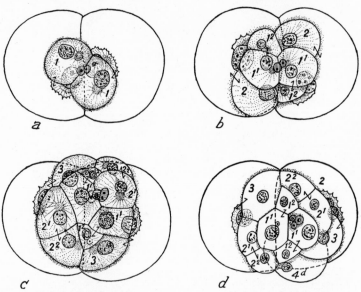

Fig. 29. Formation of micromere duets in eggs of *Crepidula plana* subjected to cold at the two-cell stage. (a) First set of micromeres (*1*) formed in a dexiotropic direction. (b) Second set of micromeres (*2*) formed in laeotropic direction. First micromeres have subdivided into a large apical (*1¹*) and a small peripheral cell (*1²*). (c) Three sets of micromeres present in typical positions and shapes, but double in size and half the number of those in typical eggs. (d) First, second and third micromeres are typical, but a large fourth micromere (*4d*) has separated from the right macromere in a dexiotropic direction. After CONKLIN, 1938.

While in these experiments cleavage divisions were omitted, in other cases extra divisions are intercalated in the mitotic cycle. In *Crepidula* eggs, compressed during third cleavage perpendicular to the egg axis, this cleavage is meridional and equal, so that eight cells in one layer are formed (sometimes this occurs only in some of the quadrants). During the next cleavages all cells adjoining the animal pole form the typical number of micromeres (CONKLIN, 1912). It is evident that a cleavage step as such is not decisive, and that all cells reaching from the animal to the vegetative pole may function as quadrants. The latter conclusion also follows from SCHLEIP's results (1925) with dispermic *Dentalium* eggs, in which all primary 3–cell stages and 'plane' 4–cell stages undergo one more meridional division, after which each of the six or eight blastomeres begins micromere formation at the next cleavage.

The relative sizes of the micromeres and macromeres depend on the position of the cleavage spindles at the moment of cleavage. If the eggs of *Crepidula* are centrifuged during third cleavage in reversed orientation, so that the yolk is accumulated at the animal side of the cells, the 'micromeres' are large and yolk-rich, while the 'macromeres' are small and consist mainly of clear cytoplasm (CONKLIN, 1917).

One might expect that the asymmetric position of the cleavage spindles leading to micromere formation depends on cortical factors. This is confirmed by experiments of RAVEN, BEZEM and ISINGS (1952) in *Limnaea*, in which it was shown that the relative size of the micromeres was reduced by a treatment of the eggs with lithium chloride solutions during third cleavage. This reduction in size became more pronounced as the concentration of the LiCl solutions increased (from 0·02 to 0·1 per cent); in the last-mentioned solution, the average volume of each micromere was $\frac{1}{45}$ of the egg volume instead of $\frac{1}{31}$ in the normal egg. The effect must be due to a displacement of the spindles towards the animal pole.

An influence of cortical factors on the position of the cleavage spindles is also apparent in PASTEELS' experiments (1931) on *Barnea* eggs irradiated with ultraviolet light. In some of these eggs not only the first and second cleavage division, but also the third had become equalized; only at the fourth cleavage unequal division occurred.

The following hypothesis seems to account for the greater part of the observations recorded above. Cleavage pattern is dependent on some fundamental progressive change in the cytoplasm, which proceeds more or less independently of nuclear and cellular divisions. This controls the direction and place of the cleavage spindles, either by setting in motion an ordered sequence of protoplasmic currents, or by setting up regular patterns of attractive and repulsive forces in the egg cortex which by their interplay determine the spindle positions, or by a combination of both mechanisms. The position of the spindles determines, in its turn, in conjunction with more or less autonomous kinetic activities of the cortex (cf. below, p. 103), the direction of the cleavage planes. External agencies may interfere with these processes either by throwing the fundamental cytoplasmic process out of gear with the nuclear divisions (e.g. cold treatment), or by disturbing the cytoplasmic currents (e.g.

H

through viscosity changes), by upsetting the cortical pattern, or, finally, by hindering in a purely mechanical way the displacement of the spindles.

3. Cleavage of isolated blastomeres

Experiments on isolation of blastomeres have been made by CRAMP-TON (1896: *Ilyanassa, Urosalpinx, Anachis*), WILSON (1904b: *Dentalium, Patella*), CONKLIN (1912: *Crepidula*), RATTENBURY and BERG (1954: *Mytilus*) and HESS (1956a: *Bithynia*). The results are similar in all these cases.

Isolated blastomeres round off and become more or less spherical. After isolation at the 2–cell stage AB cleaves as it does in normal development. The same holds for CD, whereby in *Dentalium, Ilyanassa* and *Mytilus* polar lobes are formed in a normal way. Similarly, A, B, C and D, isolated at the 4–cell stage, pursue their cleavage in the same way as they would have done in the whole egg, D once more forming a polar lobe in *Dentalium*. Blastomeres isolated at later stages (micromeres and macromeres of the 8–cell stage, trochoblasts, etc.), in so far as they develop at all, likewise exhibit a typical partial cleavage, giving rise to the same sequence of cells as in normal development. However, in *Patella* all unequal cleavages in isolated blastomeres have a tendency to be less unequal than in normal development. Moreover, one can distinguish here between an 'open' cleavage type, in which the blastomeres more or less retain their normal topographical relationships, and a 'closed' type, in which the wall of the blastula is closed by an extensive shifting of the cells. The same holds for *Bithynia*.

We may conclude from these experiments that the factors controlling the cleavage pattern are apparently bound more or less rigidly to the single cleavage cells. This is understandable in so far as cleavage pattern is determined by cortical factors, since the cortex is parcelled out during cleavage among the blastomeres. Apparently, the 'attraction fields' set up in the cortex at a certain moment, have a tendency to retain their configuration even after isolation of the cells. However, observations by PELTRERA (1940) in *Aplysia* seem to show that under certain circumstances transformations of a regulative nature may occur. By centrifuging at the 2– or 4–cell stage PELTRERA claims to have obtained a 'physiological isolation' of the cells, leading to an aberrant cleavage pattern, in which the single blastomeres have a tendency to cleave as a whole egg. Sometimes in eggs centrifuged at the 2–cell stage AB and CD are separated from one another. Both cells first divide equally, then unequally, and further behave as 4–cell stages. We may perhaps presume that in such eggs, submitted to considerable stretching by the action of a strong centrifugal force, a partial disruption of the cortical attraction

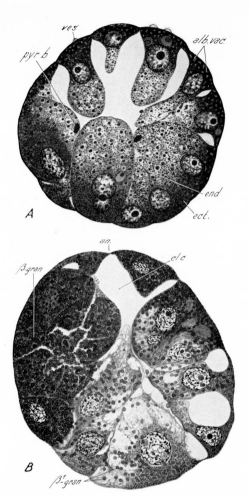

Plate VII. Later cleavage stages of *Limnaea stagnalis*. (A) Normal egg, about 40-cell stage. Blastomeres consisting of ectoplasm (*ect.*) and endoplasm (*end.*). Albumen vacuoles (*alb.vac.*) in ectoplasm of animal blastomeres. 'Ectosomes' (*pyr.b.*) in central end of cells of fourth quartette. Vesicular outgrowths (*ves.*) on surface of supraequatorial cells. (B) Egg, centrifuged immediately before first cleavage, and fixed $21\frac{1}{2}$ hours later. Several cells are crowded with proteid yolk granules (*β-gran.*), other cells poor in yolk. In the latter cells there has appeared a special kind of granules (*β¹-gran.*), pointing to a transport of proteid matter through the cell membranes.

[*Facing page* 102

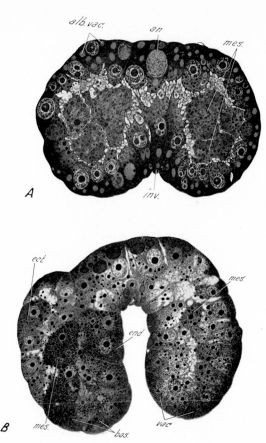

Plate VIII. Gastrulation in *Limnaea stagnalis*. (A) Early gastrula. Beginning invagination of archenteron (*inv.*). Pseudopodia from inner end of invaginating cells to animal side. Albumen vacuoles (*alb. vac.*) in ectoplasmic part of the cells; at animal pole (*an.*) cells with giant albumen vacuoles. *mes.*, mesodermal cells. (B) Late gastrula from egg, centrifuged immediately before first cleavage, and fixed 50 hours later. The left side still shows a greater density of basophil yolk granules (*bas.*), but morphogenesis is normal. *ect.*, ectoderm; *end.*, endoderm; *mes.*, mesoderm; *vac.*, albumen vacuoles in ectoderm and endoderm.

field, with subsequent reinstatement of a field adjusted to the new conditions, may occur.

4. The polar lobe

As we have seen above (p. 94), vegetative fragments of unfertilized eggs of *Dentalium* mostly form a polar lobe at cleavage, whereas animal fragments as a rule do not (sometimes they form a small polar lobe). The polar lobes formed by vegetative fragments of unfertilized eggs are more or less proportional to the size of the fragment. On the other hand, polar lobes formed by vegetative fragments of fertilized eggs (cf. below) are of the same size as those in normal eggs, so that no size regulation takes place in this case (WILSON, 1904a).

In *Ilyanassa* eggs centrifuged at the uncleaved stage, a polar lobe forms at cleavage at the original vegetative pole, irrespective of the egg substances lying in this region. Hence, the lobe may contain oil, hyaloplasm, or yolk, according to circumstances (MORGAN, 1933, 1935a). It is evident that the determining factors of polar lobe formation do not reside in the inner protoplasm, but in the egg cortex.

Vegetative fragments of *Dentalium* eggs transected after fertilization as a rule do not contain a nucleus, and, therefore, do not cleave. Nevertheless, they form a polar lobe, which appears three times synchronously with the divisions of the corresponding animal fragments, while their contour rounds off again in between the divisions. During the fourth cleavage of the animal fragment a polar lobe forms again at the vegetative fragment, but this persists (WILSON). Similarly, in *Ilyanassa* a vegetative half without a nucleus forms a polar lobe twice in succession (MORGAN, 1935b, 1936), but not in a quite typical way.

Polar lobes, isolated by transection, exhibit both in *Dentalium* and *Ilyanassa* a rhythmic activity more or less synchronously with the rest of the egg, periods of amoeboid motility alternating with rest phases in which the outline of the lobe rounds off. Even fragments cut off from a polar lobe show the same phenomenon. In *Ilyanassa* this activity of the isolated lobe does not strictly correspond to its normal behaviour, however. A lobe cut off at first cleavage exhibits three periods of surface activity, whereas it would have appeared only once more in normal development. Also, these periods of activity are not strictly synchronous with the divisions of the egg, but occur with some delay (MORGAN, 1933, 1935c). Presumably the later activity periods reflect the processes taking place during micromere formation.

Anyhow, it is evident that the surface changes of the isolated polar lobe point to an autonomous rhythmic activity of the cytoplasm which is independent of the presence of a nucleus, and which leads to local changes in the properties of the cortex. In normal development this cytoplasmic activity is co-ordinated with the above-mentioned factors determining the positions and directions of the cleavage spindles.

5. Normal and reversed cleavage

It was mentioned above (p. 69) that cleavage is the mirror image of the ordinary pattern in those snail species, where the shell is coiled according to a left-handed spiral. It is not known whether the same holds for exceptional sinistral individuals or sinistral races in otherwise dextral species, but, in the absence of proof to the contrary, it may be assumed that cleavage is reversed also in these cases. Therefore, the following experiments may for the time being be considered to have a bearing on the determination of cleavage type.

BOYCOTT and DIVER (1923) observed that the offspring of isolated self-fertilizing individuals of *Limnaea peregra* were all either dextral or sinistral, irrespective of the direction of coiling of the parent. STURTE-VANT (1923) then put forward the hypothesis that the direction of coiling is due to one pair of Mendelian factors, in which dextral is dominant over sinistral. The direction of coiling of an individual is not dependent on its own genotype, however, but on that of its mother. Presumably, the asymmetry of the egg structure, which is responsible for the direction of cleavage and, thereby, for that of coiling, is laid down in the immature, hence diploid, egg during oogenesis. In this way the expression of the genotype is shifted one generation.

Although DIVER (1925) at first thought that the numerical data in *Limnaea peregra* were at variance with STURTEVANT's hypothesis, later it became clear that this hypothesis in the main fits the facts. The relationships are only complicated by the fact that in sinistral lines genotypical dextrals may arise by mutation, and phenotypical dextrals, possibly through the action of modifying factors (BOYCOTT, DIVER, GARSTANG, and TURNER, 1931; DIVER and ANDERSSON KOTTÖ, 1938).

6. The shape and coherence of the blastomeres

In normal cleavage, after each division the more or less spherical blastomeres flatten against each other, with the formation of a separating interblastomeric wall. In a calcium-free medium, however, the vitelline membrane loses its contact with the egg surface; the blastomeres do not flatten against each other, but retain their rounded shapes. Since their planes of contact are much reduced, they tend to lose their coherence at later stages and fall apart into a loose cell aggregate (*Limnaea*: RAVEN and KLOMP, 1946; *Mytilus*: BERG, 1950) (Fig. 30). A cleavage cavity does not form in *Limnaea* in these circumstances. Addition of

$CaCl_2$, at a concentration of 0·005 per cent or more, gives normal cleavage (RAVEN and KLOMP; HUDIG, 1946). Treatment of *Limnaea* eggs in their capsule fluid with Na oxalate or Na citrate prevents the flattening of the blastomeres and the formation of a cleavage cavity (STALFOORT, 1952). If the eggs are pretreated with a strong $CaCl_2$ solution, normal cleavage may occur in distilled water (RAVEN and MIGHORST, 1946).

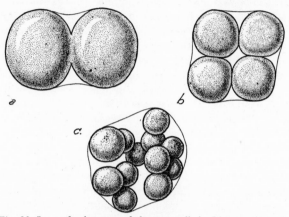

Fig. 30. Loss of coherence of cleavage cells in *Limnaea stagnalis* in calcium-free media. (a) Two-cell stage. (b) Four-cell stage. (c) Later cleavage stage. Cf. Fig. 20.

It is evident that calcium is necessary for preserving the normal properties of the egg cortex. This role of calcium may, however, be taken over by magnesium, and also by lithium in certain concentrations (DE GROOT, 1948; GRASVELD, 1949); on the other hand, sodium produces abnormal, potassium still more abnormal cleavage. The sequence Ca, $Mg < Li < Na < K$, found in these experiments, indicates that a complex colloid system, in which phosphatides take part, is involved.

Rounding off and loss of coherence of the blastomeres may also occur in *Mytilus* eggs after treatment with sperm extracts (BERG, 1950), in *Teredo* eggs treated with KCl or anionic detergents (FAURÉ FREMIET and MUGARD, 1948; FAURÉ FREMIET and THAUREAUX, 1949), and in *Spisula* eggs in cysteine solution (RUGH, 1953). Presumably in all these cases a direct action on the cortex is involved.

7. Differentiation without cleavage

In some cases, a certain amount of differentiation may take place in eggs, in which cleavage is blocked. KOSTANECKI (1908) activated *Mactra* eggs by treatment with KCl–seawater mixtures. Under certain circumstances both polar bodies were extruded, but no cleavage occurred. Nuclear division took place, however, and after twenty-four hours the eggs had formed multi-nuclear ciliated spheres. The nuclei in the common cytoplasmic mass divided synchronously, as a rule; the numerous asters arranged themselves at regular distances from each other, and a system of pluripolar spindles was formed between them, among which the chromosomes were distributed fortuitously into a kind of network. The nuclei arising in this way grouped themselves preferentially at the animal side and along the periphery, leaving free the vegetative pole and the centre of the egg, thus more or less simulating the position of the nuclei in a normal blastula. Later, cell boundaries might appear between the nuclei. When this had occurred, subsequent nuclear divisions in separated cell territories were no longer synchronous. In this case even a cleavage cavity might appear.

A similar differentiation without cleavage may incidentally occur in *Cumingia* eggs after parthenogenetic stimulation (MORRIS, 1917).

These observations indicate in the first place that the rhythm of nuclear divisions is controlled by cytoplasmic factors. Secondly, it appears that the position of the nuclei is not entirely dependent on a normal course of cleavage, but is partly due to general factors affecting the whole egg. In this connection experiments by RAVEN and DUDOK DE WIT (1949) may be mentioned, which suggest that these factors are located in the egg cortex. If *Limnaea* eggs are treated with LiCl at the 24–cell stage, the nuclei, at least in the animal cells, are displaced towards the surface.

8. Chemodifferentiation

In the segregation of cytoplasmic substances taking place during cleavage various phenomena must be distinguished.

In the first place the polar segregation of substances, which came into operation already at the uncleaved stage, in many cases continues during cleavage, so that a distinct animal-vegetative gradient in the distribution of substances comes about.

Furthermore, however, for the first time a clear bilateral symmetry in the distribution of substances now appears. This may occur in various ways.

In some cases, the segregation of cytoplasmic substances takes place along the primary egg axis, but by the asymmetry of early cleavage these substances are divided unequally among the cleavage cells. A clear example of this is given by the distribution of proteid yolk, oil and Golgi bodies, with their associated substances, during early cleavage in *Aplysia* (Pl. II; Fig. 12).

In other instances, there is likewise a polar segregation of cytoplasmic substances. By the repeated formation of a polar lobe and its secondary fusion with certain cleavage cells, some of these substances are shunted into special blastomeres. (Fig. 28). The eggs of *Dentalium*, *Ilyanassa*, etc., represent this type.

Finally, there are cases (as e.g. many gastropods) in which early cleavages are equal, and the distribution of substances remains at first mainly radial. Bilaterality only becomes manifest with the formation of 4d, which differs in its composition from the surrounding cells in consequence of the manner in which it is formed (Fig. 22e).

One gets the impression from this survey that the primary step towards the attainment of bilateral symmetry consists in the occurrence of bilateral cleavage, and that the later bilateral distribution of material arises only secondarily in consequence of this. In other words, the factors of bilateral symmetry do not directly affect the position of cytoplasmic substances (like the factors of animal-vegetative polarity), but act primarily on the cleavage pattern by way of determining the spindle positions.

There are some cases, however, which cannot fully be explained by this mechanism, but point to a more precise localization of substances which is superimposed upon the former. This holds e.g. for the later displacements of the polar lobe substance in *Dentalium* after the 8-cell stage (p. 79), the localization of the granules in *Neritina* (p. 80), of the cortical lipids in *Teredo* (p. 85) and the leucomethylene blue oxidoreductase in *Aplysia* (p. 87).

Finally, it must be mentioned that beside the polar and bilateral segregation of substances, a segregation along a radial (cortico-central) direction also may take place, as e.g. in the distribution of ecto- and endoplasm in *Limnaea* (Fig. 22).

The factors responsible for the distribution of substances can best be studied again in centrifuged eggs. Primarily, the substances accumulated during centrifuging are distributed during cleavage in an arbitrary way among the blastomeres. Cleavage may be normal or abnormal. For example in *Aplysia* (PELTRERA, 1940) and *Limnaea* (RAVEN, 1946c) in eggs centrifuged at an early stage (before or during maturation) cleavage is normal, whereas eggs centrifuged a short time before first cleavage exhibit many abnormalities of cleavage.

If the eggs are fragmented by centrifugation, so that they have lost a part of their substances, the results may differ. In eggs of Nudibranchia, in which by strong centrifugal force during the first maturation division the oil cap has been thrown off, cleavage of the remaining part is normal (COSTELLO, 1939b). If the eggs are fragmented into three parts the hyaline fragment may cleave; the first two cleavages are more or less normal in this case, but later cleavage becomes abnormal.

In *Aplysia*, egg fragments without proteid yolk, or almost entirely consisting of yolk-rich material, mostly cleave equally or irregularly. Fragments containing all substances as a rule show normal cleavage, but this stops after some divisions (RIES, 1939). This is confirmed by PELTRERA (1940); however, according to this author, under optimal conditions, when the fragments almost immediately re-assume a spherical shape, fragments of very abnormal protoplasmic composition may cleave normally.

The cleavage abnormalities in centrifuged eggs may be caused in different ways. The cleavage spindles displaced during centrifuging generally have a tendency to return to their normal positions in the cells. If, however, centrifuging continues until just before or even after the beginning of cleavage, the displaced spindles have no possibility of doing so, and the cleavage furrows appear at the places where the spindles are lying (CONKLIN, 1917; MORGAN, 1933, 1935a).

In the second place, the locally accumulated egg substances may form a hindrance to the prompt return of the spindles.

Thirdly, these substances obstruct, either by their bulk or by altering the properties of the egg cortex under which they lie, the cutting through of the cleavage furrows, so that the latter either deviate or are interrupted. For instance, in *Limnaea* eggs centrifuged just before first cleavage, the cleavage furrows are delayed or interrupted in the fat zone (RAVEN, 1946c).

Experiments by PASTEELS (1934), finally, seem to show that centrifugation may also interfere with normal cleavage by directly affecting the egg cortex. In *Aplysia* eggs, centrifuged at the uncleaved stage, cleavage may be abnormal although the egg substances have recovered their normal distribution in the meantime. On the other hand, if eggs previously irradiated with ultraviolet light are centrifuged, the effects of the first treatment on cleavage are diminished. As, presumably, the primary action of u.v. irradiation is especially upon the cortex, it appears probable that the same holds for centrifuging in this case (cf. also above, p. 94).

As regards the return of the egg substances displaced during centrifuging, the same considerations apply as mentioned above (p. 58) for the uncleaved egg. The passive redispersion of substances is also in this case of primary importance. In *Limnaea* eggs centrifuged just before first cleavage, redispersion of the mitochondria has begun after 35 minutes; 100 minutes after centrifugation the layer of mitochondria has disappeared completely (RAVEN, 1946c). The fat, which at first has a superficial position, disappears at later cleavage stages into the cell interior (RAVEN and BRETSCHNEIDER, 1942).

This redispersion of the substances is furthered by the displacements which are brought about by the cleavage process itself. Both the fat (RAVEN and BRETSCHNEIDER, 1942) (Fig. 31) and the proteid yolk (RAVEN,

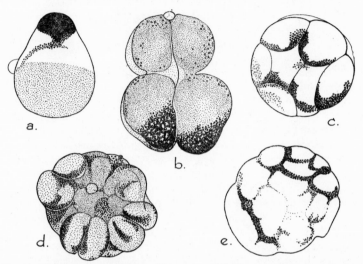

Fig. 31. Redistribution of fatty yolk in eggs of *Limnaea stagnalis* centrifuged at the uncleaved stage. (a) Forty minutes after centrifugation. Dispersal of fat by protoplasmic flow. (b) Eight-cell stage. (c-e) Later cleavage stages. Fat drawn out along the cleavage furrows.

1946c) of centrifuged *Limnaea* eggs are drawn out along the cleavage furrows when the latter cut through the egg. Furthermore, the proteid yolk, which is at first distributed passively among the cells, is mobilized at later cleavage stages, and in this form may pass through the cell walls, so that it also reappears in those cells which were yolk-free (Pl. VII, B).

Beside this passive redispersion, leading to a more uniform distribution of the substances, the processes of cytoplasmic segregation in its proper sense come into play. For instance, the redispersed mitochondria in *Limnaea* are heaped up somewhat later at the animal pole (RAVEN, 1946c).

Presumably, cortical factors play an important part also in this case. The observation that the first visible deviations in *Limnaea* eggs treated with lithium chloride concern alterations in the distribution of ecto- and endoplasm (RAVEN, 1952), argues in favour of this view.

CHAPTER IV

Gastrulation and formation of germ layers

A. DESCRIPTIVE PART

1. The blastula

CLEAVAGE in molluscs gives rise to various types of blastula.

In species, in which the eggs are poor in yolk, generally a more or less unequal *coeloblastula* with wide cleavage cavity is formed. This is e.g. the case in Polyplacophora, in *Proneomenia*, in freshwater Lamellibranchiata as *Cyclas, Sphaerium, Unio, Anodonta, Dreissensia*, in Scaphopoda, and in *Patella, Paludina, Bithynia, Planorbis*, and *Limax*.

A short time before gastrulation begins both the animal and the vegetative side of the blastula may flatten. This occurs e.g. in *Paludina* (DAUTERT, 1929), but the cleavage cavity remains wide in this case. A similar flattening takes place in *Limnaea, Planorbis, Physa*, and *Limax*. It is still more marked in some Prosobranchia as *Firoloïdes, Littorina, Pomatias*, and *Bithynia*. In these cases, the cleavage cavity is greatly narrowed or entirely obliterated in the process, and the blastula has the character of a *placula*.

In yolk-rich eggs a more or less solid, unequal *sterroblastula* is formed, e.g. in *Myzomenia*, some marine Lamellibranchiata as *Ostrea* and *Teredo*, and in *Crepidula, Fulgur, Nassa, Fusus, Urosalpynx* and *Purpura*.

Finally, in the extremely yolk-rich eggs of cephalopods the meroblastic cleavage leads to the formation of a one-layered *discoblastula*.

2. Gastrulation

In those forms which have a coeloblastula, like those mentioned above, generally there is a typical *invagination* of the archenteron. Often it is preceded by a repeated division of the macromeres into smaller cells (e.g. in Unionidae). Then the cells change in shape, beginning at the vegetative pole. The external surface of the cell is reduced, whereas the inner part increases in width, so that the cell becomes wedge-shaped, or even protrudes with a club-shaped end into the cleavage cavity (Pl. VIII, A). This causes the appearance of a pit at the vegetative pole, which becomes deeper as the narrow outer parts of the cells are more and more withdrawn. The invaginating endomeres may be connected

110

(e.g. in *Limnaea*) with the inner side of the cells of the animal hemisphere by means of pseudopodia (Pl. VIII, A). These may assist in the invagination process by providing an anchorage for the inner parts of the endomeres. With increasing invagination of the archenteron the cells arrange themselves into a regular columnar epithelium again (Pl. VIII, B). The macromeres are first invaginated, then come the cells of the fifth quartette, finally those of the fourth quartette (4a–4c). The second somatoblast 4d, insofar it had not yet disappeared into the depth, now withdraws individually from the surface, and comes to lie in the cleavage cavity behind the archenteron. Finally all yolk-rich cells have been invaginated. The margin of the blastopore is now formed by the *stomatoblasts* of the second and third quartettes, those of the second quartette lying on the radii, while the third quartette stomatoblasts are situated interradially.

Often the invagination of the archenteron is not radially symmetrical, but from the first its anterior end is deeper than the posterior one, as e.g. in *Chiton* (KOWALEWSKY, 1883a) and *Limax* (KOFOID, 1895; MEISENHEIMER, 1896).

In those cases where a flattening occurs at the end of the blastula stage, so that the germ resembles a placula, the invagination may be preceded by an incurving towards the vegetative side, e.g. in *Paludina* (DAUTERT, 1929) and *Pomatias* (CREEK, 1951). On the other hand, in more yolk-rich eggs such an incurving of the placula may also be followed by epiboly (e.g. *Firoloïdes, Carinaria, Littorina*).

In those forms where there is a sterroblastula, gastrulation takes place by *epiboly* (*Haliotis, Teredo, Crepidula, Neritina, Trochus, Vermetus, Nassa, Ocinebra, Aplysia*). The extension of the micromeres over the vegetative half of the egg may be attended by a considerable flattening of these cells. In some cases, gastrulation begins with epibolic extension of the micromeres, after which an invagination takes place (e.g. *Myzomenia, Mytilus, Ostrea, Umbrella, Clione, Cymbulia*).

By the invagination of the archenteron, and the simultaneous development of the mesoderm, an originally wide cleavage cavity may almost entirely disappear, e.g. in *Paludina* and *Physa*.

In many cases a more or less deep depression is formed during gastrulation at the animal pole by sinking in of the cells (e.g. *Neritina, Trochus, Physa, Limnaea, Limax*). It is formed by the cells of the apical rosette and the base of the dorsal arm of the cross.

A special case is provided by the very yolk-rich egg of *Fulgur* (CONKLIN, 1907). Organogenesis begins here a long time before the closure of the blastopore, while the germ still forms a small cap of cells near the animal pole. The medioventral part of this 'blastoderm' begins to extend rapidly over the yolk cells; only later the dorsal margin also begins to grow, so that the closure of the blastopore finally takes place at the vegetative pole. In a way, this case forms a transition to the relationships in cephalopods.

Gastrulation in cephalopods proceeds in a complicated way. The process begins with the formation of a layer of flat cells on the surface of the yolk, the so-called *yolk epithelium* (RAY LANKESTER) or *perivitelline membrane*. This membrane originates from the peripheral cells of the blastoderm, VIALLETON's 'blastocones'. In *Sepia* these blastocones first divide into a number of polygonal cells, which then disperse into the superficial layer of ectoplasm (VIALLETON, 1888). In *Tremoctopus*, on the other hand, no cell division takes place, but the blastocones transform directly into the cells of the perivitelline membrane (SACARRAO, 1953). This membrane spreads peripherally to the opposite pole of the egg, at the same time extending centrally beneath the germinal disc. Later it becomes a syncytium. This *yolk syncytium* begins at an early stage with the digestion of the yolk. At the same time the growth of the blastoderm commences. This extends peripherally over the perivitelline membrane, in this way forming the *external yolk-sac* (Fig. 49).

Along the margin of the germinal disc a delamination process takes place, by which this becomes multi-layered. In *Loligo* this occurs in a horseshoe-shaped area (TEICHMANN, 1903); in octopods it is a closed ring, however (SACARRAO, 1953). The deep layer produced in this way extends beneath the ectoderm, the cells arranging themselves into one layer, so that the blastoderm becomes two-layered, with the exception of its central part, which still consists of one layer of cells for a long time.

The older authors considered the deep layer as mesoderm (USSOW, 1881; VIALLETON, 1888; FAUSSEK, 1901). The definitive endoderm (gut primordium) appears in cephalopods at a very late stage as a local differentiation of the inner layer. VIALLETON supposed that it arose from the perivitelline membrane. According to FAUSSEK, however, the definitive endoderm takes its origin from the mesoderm. On the contrary, TEICHMANN considered the deep layer as a whole as endoderm. The mesoderm would be produced in *Loligo* only later, simultaneously with the genital cells, by a local proliferation of the superficial germ layer.

The most plausible view is the one upheld by NAEF (1928) and SACARRAO (1952a, 1953) according to which the deep layer forms the common primordium of mesoderm and endoderm, and only later segregates into these two components. A part of the deep layer becomes epithelial, and forms the mid-gut primordium, while the rest becomes mesoderm.

SACARRAO also regards the perivitelline membrane as a part of the endoderm. The latter is supposed, therefore, to have divided in two functionally and ontogenetically different parts. Gastrulation proceeds in two separate, but synchronous phases. This early separation of the endoderm in two parts is compared with the relationships in yolk-rich gastropods (e.g. *Nassa, Fusus, Murex*; cf. below, p. 116) (SACARRAO, 1952b).

3. The blastopore

The blastopore is at first very wide. Then it narrows considerably, as a rule by the approach of its lateral lips, so that it temporarily forms a sagittal cleft. It then closes from behind forwards, by outgrowth of its posterior margin. In many cases the anterior part of the blastopore persists, however (e.g. *Chiton, Dentalium, Aplysia, Physa, Limax*).

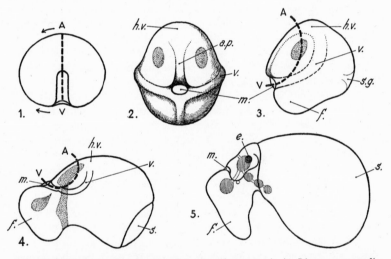

Fig. 32. Diagrammatic representation of embryogenesis in *Limnaea stagnalis*. (1) Gastrula. Arrows indicate later displacement of animal pole and blastopore. (2) Trochophore, ventral view. (3) The same, from the left side. (4) Early veliger. (5) 'Hippo'-stage. The broken line indicates the main axis through animal pole and middle of blastopore. Dotted areas indicate proliferation of ganglion cells. Ganglia (in (5)) are hatched. *A*, animal pole; *V*, vegetative end of main axis. *a.p.*, apical plate; *e.*, eye; *f.*, foot; *h.v.*, head vesicle; *m.*, mouth; *s.*, shell; *s.g.*, shell gland; *v.*, velum.

In other cases the blastopore closes completely (e.g. *Cyclas, Sphaerium, Anodonta, Mytilus, Dreissensia, Teredo, Neritina, Trochus, Fulgur*). The archenteron then forms a completely closed sac, which opens only much later to the outside again (Fig. 33). In yolk-rich eggs, instead of a sac-like archenteron a compact mass of endoderm cells filled with yolk may be found (e.g. *Teredo*).

In still other species, there is only a very temporary closure of the blastopore at the inner end of the stomodaeal invagination, which re-opens soon (e.g. *Crepidula, Planorbis*). In *Limnaea*, which also belongs to this type, at the place of closure (the future oesophagus anlage) a virtual lumen always remains (Fig. 45).

The blastopore is originally situated in the centre of the vegetative hemisphere. Then it is displaced anteriorly, however, so that it comes to lie at the ventral side (Fig. 32). This displacement of the blastopore is due to a considerable growth of the dorsal region, especially the derivatives of 2d, which form the so-called somatic plate; this may be attended with a rapid division of these cells. In Lamellibranchiata, moreover, the early formation of the shell gland, which first invaginates, but soon evaginates again, may assist in shifting the blastopore to the ventral side (MEISENHEIMER, 1901: *Dreissensia*).

This displacement of the blastopore is lacking in *Paludina*. Here the blastopore remains at the posterior end of the embryo until the end of gastrulation (DAUTERT, 1929) (Fig. 42).

At the point where the last remnant of the blastopore persists, or where its final closure takes place, the *stomodaeum* is usually formed. Only in *Paludina* does this appear at some distance from the persisting blastopore. As a rule, the stomodaeum is formed by the invagination of the stomatoblasts, which form the margin of the blastopore at the end of gastrulation. Sometimes, however, the stomatoblasts disappear from the surface by being overgrown by the adjacent cells of the ectoderm (e.g. in *Aplysia*: CARAZZI, 1905).

Paludina stands quite apart by the fact that in this form the blastopore becomes the *anus* (BLOCHMANN, 1883; VON ERLANGER, 1891; TÖNNIGES, 1896; DAUTERT, 1929; FERNANDO, 1931). It is generally admitted, how-ever, that in the other species, where the anus is formed much later, its position also corresponds to the original posterior margin of the wide blastopore. In some cases this point is marked by a pair of large, pro-truding cells, the so-called *anal cells* (e.g. in Opisthobranchia and many Prosobranchia, as *Patella, Littorina, Purpura, Nassa, Calyptraea*).

4. The ectoderm

As mentioned above (p. 70), the ectoderm of the later head region is derived from the first quartette of micromeres. Sometimes this part of the ectoderm is distinguished already at an advanced gastrula stage by a considerable flattening of its cells, forming the so-called *head vesicle* (e.g. in *Cyclas*: STAUFFACHER, 1894; *Sphaerium*: OKADA, 1936) (Fig. 33).

The ectoderm of the trunk region is derived from the cells of the second and third quartettes. Especially the descendants of the first somatoblast, 2d, play an important role here. The ectoderm cells in the dorsal region may considerably increase in size at an early stage, whereby the animal pole is shifted ventrally, e.g. in *Crepidula* (CONKLIN, 1897). By an intense multiplication of the cells in this area the so-called *somatic plate* is formed. Its anterior part forms the primordium of the *shell gland*. The posterior part, which extends towards the ventral side along with the closure and displacement of the blastopore, becomes the *ventral plate*, which is situated behind the mouth, and from which the foot develops (Fig. 33).

In most lamellibranchs the shell gland invaginates very early, more or less simultaneously with the archenteron. As the shell gland invagination is often larger than the archenteron these gastrulae show a peculiar structure. However, soon the shell gland begins to evaginate again, which may contribute to the extension of the dorsal half of the embryo and the displacement of the blastopore. In some lamellibranchs (e.g. *Sphaerium*) the invagination of the shell gland does not begin until the completion of gastrulation. The same holds for the other groups of molluscs.

5. The endoderm

In those cases where gastrulation takes place by invagination, the endomeres change directly into the cells bounding the archenteron. This remains in connection with the outside through the blastopore, or closes into a blind sac. In the latter case, the mouth is formed later as a secondary communication between the archenteron lumen and the deep end of the stomodaeum. Still later, a posterior outgrowth of the archenteron makes contact with the ectoderm; at this point an *anal plate* or a short *ectodermal proctodaeum* is formed. For instance, in *Sphaerium* the anal plate forms at the boundary between the shell gland primordium and the ventral plate (OKADA, 1936) (Fig. 33).

In those forms where gastrulation takes place by epiboly, but the yolk content is not excessive, all endomeres take part in the formation of the archenteron (*Crepidula, Clione, Cymbulia*). These cells (4A–4D and 4a–4c) are at first gradually overgrown by the ectoderm cells. There is no true invagination, but the formation of the archenteron is due to a change in shape and a displacement of the cells. Thereby the cells of the fourth and fifth quartettes slip beneath the macromeres; eventually the macromeres form the tip of the archenteron, the fifth quartette cells form the middle part, and the fourth quartette cells are situated nearest the blastopore (*Crepidula*: CONKLIN, 1897). These cells, and their descendants, then form a continuous epithelium.

In *Teredo* at first a compact mass of endomeres, filled with yolk, lies beneath the ectoderm. Later a lumen is formed in the central part of this mass, and still later it connects with stomodaeum and proctodaeum.

A peculiar phenomenon is shown by the endomeres in many cases of

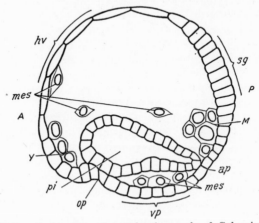

Fig. 33. Mediosagittal section of completed gastrula of *Sphaerium japonicum*. *A*, anterior end; *P*, posterior end of embryo. *ap*, anal plate; *hv*, head vesicle; *M*, teloblastic cell mass of mesoderm; *mes*, mesenchyme cells; *op*, oral plate; *pi*, archenteron; *sg*, shell gland primordium; *vp*, ventral plate; *Y*, larval mesoblast. After OKADA, 1936.

epibolic gastrulation. The nuclei of these cells are at first situated near the surface just behind the margin of the cap of ectoderm cells. During the epibolic overgrowth the nuclei maintain the same position with respect to this margin, which they precede in its vegetative displacement, so that they have reached in the end the most vegetative part of the endomeres (*Cavolinia*: FOL, 1875; *Crepidula*: CONKLIN, 1897; *Nassa*: HOFFMANN, 1902).

In very yolk-rich eggs not all macromeres are included in the formation of the archenteron, but some of these cells remain inert and form a yolk mass, which does not take part in organogenesis (Fig. 34). Later this *provisional endoderm* is replaced by *definitive endoderm* of small yolk-free cells. For instance, in *Aplysia* the cells 4A and 4B remain undivided for a long time. The derivatives of 4C and 4D, together with 4a and 4b, form an epithelium of small endoderm cells. Later 4A and 4B move apart, and in this way form a cavity, which on its other sides is bounded by the small-celled endoderm (BLOCHMANN, 1883).

In *Purpura* and *Nassa* it is the cell 4D, which is very big and yolk-rich, which remains altogether passive. The six other endomeres divide actively and form a one-layered cell plate, which is situated on the side of the blastopore. According to HOFFMANN (1902), the yolk-containing parts of these cells later fuse with the nutritive yolk in 4D to a common mass. The latter blastomere, which occupies the tip and the hind wall of the archenteron, for a long time sends a yolk-free protoplasmic protrusion containing the nucleus in between the descendants of the other endomeres, which takes the place of the archenteron lumen. Only later this lumen is formed by withdrawal of the protrusion. Then gradually 4D is overgrown by the cells of the definitive endoderm, and in this way is excluded from the archenteron lumen. The nucleus of 4D plays an important physiological role in the breakdown and mobilization of the nutritive yolk.

In the cephalopods, likewise an early separation of the endoderm in two parts with different functions occurs. The yolk mass with the surrounding perivitelline membrane may be compared to a huge macromere 4D (SACARRAO, 1952b) (Fig. 49).

6. The mesoderm

The mesoderm generally originates from the two *mesodermal teloblasts*, which are derived from the daughter cells of 4d, after the latter have produced a certain number of *enteroblasts* (Fig. 27a). The teloblasts, which are situated on the left and right behind the archenteron, bud forth a number of small cells in front, and in this way produce the two *mesoderm bands* (Fig. 33, 65).

In many cases, e.g. in most gastropods, mesoderm formation begins a considerable time before gastrulation. In other instances the process begins much later, however, e.g. in *Chiton polii*, where the future mesomeres are still lying at the gastrula stage among the endoderm cells near the blastopore lip (KOWALEWSKY, 1883a). Only after gastrulation do they move into the blastocoel, and the formation of mesoderm bands begins. In the Lamellibranchiata the cell 4d also remains superficially for a long time, sometimes up to the gastrula stage. It divides into the two teloblasts while still at the surface; then these cells sink into the blastocoel.

As a rule the mesoderm bands remain rather rudimentary, especially in the Lamellibranchiata. Sometimes, however, they are well developed e.g. in *Unio*, *Anodonta*, *Patella* and *Physa*. In these cases they embrace the archenteron in the shape of a horseshoe. They grow both by the formation of new cells at their posterior end from the teloblasts, and by division of the smaller mesomeres. Ultimately the mesoderm bands become less distinct, and the teloblasts, which diminish in size by repeated division, can no more be distinguished as such. Finally the mesoderm bands fall apart into masses of coelenchyme.

The formation of *coelomic cavities* in the mesoderm bands has been repeatedly described, but remains very questionable. KOWALEWSKY (1883a) described them in *Chiton polii*, but HAMMARSTEN and RUNN-STRÖM (1925) combat this view as a result of their observations in *Acanthochiton*. Likewise, KOWALEWSKY (1883b) claims to have observed

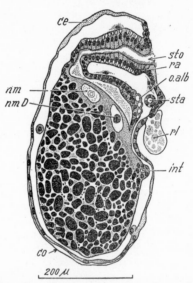

Fig. 34. Parasagittal section of early symmetric embryo of *Fusus. ce*, head vesicle; *co*, larval shell; *int*, hindgut primordium; *nm*, nucleus of macromere; *o.alb*, anlage of larval liver; *ra*, first indication of radular sac; *rl*, larval kidney; *sta*, statocyst; *sto*, stomodaeum. After PORTMANN, 1955.

a coelom in *Dentalium*, but WILSON (1904a) did not see it. In gastropods a coelomic cavity in the mesoderm bands has been described by SALEN-SKY (1887, *Vermetus*) and VON ERLANGER (1892, *Bithynia*), but both descriptions do not appear very reliable.

Special relationships are found in *Paludina*. The formation of the mesoderm in this form has been described in two completely different ways.

According to VON ERLANGER (1891), after the completion of gastrula-tion the ventral wall of the archenteron bulges out. This part is con-stricted off as a coelomic sac, which then extends on either side of the archenteron in a dorsal direction. The coelomic cavity widens laterally, and supersedes the blastocoel; at the same time, the medioventral part of the coelom disappears. Eventually, the cells of the splanchnic and somatic layers begin to lose their coherence, and disperse through the body cavity as a coelenchyme. This description is corroborated, in broad outline, by FERNANDO (1931).

A quite different course of events is described by TÖNNIGES (1896) and DAUTERT (1929). According to these authors, the mesoderm is formed some time after gastrulation by loosening of cells from the ectodermal epithelium at the ventral side of the embryo. It begins just behind the prototroch, and extends over the whole ventral surface, from prototroch to anus (Fig. 42). The mesoderm formed in this way later spreads in a dorsal and animal direction on both sides of the archenteron, but leaves free the mediodorsal region, where a direct contact between the endoderm and the ectoderm of the future shell gland area remains. No coelomic cavity is formed; the mesoderm gradually disperses into mesenchyme. As the cells of the latter are later closely applied to the ectoderm and endoderm, presumably a temporary cleft may appear between the two layers, which has been interpreted by VON ERLANGER and FERNANDO as a coelom. It is very evident from FERNANDO's paper that this author has begun his investigation at a stage when the mesoderm has long been formed. On the other hand, DAUTERT's painstaking investigation, in which the development of *Paludina* has been followed step by step, gives a very clear picture of the process.

According to DAUTERT, the mesoderm of *Paludina* is probably homologous to the ectomesoderm (larval mesenchyme) of other forms. The primary mesoderm would be lacking in this form.

On mesoderm formation in the cephalopods, cf. above, p. 112.

7. The larval mesenchyme

The initial cells of the larval mesenchyme, after they have been displaced into the depth, produce by repeated division a cell group, which is situated in the blastocoel in front of the archenteron (Fig. 33). Sometimes this joins with the mesoderm bands behind, so that a nearly continuous ring of mesoblastic elements is formed around the archenteron, e.g. in *Physa* (WIERZEJSKI). The cells of the larval mesenchyme already at an early stage form the larval musculature in the foot, head vesicle and velum.

8. Cytoplasmic differentiation

In general the cytoplasmic differentiation does not increase markedly during gastrulation. The cells which have become different in their composition during the preceding period, now come to lie in different germ layers.

For instance, in *Limnaea* the mesoderm cells have a rather dense cytoplasm, with a strong affinity for protoplasm stains (RAVEN, 1946b). Likewise, the mesodermal teloblasts in *Crepidula* stain more darkly than all other cells in their neighbourhood (CONKLIN, 1897). But whereas these cells in *Crepidula* do not contain any yolk, the mesomeres of *Limnaea* possess many large γ–granules. Since the second somatoblast 4d, by its manner of formation, is nearly devoid of ectoplasm (cf. above, p. 80), the mesomeres do not contain any albumen vacuoles. The same holds for *Limax* (MEISENHEIMER, 1896).

In consequence of the differential distribution of ecto- and endoplasm during cleavage in *Limnaea* the cells in the neighbourhood of the vegetative pole are rich in endoplasm, but contain little ectoplasm. The albumen vacuoles in the ectoplasm, which occurred first at the animal side, later increase more and more at the vegetative side (MEISENHEIMER, 1896; HOLMES, 1900; RAVEN, 1946b). At the time of gastrulation the endomeres therefore contain numerous large albumen vacuoles, which arrange themselves during invagination in rows in the narrowed peripheral parts of the cells, and are later found along the lumen of the archenteron (Pl. VIII).

In yolk-rich eggs the endomeres are nearly entirely filled with proteid yolk. The nuclei are situated, each in a small island of yolk-free protoplasm, in the cell-parts bounding the lumen.

The ectodermal cells in *Limnaea* possess much ectoplasm, which increases in amount towards the animal pole. The albumen vacuoles generally remain small, except in the cells bounding the depression at the animal pole, which have extremely large albumen vacuoles, the contents of which are often inhomogeneous (Pl. VIII).

9. Cytoplasmic inclusions

The cytoplasmic inclusions are in general more or less passively distributed among the germ layers during gastrulation. For instance, in *Physa* and *Bithynia* the fatty yolk, which was accumulated in the macromeres during cleavage, moves mainly into the inner germ layer (MANCUSO, 1953; ATTARDO, 1955a). The proteid yolk, especially in yolk-rich forms, likewise passes almost entirely into the endoderm cells. The mitochondria in *Mytilus* retain their position at the cell surface; therefore, they come to lie along the lumen of the archenteron too. The Golgi bodies in *Limnaea* (HIRSCHLER, 1918; GATENBY, 1919) and *Navanax* (WORLEY and WORLEY, 1943) are likewise passively distributed among the cells, and exhibit no segregation.

Apparently, the Golgi bodies are not in an active phase during gastrulation. An exception to this rule is found in *Mytilus*, where large oil drops are formed by the Golgi bodies during later phases of gastrulation (WORLEY, 1944). A number of Golgi bodies stick together to a common mass, in the centre of which an oil drop appears, which grows in size and finally detaches itself from the Golgi bodies. The author stresses that the oil is not formed within, but between the Golgi bodies. The process begins near the animal pole, and gradually progresses towards the vegetative side.

10. Cytochemistry

a. GLYCOGEN

In *Physa* (MANCUSO, 1953) all glycogen is found in the inner germ layer. Since some of the egg glycogen passed into the second micromeres at cleavage, this must either have been consumed or transported in the meantime.

In *Limnaea* (RAVEN, 1946b) glycogen is found at the animal side mainly around the polar depression. At the vegetative side the cells in a horseshoe-shaped area surrounding the anterior border of the blastopore, presumably the descendants of 4a, 4b and 4c, are rich in glycogen. These glycogen-rich cells are separated by a sharp boundary from the cells in the deeper part of the archenteron, which contain little glycogen. The mesoderm cells are poor in glycogen.

b. DESOXYRIBONUCLEIC ACID

In *Limnaea* the amount of DNA has strongly increased at the gastrula stage (RAVEN, 1946b; MINGANTI, 1950). The resting nuclei are now clearly Feulgen-positive, but show great differences in staining intensity. In many nuclei fine Feulgen-positive granules are arranged along the nuclear membrane and around the nucleolus.

c. RIBONUCLEIC ACID

In *Limnaea* the nucleoli are still rich in RNA, but now it is restricted to their outer shell, whereas the inner vacuoles do not stain any more. The ectoplasmic parts of the cells contain more RNA than the endoplasm; consequently, the mesomeres are rather poor in RNA. The albumen vacuoles in the ectoplasm do not stain.

d. SULPHYDRYL COMPOUNDS

Although in general the ectoplasmic parts of the cells contain more bound sulphydryl compounds in *Limnaea* than do the endoplasmic parts, yet the endoderm cells stain more deeply than the ectoderm. The nucleoli still show a strong reaction.

e. INDOPHENOL OXIDASE

In *Physa* the cytochrome oxidase is mainly found in the ectoderm (MANCUSO, 1955b).

f. IRON

In *Limnaea* (ARENDSEN DE WOLFF-EXALTO, 1947) iron granules are present in the ectoplasm of both ectoderm and endoderm cells. But the mesoderm cells, although they possess no ectoplasm, now are also rich in iron.

B. CAUSAL ANALYSIS

1. Gastrulation and formation of mesoderm after operative removal of a part of the germ

The investigations by CRAMPTON (1896, *Ilyanassa*), WILSON (1904a and b, *Dentalium* and *Patella*), CLEMENT (1952, 1956, *Ilyanassa*) and RATTENBURY and BERG (1954, *Mytilus*) provide information on the importance of various parts of the germ for gastrulation and mesoderm formation.

After isolation at the 2–cell stage, the embryos derived both from AB and CD are able to gastrulate. Likewise, A–, B–, C– and D–embryos after isolation of the cells at the 4–cell stage in *Dentalium* and *Ilyanassa* may gastrulate. But embryos developed from micromeres isolated at the 8–cell stage in *Dentalium* and *Patella* do not gastrulate, neither singly nor in combination. On the contrary, the isolated macromeres 1A to 1D do gastrulate in *Patella*.

Apparently, the presence of at least a part of the vegetative region of the egg is necessary for gastrulation. This is not the polar lobe, however, for after removal of either the first or the second polar lobe gastrulation takes place in *Ilyanassa*, *Dentalium* and *Mytilus*. In the latter even a CD–embryo without polar lobe may gastrulate. Finally, both animal and vegetative fragments of the unfertilized egg of *Dentalium* give rise to gastrulating embryos.

With respect to mesoderm formation things are different, however. It has been found already by CRAMPTON (1896) that in the development of 'lobeless' embryos of *Ilyanassa* no mesoderm bands are formed. This was later confirmed for *Dentalium* and *Mytilus*. Only the larval mesenchyme is formed in such embryos. In agreement with this, CD–embryos in *Dentalium*, *Ilyanassa* and *Mytilus* possess mesoderm, but AB–embryos do not.

Interesting observations have been made by HESS (1956a) on half-embryos from isolated blastomeres in *Bithynia*. Normal gastrulation is brought about here by a combination of endoderm invagination and epiboly. In half-embryos the invagination takes place in a rather normal way, but the epibolic movement of the ectoderm on the operated side is hampered. Since the extension of the ectoderm is not diminished, it is lifted from the endoderm and forms a vesicle. This increases in size by the accumulation of fluid. By the pressure of this fluid the invagination of the endoderm is abolished, the archenteron disappears, and an exogastrula is formed.

These observations are explained by the assumption that the epibolic movement of the ectoderm is due to a positive affinity between this layer and that part of the endoderm, which it normally overgrows. This affinity is lacking on the operated side, where a portion of the endoderm, which in normal embryos borders on the endoderm of the other half, lies on the surface.

2. Exogastrulation

Eggs of *Limnaea stagnalis*, treated at early stages with weak solutions of lithium chloride, develop in a large percentage of cases to vesicular or dumb-bell shaped embryos (RAVEN, 1942) (Fig. 35). When these structures were studied in sections, it appeared that gastrulation had entirely been suppressed (RAVEN, 1952). No invagination had taken place. The cells were arranged in one or more layers in the walls of the vesicular embryo, with the exception of some mesodermal elements filling the central cavity. Some incipient histological differentiation had taken place in various tissues.

The production of these 'exogastrulae' by means of lithium treatment is restricted to a certain period of development. There is a phase-specific sensitivity of the eggs, with a maximum at the 2- to 4-cell stage (RAVEN, KLOEK, KUIPER and DE JONG, 1947). Apparently, there is a sharp peak in the sensitivity just after the second cleavage (RAVEN and BURGERS, 1952; GEILENKIRCHEN, 1952a). Moreover, there are rhythmic changes in sensitivity in connection with the cleavage cycles (E. D. NIJENHUIS, unpublished observations). After the 12-cell stage no exogastrulation can be provoked with lithium treatment (RAVEN and RIJVEN, 1948).

Exogastrulation is not a specific lithium effect. Exogastrulae may also occur after treatment of the eggs with sodium, potassium, rubidium, caesium, magnesium, and calcium chloride. However, in all these cases the frequency of exogastrulation is much less, and it is only produced by higher concentrations of the salts (RAVEN and SIMONS, 1948; RAVEN, 1956).

The interactions between various ions were tested by exposing the eggs to various combinations of the salts. Potassium has no antagonistic effect with respect to lithium; rather, there is a weak synergism between the two ions (ELBERS, 1952; RAVEN, 1956). On the contrary, exogastrulation through lithium is entirely suppressed by certain concentrations of calcium chloride (DE VRIES, 1953). Likewise, sodium, rubidium and caesium ions diminish the lithium effect.

A weak (1.25×10^{-4} M) solution of KCN also suppresses the lithium effect (HAYE and RAVEN, 1953). But a stronger (3.75×10^{-4} M) KCN solution itself produces about 10 per cent exogastrulae, which number

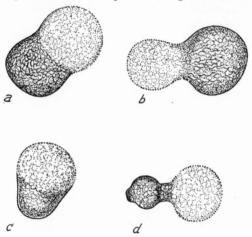

Fig. 35. Exogastrulae of *Limnaea stagnalis*, from eggs treated with lithium chloride at early stages.

is not increased, however, by addition of lithium. This corresponds to the action of a greatly reduced oxygen pressure, which also causes a certain percentage of exogastrulation, which is not increased by addition of lithium (GEILENKIRCHEN, 1952b; RAVEN and MOOY, 1954). These exogastrulae wholly agree in their structure with those produced by lithium (RAVEN and VAN RIJCKEVORSEL, 1953).

When the eggs are exposed to heat shock (one to three hours at 37°C) at early stages, they also yield a certain number of exogastrulae (VIS-SCHEDIJK, 1953). By this treatment exogastrulation may even be brought about as late as the 24–cell stage. However, these exogastrulae differ in their histological structure from those produced by lithium. The differentiation of the cells is much more disturbed (RAVEN, DE ROON and STADHOUDERS, 1955).

Finally, exogastrulation may occur after centrifugation of the eggs, particularly when it takes place just before third cleavage (RAVEN and VAN EGMOND, 1951; RAVEN and KOEVOETS, 1952). Lithium treatment and centrifugation combined gives summation, not interaction of the effects. The exogastrulae produced by centrifuging correspond in their general shape and structure to lithium exogastrulae, but differ in one important respect (cf. below, p. 193) (PARIS, 1953).

Calcium, which acts antagonistically with respect to exogastrulation produced by lithium, does not influence exogastrulation following a reduced oxygen pressure. A weak KCN solution strongly increases the number of exogastrulae produced by anaerobiosis (RAVEN and MOOY, 1954). The number of exogastrulae following heat shock is increased by calcium, coincident with a considerable reduction in mortality (RAVEN and VAN ERKEL, 1955).

HESS (1956b) obtained exogastrulation in *Bithynia* by lithium treatment, also in eggs damaged by lack of oxygen, by cold or high concentrations of vital stains. MANCUSO (1955a) produced exogastrulae in *Physa* by treatment of the eggs at early cleavage stages with sodium azide. In this case there is a maximum in sensitivity at the 4- to 8-cell stage. Some exogastrulae were also obtained in *Bithynia* by treatment with sodium azide (ATTARDO, 1955b).

The results may be interpreted in the following way. The occurrence of exogastrulation in centrifuged eggs points to the importance of ooplasmic segregation. The fact that centrifugation is most effective when it takes place immediately prior to third cleavage, hence at a moment when the concentration of the subcortical protoplasm towards the animal side and its fusion with the animal pole plasm occurs (cf. above, p. 77), speaks strongly in favour of this view. We have seen that the dense protoplasm, rich in mitochondria and β-granules, which is produced by this fusion, at later cleavage shows a differential distribution among the cells, its relative amount decreasing from the animal towards the vegetative pole (Fig. 22). This difference in composition between the animal and vegetative cells of the embryo may be a prerequisite for the normal course of gastrulation. Hence, centrifugation may lead, through mechanical interference with this process of ooplasmic segregation, to exogastrulation.

If we accept this explanation, we may presume that the other agents giving exogastrulation also disturb the normal course of ooplasmic segregation. Apparently, the latter is dependent in the first place on the respiratory mechanisms of the egg. Anaerobiosis, cyanide, azide and perhaps heat shock treatment, by upsetting the normal course of respiration, all have a disturbing effect on ooplasmic segregation, and in this way may bring about exogastrulation. Perhaps, the role played by respiration consists essentially in the generation of the energy potentials necessary for the displacement of the egg substances.

Finally, it appears that the normal course of ooplasmic segregation is, in some way or other, dependent on cortical factors. This explains why the ionic composition of the medium is of so great importance. Perhaps the primary effect of heat shock is also due to an alteration of the structure of the egg cortex (RAVEN and VAN ERKEL, 1955). It may be remembered that lithium treatment of uncleaved *Limnaea* eggs leads to visible disturbances in the distribution of ooplasmic substances (DE GROOT, 1948). Moreover, the maximum sensitivity of the egg for the production of exogastrulae by lithium lies at most half an hour before the phase of intensive protoplasmic shifting, at which centrifugation is most effective. In previous chapters we came to the conclusion that the localization of cytoplasmic substances is mainly controlled by cortical factors (cf. above, pp. 60 and 109). It is easily understandable, therefore, that agents influencing the properties of the egg cortex may lead to exogastrulation.

The observed interactions between various ions, and the 'ion spectrum' (BUNGENBERG DE JONG, 1949) of the effect, indicate that lithium and the other alkali cations act on a complex colloid, in which both calcium and phosphatides take part (RAVEN, 1956). Apparently, the colloidal structure of the cortex, upon which its other properties, such as permeability and electric conductivity, may depend, is of primary importance for its function as a regulating and controlling organ in cell life and development.

CHAPTER V

Embryogenesis

A. DESCRIPTIVE PART

1. The development of the general body plan

In most groups of molluscs, development is indirect. Typically, the first larval stage developing from the gastrula is the *trochophore*. On further development this transforms into the second larval stage, the *veliger*. After some time this metamorphoses into a young individual which has the structure of the adult animal.

A divergent larval type, the *glochidium*, is found in the Unionidae among the Lamellibranchiata, in connection with the larval parasitism occurring in this group.

The typical course of development may further be modified in various ways, because a part of or even the whole period of development is passed within the egg capsules or in a brood-pouch of the adult. In this case the larval stages are more or less suppressed, and no metamorphosis occurs. However, as a rule the larval character of the developing embryos is partly retained, and the characteristic larval organs of the free-living larvae are still clearly recognizable in these forms too.

a. THE TROCHOPHORE

The typical molluscan trochophore is a more or less top-shaped larva. Around its equator, there is a *prototroch*, consisting of from one to three rows of large cells, bearing powerful cilia. Smaller cilia may occur on the rest of the body. The prototroch divides the body into the upper or *pretrochal* region, and the lower or *posttrochal* region (Fig. 36).

The pretrochal part bears on its upper pole, which corresponds to the animal pole of the egg and is morphologically the anterior end of the larva, a long tuft of *apical flagellae*. In the posttrochal body region, the *mouth* is situated on the ventral side just behind the prototroch. It leads into the *stomodaeum*, which has in many cases a posterior outgrowth representing the rudiment of the *radular sac*. Behind the mouth, a protruding knob may be present, which is the primordium of the *foot*. On the dorsal side, opposite the mouth, the *shell gland* is represented by a thickening of the ectoderm, which first invaginates, then evaginates again, and commences the secretion of the larval shell. As a rule, the

posterior end of the gut ends blindly; no anal opening has been formed
as yet. But the lower (posterior) end of the larva may be marked by two
protruding *anal cells*, indicating the place where the anus will break
through. Sometimes, a short posterior tuft (e.g. in *Dreissensia, Ostrea,
Dentalium, Patella, Acmaea*) or a posterior crown of cilia, the *telotroch*
(e.g. in Aplacophora, *Teredo*) may occur at this place (Fig. 36).

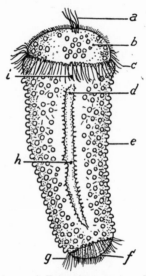

Fig. 36. Early trochophore of *Epimenia verrucosa*. Ventral view. *a*, apical
flagellae; *b*, pretrochal region; *c*, prototroch; *d*, prepedal cavity; *e*, posttrochal
region; *f*, anal region; *g*, telotroch; *h*, foot; *i*, stomodaeal pit. After Baba, 1938.

There are paired *mesoderm bands* in the posttrochal part of the body.
From the larval mesenchyme a well-developed *larval musculature* may
arise. Finally, there may be a pair of *protonephridia* (Lamellibranchiata).

Free trochophore larvae occur in the Polyplacophora, Aplacophora,
Scaphopoda, in all marine Lamellibranchiata and *Dreissensia*, and in a
number of primitive Prosobranchia (e.g. *Patella, Acmaea, Fissurella,
Haliotis*). In other cases this stage is passed within the egg capsules.

In some groups of molluscs the trochophore exhibits certain particulars. In Polyplacophora the shell gland is already at early stages subdivided into seven to eight transverse grooves. Very early, *spicules* appear
in lateral rows bordering the shell area, and in the dorsal part of the
pretrochal region. The spicules are formed in special ectoderm cells
within large vacuoles. Further a pair of *eyes* develop in the posttrochal

region immediately behind the prototroch. An invagination behind the mouth forms the so-called *pedal gland*.

In the Aplacophora (with the exception of *Epimenia*) the prototroch is strongly developed, consisting of three rows of large vesicular cells, and surrounding the whole posttrochal part of the body as a *test*. Similar relationships are found in the Protobranchia (*Nucula*, *Yoldia*) among the Lamellibranchiata.

b. THE VELIGER

In the Polyplacophora and Aplacophora the trochophore metamorphoses after some time into the adult animal. In the Lamellibranchiata, Scaphopoda and Gastropoda, however, the trochophore transforms into the veliger. This has a more complex structure than the trochophore, various organs having attained a further stage of development (Fig. 37, 52a).

The prototroch develops into a powerful organ of locomotion, the *velum*. This occurs by outgrowth of the lateral parts of the prototroch to a pair of semicircular folds, bearing ciliary cells with powerful cilia at their outer margins. As a rule the velum is bilobate, but each lobe may be subdivided into two or three lappets.

The whole pretrochal region of the trochophore is more or less involved in the formation of the velum, ultimately forming its upper side. The apical tuft may either remain or disappear. Beside it or in its place a special *apical plate* is often found in the middle of the pretrochal region, which may sometimes have the character of an *apical sense organ* (*Crepidula*). To the left and right of the apical plate lie the *cephalic plates*, from which the *cerebral ganglia*, *tentacles* and *eyes* develop. The tentacles are sometimes asymmetric (e.g. *Firoloïdes*). The eyes are vesicular, as a rule; a part of the wall develops into the retina, and a lens is formed in the cavity.

As a rule, the other ganglia are also present. The *pedal ganglia* arise by proliferation from the ectoderm covering the lateral parts of the foot; the other ganglia arise in a similar way in the neighbourhood of the *pleural groove* bounding the foot on its lateral and posterior sides, with the exception of the *buccal ganglia*, which take their origin from the wall of the stomodaeum. On either side of the anterior part of the foot a *statocyst* is formed from the ectoderm.

The rudiment of the foot grows out and begins to attain its characteristic shape. On its posterior side an *operculum* may be formed.

The intestinal tract shows further development. The stomodaeum develops into *mouth cavity* and *pharynx*, *radular sac*, and *oesophagus*, and comes into open connection with the endodermal *midgut*. The latter

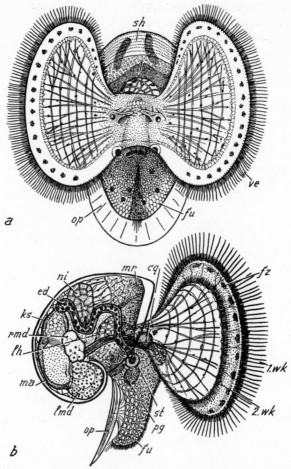

Fig. 37. Veliger of *Crepidula fornicata*. (a) front view, (b) from the right side. *cg*, cerebral ganglion; *ed*, hindgut; *fu*, foot; *fz*, pigment cells; *ks*, style sac; *lh*, larval heart; *lmd*, left liver; *ma*, stomach; *mr*, mantle edge; *ni*, kidney; *op*, operculum; *pg*, pedal ganglion; *rmd*, right liver; *sh*, shell; *st*, statocyst; *ve*, velum; 1.*wk*, 2.*wk*, ciliary bands of velum. After WERNER, 1955.

possesses, as a rule, two *hepatic lobes*, which are asymmetrical from the beginning in gastropods. The endodermal *hindgut* develops by outgrowth from the midgut; its posterior end makes contact with the ectoderm, and breaks through with formation of the *anus*. As a rule, there is no definite ectodermal proctodaeum.

The larval musculature is well developed as a rule. In particular, special *retractors of the velum* are formed, by which the latter may be wholly or partly withdrawn into the shell (Fig. 48).

True *protonephridia* only occur in Lamellibranchiata and Pulmonata. In their place one often finds larval kidneys of a different nature. They are usually unicellular, but sometimes pluricellular. Mostly they have no excretory duct, but in some cases an aperture has been found. Presumably, most of them are ectodermal in origin.

In many gastropods a *larval heart* is present. It consists of an ectodermal vesicle in the posttrochal region behind the velum, which contracts by means of mesodermal muscle cells.

The development of the *larval shell* has further advanced. It now begins to develop its typical shape in the various groups. In the Lamellibranchiata it becomes bivalve, the two valves growing lateroventrally along the body, which becomes more and more bilaterally compressed. In Scaphopoda, lateral mantle folds grow round the body in a similar way, but then they fuse with their ventral margins, so that the body is surrounded by a more or less cylindrical mantle tube, which secretes the shell on its outer surface. In the Gastropoda the shell begins to surround the body on the dorsal and posterior side (Fig. 34, 37). In the trochophore it was still situated more or less symmetrically, but now it is displaced to one side. A spiral coiling occurs by unequal growth along its margins.

In some cases (*Lamellaria, Cypraea*) two shells are formed within one another. A non-calcified larval shell lies externally. The calcified definitive shell is formed beneath it from the same matrix. As a rule, however, the formation of the adult shell does not begin until metamorphosis; it is formed along the outer margin of the larval shell, which remains as part of the definitive shell through life.

A larval shell is also formed in those species in which a shell is lacking in the adult (e.g. Nudibranchia); in these cases, the larval shell is thrown off at metamorphosis.

While the veligers of Lamellibranchiata and Scaphopoda are bilaterally symmetrical, those of the Gastropoda become asymmetrical at an early stage. This generally takes place by the occurrence of *torsion*, whereby the visceral sac and shell rotate with respect to the head and foot (Fig. 48). Thereby the midgut and anus, which were at first situated ventroposteriorly, are displaced dorsad and to the right.

Free veliger larvae are found in Scaphopoda, in marine Lamellibranchiata and *Dreissensia*, in certain Prosobranchia, and in the Opisthobranchia. Moreover, well-developed veliger stages also occur in a number of Prosobranchia, which complete their whole development in a cocoon, feeding on abortive eggs (e.g. *Purpura*), or remain in their egg capsules (*Neritina*). Likewise, in some pulmonates (*Amphibola, Oncidium*) typical veligers are formed, which stay within the egg membranes.

c. METAMORPHOSIS

In the Polyplacophora and Aplacophora metamorphosis follows directly upon the trochophore stage.

The posttrochal part of the Polyplacophora trochophore elongates and without undergoing very radical changes forms the trunk of the adult Chiton. The skin becomes covered by a *cuticule* with *spines*; the latter are formed within special cells, and connect only secondarily with the cuticule. The parts of the shell are formed in the transverse grooves of the shell gland. The latter extends anteriorly into the pretrochal region. In some species of *Chiton* there are at first only seven shell plates; the eighth plate appears only later. Along the border of the shell area the *mantle groove* appears. Behind, a *proctodaeum* is formed, which connects with the hindgut. The ciliary cells of the prototroch lose their nuclei, and disintegrate. Sometimes, however, the prototroch persists for a long time in the young Chiton. The pretrochal part of the body undergoes the greatest changes. The apical tuft disappears. The pretrochal region develops a conical shape, and flattens ventrally. The mantle groove extends into this region, and in this way delimits the *proboscis*. The mouth shifts forwards to the proboscis.

In the Aplacophora the posterior part of the larva grows out conically. It bears the anus, surrounded by a crown of cilia (telotroch) (Fig. 36). This part becomes covered with spicules. The prototroch is cast off; in those forms, where it formed a 'test', the anterior part of the animal now becomes free.

According to PRUVOT (1890), in a newly-metamorphosed specimen of *Dondersia*, seven imbricate calcareous plates on the dorsal side, consisting of rectangular spicules closely applied against each other, have been observed.

In those groups, which possess true veliger larvae, the latter have substantially the structure of the adult animal. Therefore, metamorphosis is restricted to the shedding or breakdown of certain larval organs, and the completion of the adult organism.

In most cases, metamorphosis begins during the pelagic life of the larva. Sometimes, however, spatfall takes place before metamorphosis commences (e.g. *Teredo*).

For the fully-developed veliger stage immediately preceding metamorphosis the name *veliconcha* has been proposed by WERNER (1939).

The larva at this stage is still able to swim by means of the velum, but can also use its foot for crawling.

The most conspicuous change is the loss of the velum. In Scaphopoda and most Gastropoda this is a gradual process. The velum cells become smaller, lose their nuclei and cilia, and are finally expelled. This may be due to the fact that neighbouring ectoderm cells come together beneath the velum cells (SMITH, 1935; CROFTS, 1938).

On the other hand, the shedding of the velum in the Lamellibranchiata is of a much more catastrophic nature (the same holds, however, for *Crepidula*, according to WERNER, 1955). Metamorphosis proceeds at first rather gradually, but at a certain moment the whole velum is cast off in fragments. In this way the pretrochal part loses its connection with the rest of the body. The apical plate sinks in as far as the stomodaeum, and connects secondarily with the epidermis above the mouth. It then grows out bilaterally, and contributes to the formation of the *labial palps* (MEISENHEIMER, 1901: *Dreissensia*; COLE, 1938: *Ostrea*).

The larval musculature, the larval heart, and the larval kidneys are reduced at metamorphosis. The adult musculature, the nervous system, and the intestinal tract develop their definitive structure. The same holds for the adult heart and definitive kidney. The genital organs often do not develop until a considerable time after metamorphosis.

The larval shell is cast off in some gastropods, and is replaced by the definitive shell. As a rule, however, the adult shell forms by new growth along the outer margin of the larval shell. Its shape may differ considerably from that of the latter, as in *Patella* and *Fissurella*, where the larval shell is spirally coiled, whereas the adult shell is conical.

Shedding of the larval shell at metamorphosis occurs also in those forms, which possess a shell in the larval stages, but not as adults (Nudibranchia, gymnosome pteropods, *Oncidium*).

The foot as a rule undergoes progressive changes, by which it acquires the shape it has in the adult. Very considerable changes occur in heteropods, in which the foot is transformed into the swimming organ of the adult animal. For instance, in *Carinaria* a considerable elongation of the larva occurs, while the shell and visceral sac remain very small in relation to the rest of the animal. In *Oncidium* the foot broadens greatly, and the small visceral sac closely connects with its upper side.

Apart from progressive changes of the foot, changes of a regressive nature also occur. In some Prosobranchia, in which an operculum is formed in the larva, this is lost at metamorphosis (e.g. *Patella*, *Haliotis*, *Crepidula*). In *Ostrea* the whole foot disappears.

Special relationships are found in the Protobranchia (*Nucula*, *Yoldia*). The whole body is here preformed within the prototroch ('test'). At

K

metamorphosis the prototroch, apical plate, and even a part of the stomodaeum, are suddenly thrown off. The test cells are shed off, and at once disintegrate. The whole process takes only a few minutes in *Yoldia* (DREW, 1899).

In the Nudibranchia (*Aeolidia, Tergipes*), where the larvae are provided with a shell, this is cast at the beginning of metamorphosis. The larvae remain swimming about with their enormous bilobate velum, which is much bigger than the remaining part of the animal. The body then acquires its definitive shape, after which the velum is reduced. Finally the characteristic dorsal papillae are formed.

In gymnosome pteropods (*Clio, Pneumoderma*) the velum and larval shell are thrown off. Three transverse rows of cilia develop in the much elongated posterior part of the body, so that a so-called *polytroch larva* is formed. This swims about with its ciliary apparatus, until the definitive *fins* are developed. Then the cilia are reduced.

Finally the metamorphosis of the Scaphopoda may be mentioned, in which the posttrochal part of the body elongates considerably, whereas the pretrochal part decreases in size. The shell grows in length, and becomes tubular. The foot grows out. Behind the mouth an ectodermal outgrowth is formed, which is the primordium of the *tentacular apparatus*. The anus appears at a late stage on the ventral side.

d. THE GLOCHIDIUM

Among the freshwater Lamellibranchiata, besides *Dreissensia* which has a true veliger larva, only the Unionidae have an indirect development. Their characteristic larval stage is the *glochidium*, which may be considered as a modified veliger stage adapted to a parasitic life.

The glochidium has a bivalve shell, partly covering the *larval mantle*. The two valves are connected by a powerful *larval adductor*. In some species (e.g. *Anodonta*) the margin of each valve bears a barbed tooth; this is lacking in other forms (e.g. *Unio*).

On the ventral side there is a rudimentary foot, bearing a long viscous *filament*. At the free margin of the larval mantle on both sides there are four *sense papillae* with bristles. Further sense organs include a pair of *statocysts, osphradia* and *lateral ciliary grooves*.

The intestinal sac is very rudimentary. The archenteron has formed a small endodermal vesicle, possessing two small lateral outgrowths which are the liver primordia. There is no mouth and no anus. The larval mantle functions as organ of nutrition. It consists of large strongly vacuolated cells which behave as phagocytes. There is no nephric system.

A glochidium larva is also found in some marine Lamellibranchiata

(*Philobryia*). On the other hand, South American Unionidae (Mutelidae) have another type of larva, which is known as *lasidium*.

The glochidium larva develops in a 'tumour' on its host. Within this tumour, it undergoes a gradual metamorphosis. The gut opens to the exterior, and enters upon its functions. The larval mantle atrophies, and is replaced by the definitive mantle, which develops from the epithelium of the outer edge of the mantle fold. The filament, sense papillae, and other larval sense organs disappear. The larval adductor is replaced by the adductors of the adult. The foot lengthens, and develops its definitive shape. The gills are formed. Finally the young mussel becomes free.

e. DIRECT DEVELOPMENT

Direct development without free-living larval stages is found in freshwater Lamellibranchiata (except *Dreissensia* and the Unionidae), in pulmonates and some prosobranchs (e.g. *Paludina*, *Fusus*), and in cephalopods.

In these Lamellibranchiata, the embryonic development takes place in the mantle cavity or between the gill lamellae of the mother. At first, development after gastrulation follows a fairly normal course. The stomodaeum, shell gland, and foot rudiment are formed as in a normal trochophore. But the prototroch is reduced, and occupies only a small area covered with cilia in the neighbourhood of the mouth. No velum develops. For the rest, development hardly differs from that in marine Lamellibranchiata.

In *Fusus* and the pulmonates, the eggs pass their whole development within a firm egg capsule, from which the young snail finally hatches. Otherwise, development follows a rather normal course, so that trochophore- and veliger-like stages may be successively distinguished. In the Basommatophora (*Planorbis*, *Physa*, *Limnaea*) a well-developed prototroch covered with dense cilia is formed. In *Helix* the prototroch is greatly reduced, in *Limax* and *Arion* it is lacking altogether.

In the slugs (*Arion*, *Limax*) the shell gland develops into a closed vesicle, in which a rudimentary shell is formed. The visceral sac lies originally wholly outside the foot, and is only later surrounded by the latter.

In the land pulmonates (*Arion*, *Limax*, *Helix*, *Clausilia*) already at early stages at the hind end of the strongly elongated foot a foot vesicle or *podocyst* develops. Moreover, the head vesicle exhibits a strong swelling, so that it becomes bigger than the whole rest of the body. These are pulsatile organs for the embryonic blood circulation, the podocyst functioning as the active organ for blood propulsion, whereas the head vesicle is only passively extensible. In older embryos the podocyst becomes very large; it divides into two lobes, which sometimes surround the whole embryo (*Helix Waltoni*). At the dorsal side of the base of the foot a small ectodermal vesicle forms a larval heart.

On the development of the cephalopods, cf. below, p. 174.

2. Prototroch and velum

The prototroch and velum, which represent the organ of locomotion, are naturally best developed in free-living larvae. However, these organs may, in those forms in which the embryos develop in a cocoon (e.g. *Purpura*) or in a brood-pouch (e.g. *Paludina*), also exhibit a fairly normal differentiation. In freshwater Lamellibranchiata with direct development (e.g. *Sphaerium*) the prototroch is reduced to a small ciliated area above the mouth. Among the pulmonates, the Basommatophora as a rule have a rather well-developed prototroch. In the Stylommatophora various conditions are found: *Oncidium* has a well-developed velum, in *Helix* it is greatly reduced and remains only for a short time, while in *Arion* and *Limax* no prototroch develops at all. Likewise, the prototroch is lacking in the terrestrial prosobranchiate, *Pomatias* (CREEK, 1951).

The differentiation of the prototroch may begin very early, e.g. at an advanced blastula (*Patella*) or an early gastrula stage (Polyplacophora). As a rule, however, the prototroch cells begin their differentiation after gastrulation has been completed.

The prototroch has the following cell-lineage:

(1) The cells $1a^2$–$1d^2$ each divide once or twice. In this way four inter-radial groups of two or four *primary trochoblasts* are formed.

(2) The gaps between these groups are filled up by *secondary trochoblasts*. They are descendants of the tip-cells of the ventral and lateral arms of the cross, $2a^{11}$–$2c^{11}$. Sometimes similar cells in the D–quadrant also take part in the formation of the prototroch (e.g. *Patella*: WILSON, 1904b; SMITH, 1935).

(3) To these cells *accessory trochoblasts*, derived from the cells $1a^{12}$–$1d^{12}$, may be joined (e.g. *Ischnochiton*: HEATH, 1899; *Patella*: WILSON, 1904b).

(4) Finally, behind the row or rows formed by these cells and repre-senting the prototroch in a more restricted sense, later a second row of cells often appears. Their descent is not exactly known; presum-ably, they are derived chiefly from the second quartette, but some-times third quartette cells may also be involved.

In some cases, only the ventral half of the prototroch is formed as such, from the ventral primary trochoblasts and the ventral tip-cell $2b^{11}$. The dorsal half, with the descendants of the dorsal trochoblasts

$1c^2$ and $1d^2$, and the tip-cells of the lateral and dorsal arms of the cross, $2a^{11}$, $2c^{11}$ and $2d^{11}$, enters into the formation of the head vesicle. This holds for the freshwater pulmonates *Planorbis*, *Physa*, and *Limnaea*, and also for *Crepidula* (CONKLIN, 1897).

A peculiar phenomenon was described by HOLMES (1900) in *Planorbis*. Here the basal cell of the ventral arm of the cross shifts forward between the two halves of this arm, and intercalates itself between the two daughter cells of the tip-cell, forming in this way the ventromedial part of the prototroch. A similar displacement of this cell takes place in *Physa* according to WIERZEJSKI (1905), but here it is less extensive.

During the formation of the prototroch considerable cell displacements may also take place in other cases. For example in *Patella*, the cilia on the primary trochoblasts appear already at a late blastula stage. In this way four groups of four ciliary cells each are formed. Each of these cells bears a horizontal 'comb' of cilia, so that the embryo has some resemblance to a ctenophore larva. Some hours later the prototroch is completed by the addition of secondary and accessory trochoblasts, which show a similar arrangement of the cilia, but are smaller than the primary trochoblasts. The prototroch now consists of 28–32 cells. They lie at first in two more or less alternating rows. By cell displacement an anterior row of bigger cells with powerful cilia, and a second row of smaller elongated cells with smaller cilia is formed. The latter cells later lose their cilia (WILSON, 1904b; SMITH, 1935).

Eventually the prototroch consists of one row of cells (*Acmaea*, *Haliotis*, *Trochus*, *Aplysia*, *Umbrella*) (Fig. 48), or of two rows (Polyplacophora, *Dreissensia*, *Patella*, *Paludina*, Pteropoda) (Fig. 42), or of three (*Dentalium*, *Bithynia*) or even of still more rows (*Crepidula*). In *Physa* and *Limnaea* it has ventrally only one row of cells, derived from the second quartette, but laterally on each side two primary trochoblasts are situated above this row.

In consequence of the fact that the tip-cell $2d^{11}$ as a rule does not take part in its formation, the prototroch is for some time interrupted dorsomedially. Later this gap is closed by the approach of both extremities of the horseshoe-shaped prototroch; sometimes also by the addition of some accessory elements (e.g. *Ischnochiton*: HEATH, 1899). No dorsal gap exists in *Dentalium* and *Patella* (WILSON, 1904a; 1904b). On the other hand, this dorsal gap may be very wide, e.g. in *Vermetus*, where the two halves of the prototroch run divergently from the mouth towards the dorsal side without meeting each other (SALENSKY, 1887), and in freshwater pulmonates, where the whole dorsal half of the prototroch is replaced by the head vesicle (Fig. 32). A similar situation is found in *Crepidula*, but here the prototroch laterally divides into two arms, an anterior one which runs in front of the head vesicle in the direction of the apical sense organ, and a posterior arm which runs along the posterior side of the head vesicle. The latter arm is interrupted mediodorsally, and bears no cilia at a later stage (CONKLIN, 1897).

In *Dreissensia* a postoral tuft of cilia is found behind the mouth; in *Sphaerium* there is a ciliated groove at this place; these structures are not connected with the prototroch.

In Aplacophora and Protobranchia the prototroch develops into a test, surrounding the rest of the body. It consists in Aplacophora of three rows of cells, of which the anterior one bears a crown of strong cilia, whereas the other two rows are covered with finer cilia. In the Protobranchia the test consists of four rows of which the anterior three rows each bear a crown of cilia, while the posterior row has finer cilia.

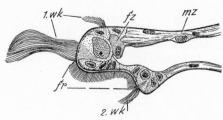

Fig. 38. Transverse section through edge of velum of *Crepidula fornicata*. *fr*, food furrow; *fz*, pigment cell; *mz*, muscle cell; *1.wk*, *2.wk*, ciliary bands of velum. After WERNER, 1955.

When the trochophore develops into a veliger, the prototroch transforms into the velum. This occurs by lateral outgrowth of the side parts of the prototroch into the *velar lobes*. Dorsomedially and ventromedially an indentation occurs. The mouth shifts forwards, and comes to lie in the ventral incision of the velum (Fig. 37). The cell rows of the prototroch telescope into each other, finally forming one row of cells. The cilia on these cells increase still more in length. In front of and behind this row of velar cells with powerful *velar cilia*, new cell rows may be added, which either bear shorter cilia or function only as supporting cells (Fig. 38).

In those cases, where the velum is highly differentiated (e.g. *Crepidula*, Pteropoda), its margin is grooved. The upper edge of this groove bears the long velar cilia, its bottom and lower edge are covered with finer cilia (Fig. 38). Besides being an organ of locomotion and respiration the velum in this case is also an organ of nutrition. A food stream is driven by ciliary movement through the velar groove towards the mouth. The two edges of the groove may diverge ventrally, with the mouth between them; the posterior edge then forms the *postoral velum*. The latter may turn backwards in the midline, and continue in a posterior direction as a median row of ciliary cells on the foot (e.g. *Crepidula*: CONKLIN, 1897).

The velar lobes are folds of the body wall. Internally, between the ectodermal layers of their upper and lower side, they contain muscle cells, which accounts for their great mobility. The muscle cells are often branched, and run in different directions (Fig. 37).

WERNER (1955) has described scattered multipolar ganglion cells in the velum of *Crepidula*, apparently forming a primitive peripheral nerve plexus.

As a rule, the velum in bilobate, but by secondary indentations each lobe may be further subdivided into two (*Creseis*, *Cleodora*, *Cymbulia*) or three (*Atlanta*) lappets.

The cells of the prototroch are characterized from an early stage by certain cytological features. They are large and have a clear cytoplasm, and a large, clear, vesicular nucleus, often with a big spherical nucleolus, which has a distinct internum in *Limnaea*. In many cases the prototroch cells contain highly refringent, often yellow-coloured granules (*Neritina*, *Umbrella*, Pteropoda, *Planorbis*, *Physa*, *Oncidium*), distinct albumen vacuoles (*Bithynia*, *Limnaea*) or droplets (*Ischnochiton*). Vacuoles with watery contents are also very common; the cells are often turgescent and protrude strongly above the surface (Fig. 42).

In *Limnaea* (RAVEN, 1946b; 1952) the prototroch cells have the following structure. At the base of the cilia there are distinct basal granules. Then follows an outer layer of dense protoplasm with innumerable very fine mitochondria. Beneath this there is a zone containing the nucleus, and numerous big albumen vacuoles. Finally, the basal part of the cell contains many watery vacuoles, within and between which are found the γ–granules of the proteid yolk. At a later stage these watery vacuoles coalesce, especially in the big primary trochoblasts, forming a basal fluid cushion which causes a strong protrusion of the cells. The yolk granules and albumen vacuoles disappear at later stages (Fig. 39).

A detailed cytological description of the velar cells of *Aeolidia* has been given by CARTER (1928). Each cell bears three cilia, which have the shape of triangular plates. Beneath each cilium, and exactly at the level of the cell surface, there is a double row of granules. These are connected by rods with the basal granules proper, which are situated at a depth of about 1μ beneath the surface. Beneath the basal granules there is a special 'ciliary protoplasm', presumably consisting of columnar elements, each corresponding to one basal granule. Half-way down, at about 4μ from the surface, each of these elements contains a third granule, strongly stained with methylene blue. The rest of the cell possesses two kinds of vacuoles: distally, at one side of the ciliary protoplasm, there are smaller vacuoles, staining heavily with neutral red, and containing fatty acids. The basal greater part of the cell has big vacuoles, which do not stain with vital dyes; they contain lipids, but no true fats. (Apparently, these two kinds of vacuoles show a certain parallelism to the 'albumen vacuoles' and 'watery vacuoles' of *Limnaea*, respectively). Nerve fibres from the cerebral ganglion penetrate into the velar cells, and end near the basal granules.

Both in *Aeolidia* and in *Limnaea* (HIRSCHLER, 1918) a group of Golgi bodies is situated distally to the nucleus. Presumably, they play an important part in the metabolism of the velar cells. A very intense activity of the Golgi bodies has been observed in *Navanax* (WORLEY and WORLEY, 1943) and *Mytilus* (WORLEY, 1944).

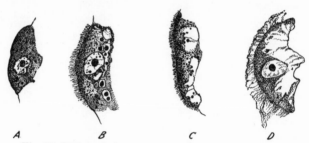

A   B   C   D

Fig. 39. Differentiation of velum cells in *Limnaea stagnalis*.

In *Navanax*, the Golgi bodies in the cells of the prototroch, but to a lesser extent also in other cells of the embryo, begin to exhibit a strong activity immediately after the completion of gastrulation, which lasts until an early veliger stage. They produce fat and protein droplets, sometimes both together in one and the same Golgi body, sometimes in separate bodies. The fat droplets are much smaller; sometimes fifteen to twenty of these droplets may occur simultaneously in one Golgi body. They are formed in the midst of the chromophil substance. At the height of fat production, one fat droplet is liberated on an average every five minutes. Fat synthesis takes place mainly during the trochophore stage; at an early veliger stage it comes to an end. The protein droplets are much bigger, and their formation takes longer. Sometimes two or three of these droplets are formed simultaneously in the same Golgi body. They arise by enlargement of the original chromophobe internum of the body. The protein globules are liberated by withdrawal of the chromophil substance. This then falls apart into smaller particles, which are uniformly dispersed through the cytoplasm, and later may once more give rise to the formation of vesicular Golgi bodies.

In *Mytilus* the formation of large oil drops, which began already at a late gastrula stage (cf. above, p. 121), continues at the trochophore stage. After completion of gastrulation, the formation of solid fat globules, two to four per Golgi body, begins. They are liberated in the cytoplasm. The Golgi bodies then coalesce to large complex bodies, which accumulate fine ultramicroscopic pigmented fat droplets from the cytoplasm, and unite them into larger pigmented fat globules, while the cytoplasm becomes colourless. Afterwards the complex Golgi bodies disintegrate into small particles, some of which once more become vesicular, and accumulate in their internum either protein, or fat containing much dark orange to brown carotenoid pigment; the formed products are set free into the cytoplasm as pigment granules.

In *Limnaea* the outer zone of the prototroch cells contains a large number of ultramicroscopic mitochondria. Larger mitochondria are scattered over the rest of the cell. In *Aeolidia* the latter lie as curved rods against the large vacuoles.

The velum cells of *Aplysia* (RIES and GERSCH, 1936), *Aeolidia* (CARTER, 1928) and *Limnaea* (RAVEN, 1946b) exhibit a selective uptake of basic vital dyes (neutral red, nile blue hydrochloride, brilliant cresyl violet). In *Limnaea* these dyes are accumulated in the albumen vacuoles. With brilliant cresyl violet a granular precipitation occurs in these vacuoles, probably by coacervation of a negative colloid (mucopolysaccharide) by the dye cations. In *Aeolidia* neutral red is especially accumulated in the distal vacuoles, the contents of which have an acid reaction. The velar cells of *Aplysia* also show a granular accumulation of acid colloid dyes (trypan blue, pyrrol blue).

The nuclei of the prototroch cells of *Limnaea* are poor in DNA; their cytoplasm is nearly devoid of RNA, but the latter substance is found in the nucleolus (RAVEN, 1946b; MINGANTI, 1950). At an advanced stage of development, the cells contain a moderate amount of fat droplets, in contradistinction to the rest of the ectoderm, which is poor in fat. In *Aeolidia* the distal vacuoles contain fat, the basal vacuoles and the granules have lipids, but no true fats (CARTER, 1928). The prototroch cells of *Limnaea* contain much glycogen, except in their outer zone. They are also rich in iron (RAVEN, 1946b; ARENDSEN DE WOLFF-EXALTO, 1947). The velum cells of *Aplysia* are especially rich in vitamin C (PELTRERA, 1940).

The velar cells of *Pleurobranchus*, *Aeolis*, *Calyptraea*, and *Littorina*, exhibit a strong benzidine peroxidase reaction (PRENANT, 1924). In *Limnaea* the reaction is very pronounced in the primary trochoblasts, both in the cytoplasm and the nucleolus; in the secondary trochoblasts it is much weaker. The nadi-oxidase reaction of the velum cells is intense in *Limnaea*, *Aplysia* (RIES, 1937) and *Bithynia* (ATTARDO, 1955a). Likewise, the oxidation of leucomethylene blue occurs very intensively in the velum cells of *Aplysia* (RIES and GERSCH, 1936). Finally, the velum cells of *Limnaea* show a positive alkaline phosphatase reaction from the fifth day on (MINGANTI, 1950).

3. The pretrochal region

The pretrochal part of the embryo may be entirely covered with short cilia at the trochophore stage, apart from the cells bearing the apical tuft, e.g. in *Epimenia*, *Dentalium*, *Patella*, and in *Nucula delphinodonta* (DREW, 1901) (Fig. 36).

In *Paludina* the cells of the pretrochal region are all strongly vacuolated (Fig. 42). A pronounced vacuolization also occurs in *Pomatias*, in which the prototroch is lacking, but the area corresponding to the pretrochal region of other gastropods becomes a 'cephalic mass', which temporarily occupies about 3/4 of the surface of the embryo (CREEK, 1951) (Fig. 46). Its cells each possess a central vacuole, filled with albumen. Vital dyes, such as neutral red and Bismarck brown, and also saccharated ferric oxide, are strongly accumulated in this vacuole. Presumably, the cephalic mass plays a part in the uptake and digestion of albumen.

In *Neritina* a gland cell is found on both sides in the pretrochal region (BLOCHMANN, 1882). In *Chiton* its dorsal part contains cells with large peripheral vacuoles, in which spicules are formed (KOWALEWSKY, 1883a).

In general, the following parts may be distinguished in the pretrochal region: (1) the dorsally situated *head vesicle*, (2) the median *apical plate*, (3) the ventrolateral *cephalic plates*.

a. HEAD VESICLE

The cells of the dorsal part of the pretrochal region soon after gastrulation begin to flatten, at the same time increasing in surface. By its increase in area the ectoderm is lifted from the endoderm, so that a large vesicle, covered by a very thin epithelium and filled with a transparent fluid, is formed (Fig. 33). Mesoderm cells penetrate into this space, forming a loose network (Fig. 46).

The head vesicle reaches its highest development in land pulmonates. It swells to such an extent that it temporarily becomes much bigger than the rest of the body. Later it lags behind in growth and is gradually taken up in the body. The head vesicle possesses no active contractility, but is passively distended by the contractions of the podocyst.

Apart from the pulmonates, the head vesicle is also well developed in *Crepidula*. In both cases it partly represents the dorsal part of the proto-troch. In *Crepidula* it is mainly derived from the dorsal primary trocho-blasts and the basal and middle cells of the dorsal arm of the cross (CONKLIN, 1897). In *Planorbis* and *Physa* the tip-cells of the lateral and dorsal arms also take part in its formation (HOLMES, 1900; WIERZEJSKI, 1905). In *Planorbis* and *Limnaea* the head vesicle consists of twelve cells.

The head vesicle of *Limnaea* is formed at an early stage by large cells with a big clear vesicular nucleus, containing one big nucleolus with distinct internum and a delicate chromatin net-work. Their cytoplasm exhibits the same three layers as the prototroch cells: an outer ecto-plasm layer with very numerous ultramicroscopic mitochondria, a middle zone with albumen vacuoles, and a basal zone with watery vacuoles and γ–granules in the meshes between them. In their behaviour with regard to vital stains and their cytochemistry they also show a great agreement with prototroch cells, but they are richer in glycogen and poorer in fat, and the nadi-oxidase and benzidine-peroxidase reactions are somewhat weaker. Moreover, at no stage of development do the head vesicle cells of *Limnaea* bear cilia (in contrast to *Crepidula*, where the head vesicle is covered with cilia). At later stages the cells flatten con-siderably. Still later, however, the cells begin to protrude strongly by a considerable vacuolization of their endoplasm (Pl. XII, A). Presumably, this is the beginning of their final degeneration.

The head vesicle of the Unionidae shows a peculiar behaviour. It consists here of six big vacuolated cells, one in the middle and five around it. The middle cell sinks in, its nucleus is shifted towards the inner extremity and vacuoles form a tubular lumen in the cytoplasm which connects with the exterior and gets a cuticular lining. In this way the cell transforms into the *thread-gland*, which grows out in a posterior direction. The adhesive thread is formed by a kind of metamorphosis from the cytoplasm of the thread-gland cell (LILLIE, 1895).

b. APICAL PLATE

A long *apical tuft*, on an ectodermal thickening at the animal pole, is found in Polyplacophora, Aplacophora (except *Halomenia*), marine Lamellibranchiata and *Dreissensia*, Scaphopoda, and *Patella* and *Acmaea* among the gastropods (Fig. 36, 51a). It consists of long, flexible, but non-vibratile sense hairs. In *Haliotis*, *Crepidula* and *Littorina* at this place some cells bearing shorter cilia are found (Fig. 48b); in *Aplysia* there is one long flagellum.

In *Crepidula* the apical cells proliferate some cells inwards into the cavity of the head vesicle. Together, these elements represent the *apical sense organ*, which is connected by a cell strand with the cerebral ganglia.

In *Patella* (SMITH, 1935) and *Acmaea* (BOUTAN, 1899) the apical tuft is flanked on both sides by a small bundle of cilia on a protruding cell. In *Cleodora* (FOL, 1875) there are two stiff cirri above the mouth, each

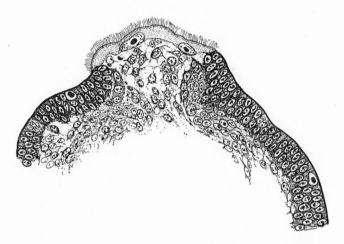

Fig. 40. Transverse section through apical plate and adjacent parts of cephalic plates in *Limnaea stagnalis*. Cf. Pl. XI A.

on a protruding cell, and two further cells each with a tuft of small cilia. Two strikingly large cells are also found above the mouth in *Bithynia* (VON ERLANGER, 1892).

In *Crepidula* (CONKLIN, 1897), seven cells of the ventral arm of the cross in front of the apical sense organ form a median plate of large, flat cells covered with fine cilia, the *apical plate*. In *Planorbis*, *Physa* and *Limnaea*, where no apical sense organ is present, the apical plate, consisting of six or seven cells, extends from the head vesicle to the ventromedian part of the prototroch (Fig. 32). A median band of cilia on the pretrochal region has also been described in *Pomatias* (CREEK, 1951), *Vermetus* (SALENSKY, 1887) and *Cleodora* (FOL, 1875), while a band of flattened epithelium between the cephalic plates is also found in *Bithynia* (VON ERLANGER, 1892). Whether the median band of 'suture cells', which runs in Unionidae from the thread-gland to the oral plate (LILLIE, 1895), is homologous with the apical plate, is not clear.

The apical tuft in those forms where it is present, and the apical sense organ of *Crepidula*, are certainly largely or wholly derived from the apical rosette cells. The apical plate in *Crepidula* originates from the cells of the ventral arm of the cross. In *Planorbis, Physa* and *Limnaea* the apical plate is formed by the apical rosette cells, supplemented by a few cells in front of them, which are either derived from the ventral arm or from the peripheral rosettes (HOLMES, 1900).

In *Limnaea* the apical rosette cells at the end of gastrulation contain extraordinary large albumen vacuoles, surpassing the nucleus in size, in the outer part of the cell (Pl. VIII). Their contents are not homogeneous, but granular owing to the presence of pseudo-crystals. At a somewhat later stage clear watery vacuoles appear in the basal part of the cells, whereas the albumen vacuoles decrease in number and size. The cells now exhibit the same three layers as those of the prototroch and head vesicle. They are densely covered with cilia. Their nuclei are big, clear, with a distinct nucleolus. The outer zone of the cytoplasm contains numerous fine mitochondria, the rest of the cell larger mitochondria. Later the cells become considerably flattened, while the vacuoles in the endoplasm disappear (Fig. 40; Pl. XI, A). In their vital staining and cytochemistry the apical plate cells resemble in broad outline the prototroch and head vesicle cells. Alkaline phosphatase appears somewhat earlier and in greater amount in the former; it is mainly localized in the superficial layer and the cilia (MINGANTI, 1950).

c. CEPHALIC PLATES

The two halves of the cross, separated by the formation of the apical plate, by rapid cell multiplication form a pair of small-celled areas, the cephalic plates (Fig. 32, 46). From these plates the cerebral ganglia, tentacles and eyes develop.

In many cases the cerebral ganglia are formed by an invagination of the cephalic plates. This invagination is either paired from the beginning (e.g. *Epimenia, Dentalium, Vermetus, Limax*), or it is at first unpaired but is divided secondarily into two separate grooves by outgrowth of its lateral extremities in divergent directions (e.g. *Dreissensia, Yoldia, Patella, Cavolinia*). The walls of these invaginations consist of small columnar cells, and are at first single-layered. Then they thicken and become multi-layered; the lumen disappears, and the inner ends of the invaginations, which come to lie on either side of the stomodaeum, differentiate into the cerebral ganglia, which detach themselves from the epithelium.

In other cases (*Sphaerium, Haliotis, Trochus, Crepidula, Planorbis*) there is no invagination, but the cerebral ganglia develop by cell proliferation from the thickened cerebral plates. The same holds for *Physa* and *Limnaea*, but here a very circumscribed invagination takes place in the dorsolateral part of each cephalic plate. This *cerebral tube* gives rise in *Limnaea* to an accessory lobe of the cerebral ganglion.

In front of the cerebral ganglia, the tentacles develop as outgrowths of the ventrolateral parts of the cephalic plates, covered by an epithelium of high columnar cells.

The eyes are formed in the lateral or dorsolateral part of the cephalic plates, mostly as small invaginations, which are constricted off from the surface (Fig. 61).

In *Ischnochiton* (HEATH, 1899) the cerebral ganglia are probably mainly derived from descendants of the peripheral rosette cells, $1a^{112}$– $1d^{112}$, with perhaps the addition of cells from the apical rosettes. In *Crepidula* (CONKLIN, 1897) and *Fulgur* (CONKLIN, 1907) the cerebral ganglia arise mainly from the ventral rosettes $1a^{112}$ and $1b^{112}$. In *Planorbis* (HOLMES, 1900) six of the eight daughter cells of the peripheral rosette cells are included in the cephalic plates, but various derivatives of the ventral and lateral arms of the cross also take part in their formation.

In *Limnaea* the proliferation of cells from the cephalic plates continues some time after the cerebral ganglia have been formed. Presumably mesenchyme of the head region, which later forms a dense layer immediately beneath the epithelium of the tentacle field, is produced in this way.

4. The posttrochal region

a. THE SHELL GLAND

The shell gland develops, on the dorsal side behind the prototroch, from descendants of the first somatoblast 2d.

The primordium of the shell gland is represented by an ectodermal thickening, formed by elongation of the cells, which, however, remain in one layer (Fig. 33). In the centre of the thickening an invagination takes place (Fig. 42). It has often been observed that the cells at this time are radially arranged around the central pit forming a kind of rosette (FOL, 1875; JOYEUX LAFFUIE, 1882; BOUTAN, 1899). This is probably due to an active or passive stretching of the cells during their invagination. The invaginated shell gland possesses a thick wall, which consists, however, of only one layer of elongated, regularly arranged cells. The lumen is sometimes wide, but may in other cases entirely disappear (Fig. 41). The shell gland is very large especially in Lamellibranchiata; here it often exceeds the archenteron in size. After having remained in this state for some time, the shell gland begins to roll out again onto the surface (Fig. 43).

In *Limnaea* the shell gland primordium has from its first appearance a close contact with the small-celled endoderm of the midgut. The extension of the thickened shell gland epithelium corresponds from the beginning accurately with this area of contact. A very close connection between shell gland and small-celled midgut epithelium remains during the whole invagination period (Fig. 41), and is only broken when the

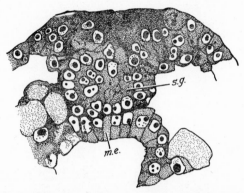

Fig. 41. Intimate contact between invaginated shell gland (*s.g*) and small-celled midgut epithelium (*m.e.*) in *Limnaea stagnalis*.

evagination of the shell gland has well advanced. The period of contact lasts about two days (RAVEN, 1952).

From the figures drawn by the authors it is evident that a similar close contact between shell gland primordium and small-celled endoderm exists in *Paludina* (VON ERLANGER, 1891; TÖNNIGES, 1896; DAU-TERT, 1929) (Fig. 42), *Umbrella* (HEYMONS, 1893), *Aplysia* (SAUNDERS and POOLE, 1910), *Planorbis* (RABL, 1879), *Physa* (WIERZEJSKI, 1905), *Limax* (MEISENHEIMER, 1896) and *Agriolimax* (CARRICK, 1939). Presumably, therefore, it is a general phenomenon in gastropods.

During its evagination the shell gland spreads on the surface in a lateral and ventral, but above all in a posterior direction. The cells in its central part flatten greatly. The peripheral cells remain highly columnar, and form an annular fold surrounding the thin centre (Fig. 43). This *mantle fold* now extends over the visceral hump. In Lamellibranchiata and Scaphopoda this occurs mainly in a lateral and ventral direction, so that two lateral mantle flaps are formed, which envelop the body, and in Scaphopoda fuse with their ventral free margins. In gastropods the mantle first overgrows the posterior end of the body, and then extends anteriorly towards the head and foot (Fig. 32, 43).

A transparent secretion may already be extruded into its lumen during the invagination of the shell gland. This spreads during evagination as a thin chitinous pellicle over the thinned-out middle part of the shell area, and forms in this way the *larval shell* (Fig. 34, 43, 46). Peripherally, it is bordered by the mantle fold. Here further growth of the shell takes place by secretion from the mantle fold. Although the larval shell is mainly a cuticular structure, it may contain calcium salts from the beginning (FOL, 1875).

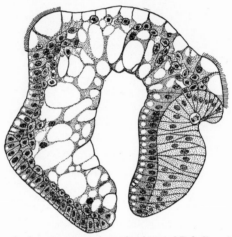

Fig. 42. Mediosagittal section through trochophore of *Paludina vivipara*. Ventral side at left, dorsal at right. Protruding prototroch cells. Formation of mesoderm by proliferation of ventral ectoderm. Ventral and apical wall of archenteron formed by big-celled endoderm, dorsal wall by small-celled endoderm. Intimate contact of the latter with shell gland primordium. After DAUTERT, 1929.

The shape of the shell reflects that of the mantle field. In Lamellibranchiata it is at first unpaired, bent over the dorsal edge of the body. Then it grows out towards the two sides, and folds into two valves. Mediodorsally the epithelium remains thick, and a close connection between the shell and the underlying epithelium is preserved; in this region the suture between the valves is formed (MEISENHEIMER, 1901). In Scaphopoda the two halves of the shell fuse in the ventral midline, so that a tubular shell is formed. In gastropods the shell is, as a rule, at first cup-shaped, but spiral coiling begins to appear already at the veliger stage by a more rapid growth on one side (Fig. 37, 48, 52a).

After the larval shell has reached the height of its development, a short pause may occur. After this, growth continues, but often in a somewhat different way, so that the newly formed part has the character of the adult shell. The two parts are often separated by a distinct boundary-line; they may exhibit differences, e.g. in surface sculpture. In *Patella* and *Fissurella* the larval shell has the shape of a flat spiral, whereas the adult shell is conical. The larval shell is thrown off in this case after some time. In *Patella* this is an active process, initiated by the secretion of an annular horny layer by the mantle beneath the larval shell (SMITH, 1935). As a rule, however, the larval shell remains as part of the adult shell.

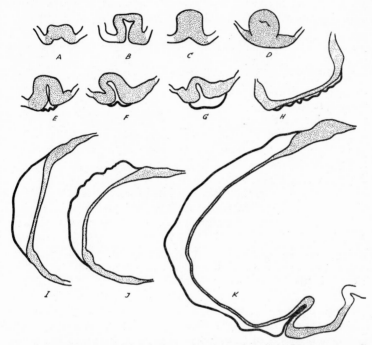

Fig. 43. Development of the shell gland and larval shell in *Limnaea stagnalis*. (A-H) transverse, (I-K) sagittal sections. (A-C) invagination; (D-H) evagination and secretion of larval shell; (I-K) extension and surrounding of visceral hump.

Sometimes the secretion of the definitive shell begins already at the veliger stage beneath the larval shell (e.g. *Lamellaria*, *Cypraea*). In this case the larval shell is thrown off at metamorphosis.

Shell formation may be reduced in a greater or less degree. In Nudibranchia and gymnosome pteropods, possessing no shell in the adult state, a well-developed larval shell is formed, which is, however, thrown off at metamorphosis without being replaced by an adult shell. In *Cymbulia* the shell gland invaginates, and a dark strongly refringent

L

mass is secreted in its lumen; then, however, the opening of the invagination closes, and the larval shell is formed on the outlying parts of the ectoderm surrounding the opening, whereas the invaginated part is resorbed later (FOL, 1875). In *Arion* and *Limax* the shell gland likewise develops into a closed sac, in which a rudimentary shell is secreted. In *Agriolimax* there is no true invagination, but a local proliferation of ectodermal cells, by which a cell mass is formed, in which later a lumen appears and granules of $CaCO_3$ are secreted (CARRICK, 1939). Finally, in the nudibranchiate *Cenia* only an ectodermal thickening is formed, which does not invaginate.

In the Protobranchia (*Yoldia*, *Nucula*) the shell gland and shell develop beneath the 'test'.

In the Polyplacophora the shell gland exhibits already at an early stage, instead of a single invagination, a series of seven to eight transverse grooves, separated by epithelial folds. The first of these folds lies a short distance behind the prototroch. Later the shell gland area extends secondarily forwards into the pretrochal region. On the epithelial folds, in which later a transverse furrow is formed, a rapid secretion of cuticular substance begins, which forms the *periostracum*. This cuticular layer initially covers the whole dorsal side. In the grooves, where the epithelium is thinner, the cuticule is lifted from the epithelium. Here lime is secreted beneath the cuticule, and the *tegmenta* are formed (HAMMARSTEN and RUNNSTRÖM, 1925). According to KOWALEWSKY (1883a) this occurs in *Chiton* by the secretion of small calcareous plates that fuse secondarily, beginning near the anterior edge of the grooves and extending gradually backwards. The *articulamenta* appear only later, while the lateral apophyses are formed in pouch-like folds of the mantle.

The shell gland of gastropods lies at first in the dorsal midline. When it begins to evaginate, however, this occurs asymmetrically, on the left side more rapidly than on the right; in this way the shell gland area as a whole is displaced toward the left (CONKLIN, 1897; FRANC, 1940; RAVEN, 1952). In the sinistral species of *Planorbis*, on the contrary, the shell gland is shifted to the right side (RABL, 1879).

The *mantle cavity* is formed in Lamellibranchiata by an invagination of the ventral body wall surrounding the foot rudiment, which penetrates beneath the shell valves. In Gastropoda and Cephalopoda the formation of the mantle cavity is due to the fact that the mantle fold, in growing forwards along the body, is elevated from the body wall, arching over the anal region. In gastropods this may be preceded, however, by the formation of one or two special grooves in the body wall, which are secondarily overgrown by the mantle (DRUMMOND, 1902; HEYDER,

1909; CROFTS, 1938; CARRICK, 1939; CREEK, 1951). When it first becomes visible, the mantle cavity lies either in the ventral midline behind the foot (e.g. *Patella*, *Paludina*, *Pomatias*) or on the right side of the body; this depends on the time relations between its formation and the torsion of the visceral hump (cf. below, p. 171).

The cells of the not yet invaginated shell gland rudiment of the early trochophore stage of *Limnaea* are characterized by a layer of dense ectoplasm. After invagination has taken place, this outer part of the cells contains a filamentous secretion, which is continuous with a similar substance in the lumen. At a later stage, the cells of the mantle fold have a strongly osmiophil ectoplasm. According to HIRSCHLER (1918), in this part lamellar Golgi bodies are found, while filamentous mitochondria are distributed more or less uniformly throughout the cytoplasm.

The cells of the shell gland and mantle fold of *Limnaea* contain small fat droplets (RAVEN and BRETSCHNEIDER, 1942). Their nuclei are rich in DNA, their cytoplasm rich in RNA. In the invaginated shell gland the RNA is especially localized in the basal part of the cells, and (to a lesser extent) half-way between nucleus and cell surface; also in the nucleolus and around the nuclear membrane (RAVEN, 1946b). Later the cells of the mantle fold are rich in RNA, but the flat epithelium beneath the shell much less so; here only the superficial part of the cells is strongly basophil (MINGANTI, 1950). In the invaginated shell gland there is a positive alkaline phosphatase reaction in the lumen, the superficial cytoplasm, and the nucleoli. After evagination the cells beneath the shell show a positive reaction near the surface and in the nuclei; the reaction is much stronger along the mantle fold, where shell secretion continues (MINGANTI).

RIES (1937) observed in *Aplysia* numerous granules giving a nadioxidase reaction in the shell gland. In *Physa* (MANCUSO, 1953), only the cells of the margin of the shell area exhibit a strong M–nadi oxidase reaction; this is more pronounced on the left than on the right side. It is due to a stable oxidase, which is not destroyed by fixatives, and is inhibited by KCN, Na_2S and NaN_3 (MANCUSO, 1955b). A similar oxidase is found in the shell gland of *Bithynia* (ATTARDO, 1955a). In *Limnaea* at the veliger stage especially the shell shows a strong reaction, the mantle fold somewhat less (RAVEN, 1946b). The benzidine peroxidase reaction is especially pronounced in the margin of the shell area, both in *Physa* (MANCUSO) and *Limnaea* (RAVEN; PRENANT, 1924). In *Physa* (sinistral) the reaction is on the left side stronger than on the right, in *Limnaea*, on the contrary, it is stronger in the right mantle fold (Mrs H. E. HUISINGA-BLOK, unpublished observations). In the shell of *Limnaea* the reaction begins even earlier than in the mantle fold, but it remains rather weak. In *Planorbis*, on the contrary, it is especially the shell which gives the reaction (PRENANT).

The mantle fold of *Aplysia* shows a selective accumulation of acid colloidal dyes (trypan blue, pyrrol blue), and of basic vital dyes (RIES and GERSCH, 1936). The shell gland of *Anodonta* exhibits a less intense reduction of redox indicators than the rest of the egg (STRELIN, 1939b).

b. THE FOOT

The foot originates as an ectodermal thickening on the ventral side behind the mouth. As a rule, it is first indicated by an area of high columnar cells. Later an outgrowth appears in this region, which is filled with mesenchyme. In Lamellibranchiata the foot rudiment may be delimited from its surroundings by the ingrowth of ectodermal furrows on its lateral, posterior and anterior sides (e.g. *Dreissensia*: MEISENHEIMER, 1901).

In Gastropoda the foot rudiment may originally be more or less paired or bilobed (e.g. *Acmaea, Trochus, Littorina, Fulgur*). In Scaphopoda it becomes trilobate at an early stage.

In Polyplacophora the foot is attached with a broad base to the whole ventral side of the body behind the prototroch.

In Aplacophora (*Epimenia*: BABA, 1938) the foot arises as a narrow longitudinal depression on the ventral surface of the trochophore (Fig. 36), the bottom of which becomes more and more arcuate ventrally. The ridge formed in this way is lined by high columnar cells with a thin cuticle and short cilia on the free surface. On each side of the foot there is a continuous row of mucous glands (pedal glands). An invagination at the foremost end of the foot, with the cells bearing more powerful cilia, forms the so-called *prepedal cavity* (Fig. 60).

On the posterior side of the foot an *operculum* is formed in many gastropods (Fig. 37, 48, 52a). This is secreted by an area of glandular epithelium; there is no counterpart of the dorsal shell gland. In *Haliotis* the operculum does not lie exactly in the midline, but somewhat to the left (CROFTS, 1938).

The *pedal ganglia* arise by proliferation of the ectoderm in the lateral parts of the foot. The *statocysts* are formed by invagination or proliferation of cells from the epithelium on the boundary between foot and trunk. There are some indications that the mesenchyme of the foot originates at least in part by proliferation from the ectoderm (MEISEN-HEIMER, 1901; DELSMAN, 1912; HERBERS, 1913; RAVEN, 1952) (Fig. 44).

The foot rudiment is, as a rule, either from the first or from an early stage, wholly or for the greater part covered with cilia (Fig. 37, 52a). In many gastropods (*Crepidula, Littorina, Vermetus, Planorbis, Limnaea*) there is a median row of large clear elongated ciliated cells with long cilia (Fig. 32). In *Crepidula* it is continuous with the postoral velum. These cilia beat towards the mouth; presumably, they serve for food supply.

In *Acanthochiton* the cilia are continued into the cytoplasm of the cells forming a fibre cone extending towards the cell base (HAMMARSTEN and RUNNSTRÖM, 1925). The large ciliary cells of the median row of the foot in *Limnaea* resemble the velum cells. They are poor in DNA and

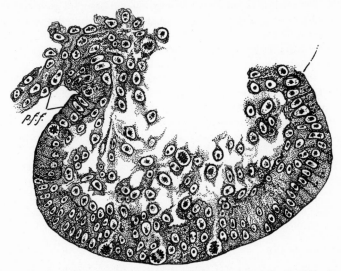

Fig. 44. Sagittal section of foot of veliger of *Limnaea stagnalis*. Proliferation of foot epithelium. *p.f.f.*, posterior foot furrow.

RNA, in contrast to the surrounding foot cells, which are strongly basophil especially in their superficial parts. The outer zone of the large ciliary cells is filled with fine mitochondria, and shows a positive alkaline phosphatase reaction. The rest of the cell contains rather large mitochondria, and a large amount of glycogen and of iron.

The foot epithelium of *Aplysia*, especially in the opercular region, exhibits a selective accumulation of trypan blue and pyrrol blue in granular form. It also shows a selective uptake of basic dyes (RIES and GERSCH, 1936). The median foot row of *Limnaea* stains selectively with brilliant cresyl violet.

The early foot rudiment of *Bithynia* contains cytochrome oxidase (Fig. 24); at later stages a stable M–nadi oxidase is found in the operculum (ATTARDO, 1955a).

In Polyplacophora a peculiar larval organ, the *foot gland*, is found in the anterior part of the foot, behind the mouth. In *Chiton* (KOWALEWSKY, 1883a) and *Ischnochiton* (HEATH, 1899) it is a pouch-like invagination. Its cells contain granules; later a mass of secretion appears in its lumen. In *Acanthochiton* (HAMMARSTEN and RUNNSTRÖM, 1925) it consists of a mass of greatly elongated ectodermal gland cells, each opening with a neck-shaped part on the surface. In their cytoplasm basophil granules and large vacuoles are found. Cyclic changes take place in the nuclei, the nuclear membrane disappearing and basophil granules from the nuclei passing into the cytoplasm. Here these granules apparently swell, forming the secretion product.

Foot glands have also been described in the larvae of some Prosobranchia (e.g. *Nassa, Murex, Vermetus, Firoloïdes*) (Fig. 46).

The foot may play a part as an organ of circulation. In pteropods (FOL, 1875) it temporarily exhibits contractions, by which the foot sinus is compressed. In all Stylommatophora, except *Succinea, Bulimus, Oncidium* and *Vaginula*, at the posterior extremity of the foot a *foot vesicle* or *podocyst* is formed at an early stage, by flattening of the epithelium. It contains in its interior muscular elements, originating from the mesenchyme. The podocyst shows powerful contractions, driving the blood into the body. In older embryos it becomes very large, and divides into two lobes, which may surround the whole embryo (*Helix Waltoni*). Towards the end of the embryonic period it decreases again, and finally is thrown off.

c. LARVAL HEART

In many Prosobranchia (*Crepidula, Nassa, Fusus, Littorina, Buccinum, Purpura, Vermetus, Bithynia, Fulgur, Ocinebra*) there is an ectodermal vesicle behind the velum, which exhibits rhythmic contractions by means of mesodermal muscle cells (Fig. 37). Originally it is situated on the right side in front of the mantle fold, but by the torsion of the larva it is displaced towards the dorsal side. Moreover, it is overgrown by the mantle fold, so that it comes to lie in the mantle cavity.

WERNER (1955) has made some observations on the function of the larval heart in *Crepidula*. The organ is provided here with an anterior and posterior valve. Anteriorly it is connected with the lacunar spaces of velum and foot, posteriorly with those of the visceral mass. The body fluid flows in an anteroposterior direction through the heart, so that the visceral organs are bathed by the oxygen-rich blood coming from the velum. Moreover, the larval heart may play a part in the extension of the velum and foot, after these organs have been withdrawn into the shell. In the extended veliger, the rate of pulsation of the larval heart is about 60 per minute. During contraction of the larva, the pulsation is greatly reduced.

In Pteropoda (FOL, 1875) a similar organ is found in the inner wall of the dorsal part of the mantle cavity. In land pulmonates it lies dorsally on the base of the foot.

d. ANAL CELLS

The posterior end of the trochophore sometimes bears a tuft of stiff coarse cilia (e.g. *Dreissensia, Dentalium, Patella, Acmaea*) or a crown of cilia, *telotroch* (Aplacophora, *Teredo*) (Fig. 36). The two cells, which bear the ciliary tuft in *Patella*, later protrude strongly above the surface (SMITH, 1935). At this place the anal orifice is formed.

In other cases only two protruding *anal cells* are found in this region, which may bear some fine cilia, but no ciliary tuft. This is especially the case in Opisthobranchia, also in *Crepidula*, the Heteropoda, *Physa* and *Limnaea*. The distal end of the hindgut makes connection with the ectoderm at this place; later the anus breaks through.

The anal cells of *Aplysia* are, according to CARAZZI (1905), the cells $2d^{22221}$ and $2d^{22222}$.

Generally the anal cells are large cells with clear protoplasm and light-staining nucleus, which protrude strongly especially in the Opisthobranchia. Often they have a large central vacuole, or numerous smaller vacuoles, which are filled with albumen in *Physa* according to WIERZEJSKI (1905). In *Aplysia* there is a selective accumulation in the central vacuole both of trypan blue and of basic vital dyes (RIES and GERSCH, 1936); this may point to an excretory function of these cells. The anal cells of *Limnaea* have little RNA (MINGANTI, 1950); they show a very strong selective benzidine peroxidase reaction (RAVEN, 1946b).

5. The internal organs

a. STOMODAEUM

The stomodaeum originates as an invagination on the ventral side immediately behind the prototroch, at the point where the blastopore eventually closed, or in direct connection with the remaining blastoporal opening. During its invagination temporarily a rosette-like arrangement of the cells, due to their radial elongation, may be seen (FOL, 1875). In *Physa* no actual invagination takes place, according to WIERZEJSKI (1905), but the stomodaeum cells sink beneath the surface by local cell proliferations in their neighbourhood.

The stomodaeal invagination is at first funnel-shaped (Fig. 45a). Its inner end is often closed, but may sometimes remain in open communication with the lumen of the archenteron (Fig. 34). The closed inner end or the narrowest part of the stomodaeum later gives rise to the *oesophagus*. In *Limnaea* at this place the lumen is temporarily obliterated, but the future oesophagus cells remain radially arranged

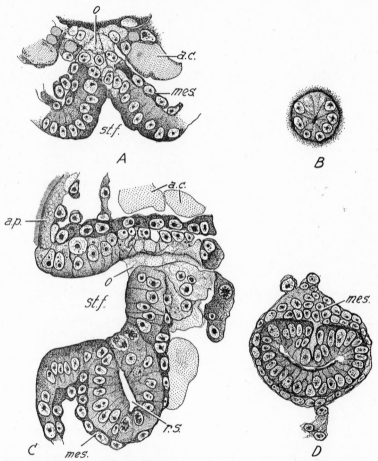

Fig. 45. Development of the stomodaeum in *Limnaea stagnalis*. (A) Stomodaeal funnel (*st.f.*) of trochophore. Lumen obliterated in region of oesophagus anlage (*o.*). (B) Same stage, transverse section of oesophagus anlage. (C) Mediosagittal section of stomodaeum of early veliger. Oesophagus (*o.*) with distinct lumen, connected with midgut. Radular sac (*r.s.*) as posterior outgrowth of stomodaeal funnel (*st.f.*). (D) Transverse section of radular sac of older larva. *a.c.*, albumen cells of midgut; *a.p.*, apical plate; *mes.*, mesoderm cells.

around a virtual lumen (Fig. 45b). Later this part grows out, becomes tubular and elongates strongly. Now its inner end opens into the midgut (Fig. 45c).

According to some authors, the oesophagus is derived from the endoderm (cf. HAMMARSTEN and RUNNSTRÖM, 1925). This is probably incorrect; presumably in all molluscs the oesophagus develops from the stomodaeum.

The posterior wall of the stomodaeum gives rise to the *radular sac*. This begins with a thickening of the epithelium (Fig. 34); then a posteriorly directed outgrowth occurs, which may at first be solid, but soon develops a lumen. Mesoderm cells then begin to surround the rudiment of the radular sac (Fig. 45c, 46).

In some cases the formation of the radular sac begins before the stomodaeum has been completely invaginated. For some time the radular sac rudiment then forms an independent invagination at the surface behind the stomodaeum anlage, e.g. in *Helix* (FOL, 1880).

According to WIERZEJSKI (1905), the first anlage of the radular sac in *Physa* also arises quite independently of the stomodaeum. Behind the latter, two round bilaterally situated cell masses are found, surrounded by an epithelial wall. Paired invaginations lead to two divergent pouches, separated by a median edge. These pouches unite only later, and their common entrance is secondarily taken up in the posterior wall of the stomodaeum. This description, which differs from what has been observed in all other molluscs, may perhaps find its explanation in DELSMAN's (1912) observations in *Littorina*. In this form also paired invaginations occur, but they later give rise to the sublingual clefts, and the radular sac proper forms between them.

No radular sac is formed in Lamellibranchiata.

The remaining outer part of the stomodaeum gives rise in *Limnaea* to the bilaterally compressed *mouth cavity*, and the *pharynx*, which is at first wide, but later has a dorsoventrally compressed lumen (Pl. IX; Pl. XII, A).

The cells of the stomodaeum are in many cases covered with cilia at an early stage (Fig. 34). The tubular oesophagus often possesses cilia too. In those embryos, which develop inside their capsules, the albumen is conveyed into the midgut by ciliary movement. Presumably, long cilia which are found on a dorsomedian row of ciliary cells in the stomodaeum of pulmonates, here play an important part. This row is either single (*Agriolimax*) or double (*Limnaea*) (Pl. XI, D), and consists of cells with pale cytoplasm, which is sometimes strongly vacuolated (*Limax, Agriolimax*). In *Crepidula* a similar double row of big clear cells with long cilia is found in the *ventral* wall of the stomodaeum; it is in direct continuity with the median row of ciliary cells on the foot (CONKLIN, 1897).

According to PORTMANN (1955), the uptake of albumen into the mid-gut in *Fusus* is not due to ciliary action, but to swallowing movements of the stomodaeum. To this end a transitory thickening is developed in the dorsal wall of the stomodaeum, through which a rhythmic closure is effected (Fig. 34). This thickening disappears after the period, in which the albumen uptake occurs, has ended. Only then does the differentiation of the stomodaeum, which had been temporarily arrested, recommence, and the radular sac is formed.

In *Limnaea* the stomodaeum originally consists wholly of cells with small oval nuclei, which have as a rule two nucleoli. Their cytoplasm is dense, and contains a few albumen vacuoles. At a somewhat later stage a differentiation occurs. The outer part still consists of small columnar highly basophil cells. Later these cells, which give rise to the mouth cavity and pharynx, exhibit a characteristic broad zone of very dense basophil ectoplasm along the lumen (Fig. 45 A, C). A similar ectoplasm layer has also been observed in *Chiton* (KOWALEWSKY, 1883a). The radular sac consists of similar cells, but they have a clearer cytoplasm and lack the distinct ectoplasmic layer. The inner part of the stomo-daeum, which forms the rudiment of the oesophagus, at first consists of cubic cells with clear cytoplasm, which then becomes strongly vacuo-lated, so that the cells get the appearance of turgor cells. Similar vacuolated cells in the oesophagus rudiment have also been observed in *Dreissensia* (MEISENHEIMER, 1901), *Littorina* (DELSMAN, 1912), *Fusus* (PORTMANN, 1955), *Physa* (WIERZEJSKI, 1905) and *Limax* (MEISEN-HEIMER, 1898).

The cells of mouth cavity and radular sac in *Limnaea* possess numer-ous Golgi bodies in the ectoplasm, and filiform mitochondria in the basal cell part (HIRSCHLER, 1918; RAVEN, 1946b). The large ciliary cells of the dorsomedian row have an outer zone with Golgi bodies and innumer-able fine mitochondria, whereas rather big mitochondria are found in the rest of the cell.

Small fat droplets are present in the stomodaeum cells of the *Limnaea* trochophore (RAVEN and BRETSCHNEIDER, 1942). MANCUSO (1953) found in *Physa* much glycogen in some small transparent cells between stomo-daeum and gut, apparently the oesophagus anlage. The nuclei in the stomodaeum and radular sac are rich in DNA in *Limnaea*. The cells of the mouth cavity possess much RNA, especially in the layer of ecto-plasm. In the cells of the radular sac RNA is mainly concentrated around the nuclear membranes. The oesophagus cells are very poor in RNA. Likewise, the big ciliary cells of the dorsomedian row contain practically no RNA. They are, however, rich in alkaline phosphatase and in iron (RAVEN, 1946b; ARENDSEN DE WOLFF-EXALTO, 1947; MINGANTI, 1950).

b. GUT

In yolk-rich forms the endoderm is subdivided from the beginning into large, yolk-filled, more or less passive cells, and smaller ones, which actively divide and in this way form the gut epithelium (e.g. *Buccinum*, *Purpura*, *Nassa*, *Aplysia*) (Fig. 34). However, in those species, where the wall of the archenteron at first consists of more or less equivalent cells, a separation soon occurs into two regions, the large-celled and the small-celled endoderm, respectively; this is brought about by a strong swelling of the cells, attended with the formation of large vacuoles, in a certain part of the gut wall. This is, for instance, the case in *Dreissensia*, *Paludina*, *Bithynia*, *Pomatias*, *Planorbis*, *Physa*, *Limnaea*, *Limax* and *Agriolimax* (Fig. 42, 46).

The relative positions of large- and small-celled endoderm are given somewhat differently by the authors, which is partly due to the confused terminology existing with respect to the main axes of the body in molluscan embryos (cf. above, p. 68), partly to the occurrence of a torsion in gastropods and the concomitant displacements in the gut primordium. Generally it may be said, however, that the small-celled endoderm, at least in gastropods, initially corresponds to the place of the shell gland in the ectoderm. In *Paludina* it therefore lies dorsally, on one side of the blastopore (Fig. 42). In the other forms, where the blastopore has shifted ventrad during its closure, it lies more or less opposite the blastopore in the tip of the archenteron. Perhaps it is permissible to conclude from this that the small-celled endoderm is derived from the macromeres 5A–5D.

From this region it later extends in *Limnaea* and *Physa* mainly in the dorsal and ventral wall of the midgut in the direction of the oesophagus. Still later it also encroaches upon the lateral walls, and in this way grows round the lumen of the midgut, which is transformed into the *stomach*.

The *hindgut* arises as a posteriorly directed outgrowth from the small-celled part of the midgut (Fig. 34, 46). According to CONKLIN (1897, 1907), CASTEEL (1904) and WIERZEJSKI (1905) it is derived from the enteroblasts, which are descendants of 4d. In the Basommatophora the hindgut primordium is at first a solid cell mass, in which a lumen appears only afterwards. According to WIERZEJSKI, this cell group is in *Physa* at first entirely separated from the midgut, with which it connects only secondarily.

MEISENHEIMER's view (1898), according to which the whole hindgut in *Limax* is derived from an ectodermal invagination, appears very un-likely, the more so as it develops in *Agriolimax* (CARRICK, 1939) in the normal manner.

The hindgut connects with its tip with the ectoderm between shell gland and foot anlage (Fig. 33), at the place where the anal cells are lying if these are present. Often a shallow ectodermal *proctodaeum* is formed here. In Polyplacophora and *Dreissensia* this is larger, and gives rise to a great part of the hindgut (MEISENHEIMER, 1901). In the Apla-cophora (*Epimenia*: BABA, 1938) the proctodaeum gives rise to a *cloaca*. No ectodermal proctodaeum is formed in cephalopods.

In *Paludina* the blastopore becomes the anus.

The hindgut primordium lies at first medioventrally, but in gastro-pods it is soon displaced towards the right side (the left in sinistral species) in consequence of torsion. At the same time the anus shifts forwards, so that the hindgut forms a loop towards the right (Fig. 37).

The small-celled endoderm generally forms a regular one-layered epithelium of prismatic cells. The nuclei are situated in the basal cell part. In *Limnaea* they contain as a rule one nucleolus without internum, except in the early solid hindgut primordium, where there are often two or more small nucleoli per nucleus. The apical part of the cell is originally filled with numerous small albumen vacuoles in *Limnaea*, but they soon disappear, and the nucleus comes to lie in the middle of the cell. In *Paludina* (DAUTERT, 1929) each cell at an early stage contains one vacuole; these vacuoles are arranged in a regular row in the peri-pheral cell parts (Fig. 42).

The small-celled endoderm of *Limnaea* contains Golgi bodies in the ectoplasmic cell parts near the lumen (HIRSCHLER, 1918; RAVEN, 1946b).

The stomach epithelium of *Physa* shows a positive glycogen reaction (MANCUSO, 1953). The nuclei of the small-celled endoderm of *Limnaea* are rich in DNA, the cytoplasm contains much RNA. In the midgut the RNA is found especially in the basal cell parts and around the nuclear membranes, to a lesser extent in the nucleoli; in the hindgut prefer-entially along the nuclear membranes. The small-celled endoderm is rich in bound sulphydryl compounds. The hindgut exhibits a positive alkaline phosphatase reaction (RAVEN, 1946b; MINGANTI, 1950).

The large-celled endoderm is during further development more or less displaced from the gut lumen. It bulges out, mostly in form of two lateral outgrowths (e.g. *Sphaerium*, *Dreissensia*, *Paludina*, *Umbrella*) (Fig. 65b). Their position may, however, in gastropods change second-arily in consequence of the torsion occurring in this group. They form the *larval liver*. In *Pomatias* the future left lobe of the liver is formed at an early stage, prior to torsion, whereas the right one develops only later, when torsion is well under way (CREEK, 1951). In *Littorina* the liver primordium is unpaired, according to DELSMAN (1912). In *Aplysia* the left liver originates from the large endomeres 4A and 4B, which are

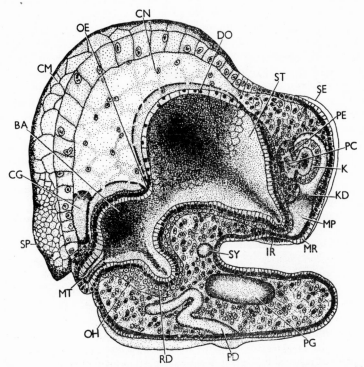

Fig. 46. Reconstruction of right half of embryo of *Pomatias elegans* at mid-veliger stage before torsion. *BA*, buccal cavity; *CG*, cerebral ganglion; *CM*, cephalic mass; *CN*, connective tissue of cephalic mass; *DO*, rudiment of left larval liver; *IR*, hindgut rudiment; *K*, kidney; *KD*, kidney duct; *MP*, right invagination of mantle cavity; *MR*, rudiment of mantle fold; *MT*, mouth; *OE*, oesophagus; *OH*, odontophore; *PC*, pericardial cavity; *PD*, pedal gland; *PE*, pericardium; *PG*, pedal ganglion; *RD*, radular sac; *SE*, shell; *SP*, cephalic plate; *ST*, stomach; *SY*, statocyst. After CREEK, 1951.

more and more displaced from the gut lumen, whereas the right liver arises only later by outgrowth from the small-celled stomach wall (SAUNDERS and POOLE, 1910).

In some cases the larval liver passes directly into the adult liver. BLOCH (1938) showed, however, that the larval liver in *Planorbis, Physa* and *Limnaea* is a typical larval organ, the cells of which have lost the capacity to divide. At the end of the embryonic period it disappears, and is very rapidly replaced by the definitive liver, which arises by proliferation from the wall of the stomach.

The cells of which the larval liver is formed, are characterized already at an early stage by their large size and pale colour. They have large, clear nuclei, often with a big nucleolus. Their most striking characteristic is the appearance of vacuoles, however. Often, these vacuoles first occur in the apical part of the cell directed towards the lumen. Later, however, they occupy the greater part of the cell, and reach huge dimensions (Fig. 42). The nuclei may be wholly displaced towards the periphery, whereas possible yolk granules still present in the cell are mostly crowded together in their basal part. The biggest vacuoles in *Limnaea* often contain pseudo-crystals of albumen.

In free-living gastropod veligers the food taken up in the larval stomach may be kept in rotatory movement, presumably by ciliary action. From time to time, by contractions and expansions of the walls of stomach and liver, the stomach contents are pushed into the larval liver, which represents the main digestive organ of the larva.

In those forms, where the embryos develop inside the egg capsules, the larval liver plays an important part in the uptake and digestion of the albumen (e.g. *Paludina, Bithynia, Fusus, Planorbis, Physa, Limnaea, Limax, Agriolimax*). The ingested albumen is first accumulated in smaller vacuoles in the apical part of the cell, then in much bigger irregular vacuoles in the basal part. The albumen is strongly PAS–positive in *Limnaea* (H. VAN DER HEÌDE, unpublished observations). Often, a change in stainability of the albumen in the vacuoles indicates that chemical transformations are taking place (RABL, 1879; RAVEN, 1946b). In *Limnaea* the contents of the larger vacuoles show an acid reaction. Presumably, the intracellular digestion may often be preceded by an extracellular digestion in the gut lumen, by means of enzymes secreted by the cells. Often clear unstained vacuoles are found in the albumen in contact with the liver cells (BLOCH, 1938; RAVEN, 1946b). The extrusion of secretion droplets into the gut lumen by the large endoderm cells has been observed in some cases. In *Limnaea* these cells at the early trochophore stage even temporarily exhibit a distinct apocrine secretion, whereby apical cell parts containing spherical droplets are constricted off into the lumen (RAVEN, 1952).

Other relationships are found in those forms, where the embryos develop in a cocoon, and feed on abortive eggs (e.g. *Purpura, Buccinum*). As soon as the stomodaeum has broken through, these nutritive eggs are taken up into the gut. This is distended to a large pouch filled with nutritive eggs. In connection with this, the differentiation of the midgut is greatly delayed. In *Purpura* even the differentiation of other organs is arrested during this period (PORTMANN, 1925).

In yolk-rich forms the endoderm cells are initially crowded with yolk granules. Presumably, the nucleus plays a part in the digestion of the yolk (e.g. *Acanthochiton*: HAMMARSTEN and RUNNSTRÖM, 1925; *Nassa*: HOFFMANN, 1902). The nuclei are generally found in the apical cell part near the lumen, and are surrounded by an area of perinuclear cytoplasm (Fig. 34). Sometimes they are lobate (*Acanthochiton*). They possess a big, often irregular and constricted nucleolus, which is often vacuolated, and may form protrusions towards the yolk. Vacuoles may also occur in the nucleoplasm. Presumably substances pass from the nucleus into the cytoplasm. The nuclear membrane may be folded, or may even disappear in places. The nucleolus lies preferentially at this point. The perinuclear cytoplasm in this region is deeply stained; basophil granules are seen to pass from the nucleus into the cytoplasm. In *Acanthochiton* after the extrusion of these substances a restitution of the nucleus may start from the nucleolus.

Apparently, in those forms where the large-celled endoderm is involved in albumen digestion, the nuclei also play a part in the process. The albumen cells of *Limnaea* have big, often irregular nucleoli, indicating a certain nuclear activity.

In the large endoderm cells of *Limnaea* Golgi bodies are found throughout the cytoplasm, but especially basally near the big albumen vacuoles. Innumerable small mitochondria are scattered through the cytoplasm (HIRSCHLER, 1918; RAVEN, 1946b).

The albumen cells of the larval liver of *Pomatias* (CREEK, 1951) and *Limnaea* (RAVEN, 1946b) selectively take up basic vital dyes, which are accumulated in the albumen vacuoles. The colour, in which the albumen in the vacuoles is stained at an advanced trochophore stage by neutral red, nile blue hydrochloride, and cresyl echt violet, points to a low pH.

The albumen cells of *Bithynia* (ATTARDO, 1955a), *Physa* (MANCUSO, 1953) and *Limnaea* contain numerous fat droplets in the meshes between the vacuoles. They also show a positive glycogen reaction (Fig. 23). Their nuclei are rich in DNA. In the nucleoli and around the nuclear membranes there is some RNA, but the rest of the cytoplasm contains little of this substance. Initially there are many iron granules in the meshes between the vacuoles, but at later stages ionic iron decreases, and finally it disappears altogether. The alkaline phosphatase reaction is negative (RAVEN, 1946b; ARENDSEN DE WOLFF-EXALTO, 1947; MINGANTI, 1950).

c. LARVAL KIDNEY

The larval kidneys of molluscs belong to various types. Well-developed paired protonephridia occur in Lamellibranchiata and Pulmonata. Moreover, protonephridia are also found in *Paludina* according to VON ERLANGER (1891).

In marine Prosobranchia larval kidneys occur in the form of a pair of protruding ectoderm cells behind the velum (e.g. *Littorina, Ocinebra, Crepidula, Buccinum, Purpura, Fulgur, Fusus*).

In Opisthobranchia there are two types of larval kidneys: (1) paired unicellular nephrocysts or primitive kidneys, situated in the body cavity; (2) unpaired pluricellular secondary kidneys, situated on the right side, and opening at the surface.

In Polyplacophora no larval kidneys have been found.

The *protonephridia* of the Lamellibranchiata are paired tubes, more or less straight, and debouching on the ventral surface (according to STAUFFACHER, 1897, there is only a left protonephridium in *Cyclas*). Each protonephridium consists of two or three cells: a *terminal cell* with a 'flame' of cilia, a *canalicular cell* with an intracellular canaliculus, and possibly an *aperture cell* containing the nephric pore. The terminal cell sends long protoplasmic protrusions into the body cavity. The canalicular cell may contain many excretion granules.

According to MEISENHEIMER (1901) the protonephridium in *Dreissensia* originates from the ectoderm. STAUFFACHER (1897) derives the outer part of the protonephridium of *Cyclas* from the ectoderm, but the inner part from the mesoderm. The development of the protonephridium in *Sphaerium* has been accurately studied by OKADA (1936, 1939). According to this author, the protonephridium in this species comes entirely from the mesoderm. At the third division of each mesodermal teloblast M there is formed a daughter cell 3 $m = N$, the *nephroblast*. This is a large cell with vesicular nucleus, with a distinct nucleolus and granular cytoplasm (Fig. 65a). It moves anterodorsad, and divides once. The anterior daughter cell N_1 extends towards the body wall. It contains granules and a vacuole, which opens towards the exterior, and in this way becomes the nephric channel. The posterior cell N_2 divides once more into aN_2 and pN_2; aN_2 becomes the *primary flame cell*, which however disappears soon, and is replaced by a *secondary flame cell* from pN_2. Soon after this the protonephridium degenerates.

The protonephridia of the Basommatophora (*Ancylus, Planorbis, Physa, Limnaea*) show a great resemblance to those of the Lamellibranchiata. They are looped or bent protonephridia, consisting of four cells, with an intracellular canaliculus and a terminal cell with ciliary flame (MEISENHEIMER, 1899). One end of the loop is directed forwards toward the cephalic plate, the other end ventrad; both limbs meet in the cell body of a huge nephroblast, situated beneath the ectoderm at the level of the lateral edges of the velum. The four component cells are: the terminal cell, canalicular cell, giant excretory cell, and aperture cell.

According to MEISENHEIMER the protonephridium of *Ancylus* originates from the ectoderm. All other authors (e.g. RABL, 1879; HOLMES, 1900; WIERZEJSKI, 1905) agree that the basommatophore protonephridium is derived from the mesoderm. According to RABL and WIERZEJSKI,

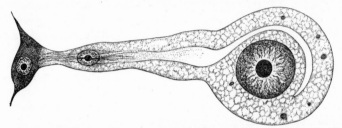

Fig. 47. Longitudinal section of protonephridium of *Limnaea stagnalis*. From left to right: terminal cell, canalicular cell, giant excretory cell. The aperture cell is in another section.

the nephroblasts originate on either side as large cells in the anterior half of the mesoderm bands. Each nephroblast N divides equally into N_1 and N_2. The posterior cells (N_1) differentiate into the giant excretory cells, whereas the terminal and canalicular cells are probably derived from N_2. In the giant excretory cell an intracellular canaliculus appears, which extends secondarily into two smaller mesoderm cells in front, and one behind. The most anterior cell becomes the terminal cell (Fig. 47). The latter has a dense cytoplasm, filled with excretion granules. It forms a long tuft of cilia in the nephric channel, and has often a big terminal vacuole at its opposite end. This side of the cell extends with filiform prolongations into the body cavity between neighbouring mesenchyme cells. The canalicular cell is perforated by the nephric channel; it takes part in the excretion process, and is filled with excretion granules. Then follows the giant excretory cell, which has a large vesicular nucleus with huge nucleolus. The chromatin forms a peripheral network beneath the nuclear membrane. The nucleolus often has an internum, consisting of several droplets. The nucleus lies in the anterior part of the cell, the intracellular canaliculus bends around its posterior side. The cytoplasm of the giant cell remains pale in ordinary staining procedures, but is strongly osmiophil. Golgi bodies are arranged along the lumen of the

M

canaliculus, rod-shaped mitochondria mainly in the periphery of the cell (HIRSCHLER, 1918). The aperture cell is a mesoderm cell, which has intruded secondarily between the ectoderm cells. The intracellular channel debouches here, forming a nephric pore situated immediately behind the velum. The nucleus of the cell is situated near this pore.

In later stages the cytoplasm, especially of the giant cell, becomes more and more vacuolated, and the entire organ less and less basophil. Finally it degenerates.

The giant excretory cell in *Limnaea* contains numerous fat droplets in its cytoplasm. Much glycogen is found in the giant cell throughout the cytoplasm; in the terminal and canalicular cell it is mainly accumulated near the nuclei. The nucleus of the giant cell is at first rich in DNA, but becomes strikingly poor in this substance at an advanced trochophore stage. The whole protonephridium contains very little RNA; most of this substance is found in the terminal cell, and a little around the nuclei of canalicular cell and giant cell. The nucleolus also contains some RNA. The alkaline phosphatase reaction is positive in the surface of the giant excretory cell, along the nephric channel, and in the outer layer of the nucleolus. Finally, the giant cell at first contains much iron (RAVEN, 1946b; ARENDSEN DE WOLFF-EXALTO, 1947; MINGANTI, 1950).

In the Stylommatophora (*Succinea, Helix, Arion, Limax, Agriolimax*) the protonephridia have a very different structure. They consist of a large number of cells, bordering an intercellular nephric channel, which begins with several terminal cells. Each protonephridium forms a tube, bent in several places, the front end of which is situated beneath the cephalic plates (MEISENHEIMER, 1898, 1899). The terminal cells, which often possess terminal vacuoles, generally resemble those of the Basommatophora. In *Succinea* there are two terminal cells to each protonephridium, in the other species there are more. The proximal part of the tubule consists of cells with vacuoles and excretion granules; the vacuoles may become very large. The middle part of the protonephridium is in *Limax* a thin-walled tubule consisting of flattened cells. The following part again has an epithelium of highly columnar cells, with vacuoles in the cytoplasm. Finally, the distal part may be composed of a more or less indifferent epithelium (e.g. in *Helix*). It opens in the lateral body wall.

According to MEISENHEIMER (1898) the whole organ in *Limax* is of ectodermal origin. The first rudiment is formed by an ectodermal invagination on either side, which grows out in an anterior direction. Its front end is at first closed. The cells situated here have clear nuclei with a big nucleolus, and dark-staining cytoplasm. They begin to form amoeboid projections, and lose their regular arrangement, but remain connected by fine membranes. They then develop flames of cilia, and become the terminal cells.

In *Agriolimax*, according to CARRICK (1939) only the distal part of the tube, consisting of small compact cells without vacuoles, is derived from the ectoderm. The inner, secretory part with the terminal cells is of mesodermal origin, however.

The veliger larvae of Prosobranchia as a rule have a pair of big larval kidneys situated behind the velum, to the left and right of the oesophagus. They are mostly unicellular, but sometimes consist of several cells (*Crepidula, Fulgur*). In *Ocinebra* there is at first one large cell, but later a second cell beneath it becomes strongly vacuolated, and forms a kind of stalk (FRANC, 1940).

The larval kidneys of the Prosobranchia are ectodermal structures. They arise by growth of one or more ectodermal cells, which become very large and protuberant (Fig. 34). They have a pale cytoplasm, and a large nucleus with big spherical nucleolus. The cytoplasm is filled with clear droplets or vacuoles. The latter as a rule contain excretion granules. At a later stage the vacuoles coalesce into one or a few larger vacuoles. The nucleus is pushed to one side, and finally degenerates. In pluricellular kidneys the cell boundaries become indistinct. Often the organ becomes constricted at its base, either by considerable growth of a special stalk cell (*Ocinebra*), or by neighbouring cells growing together beneath it (*Crepidula*). Finally the larval kidney becomes constricted off and is cast.

PORTMANN (1930) has made interesting observations on the function of the larval kidneys in *Buccinum*. Amoebocytes in the body cavity of the larva, filled with small vacuoles, apply themselves against the kidney cell, and are ingested by it. Their nuclei disappear and the contents of their vacuoles are taken up by the big vacuoles of the kidney cell. Amoebocytes of another kind penetrate into the kidney cells, and become filled with crystalline concretions. Then these 'crystal cells' are extruded through a slit between the kidney cell and the neighbouring ectoderm cells. In addition, a direct extrusion of the contents of the big vacuoles, breaking through the surface of the kidney cells, takes place.

The larval kidneys of *Ocinebra* show no selective accumulation of carmine or indigo carmine (FRANC, 1940).

In the Opisthobranchia there are two kinds of larval kidneys: (1) *primitive kidneys* or *nephrocysts*, which are paired unicellular structures, situated at some distance beneath the surface. For instance, in *Aplysia* there is a pair of big strongly vacuolated cells with small nuclei lying on either side at the base of the velum; they contain brightly coloured oily droplets (SAUNDERS and POOLE, 1910).

(2) *secondary kidneys*, which are as a rule unpaired, but may exceptionally be paired (*Umbrella*: HEYMONS, 1893). They consist of several large vacuolated cells, and open on the surface by means of a short duct. They are situated on the right side a short distance in front of the anal cells.

According to MAZZARELLI (1898) the secondary kidneys have a mesodermal origin. In *Aplysia* two large mesodermal cells, coming together from the two sides near the anus, by cell division produce a cell group, in which a lumen appears, that connects by a short invagination of the ectoderm with the outer world. According to other authors (e.g. HEYMONS, 1893; CASTEEL, 1904; SAUNDERS and POOLE, 1910), however, the organ is derived from the ectoderm. Large cells, situated on the right side in front of the anal cells (according to CASTEEL, 1904, and CARAZZI, 1905, they are descendants of $3c^1$), sink into the depth, and are for the greater part overgrown by neighbouring ectoderm cells. They have a large clear nucleus with distinct nucleolus. Their cytoplasm is pale, and finely vacuolar at first. Later the vacuoles coalesce to larger cavities, or into one distally situated vacuole. These vacuoles converge towards the aperture, where a few small ectoderm cells may form a short excretory duct. In living larvae the vacuoles are filled with a coloured fluid.

Neither the primitive nor the secondary kidneys of *Aplysia* accumulate acid colloidal dyes, as trypan blue or pyrrol blue (RIES and GERSCH, 1936).

d. NUCHAL CELLS

The nuchal cells are a loose heap of large cells lying above the oesophagus in the dorsal part of the nuchal region (Pl. IX; Pl. XI, C). They are found in two groups of freshwater gastropods: (1) the Prosobranchia *Paludina* and *Bithynia*, (2) the Basommatophora *Planorbis*, *Physa*, *Limnaea* and *Ancylus*.

According to FOL (1880) and VON ERLANGER (1891) they originate from the ectoderm. Most authors, however, derive them from the mesoderm. At first there are paired groups of mesoderm cells, which later unite.

The nuchal cells are very large elements; in Basommatophora they are larger than any other cells except the albumen cells of the gut. They are spherical or oval, polyhedral or pointed. They have large vesicular nuclei, with a peripheral chromatin network against the inner side of the nuclear membrane, and a big nucleolus with clear internum. Their cytoplasm is at first dense, sometimes with scattered vacuoles. Soon, however, granules appear which transform into highly refringent, rod-shaped, crystal-like and often yellow-coloured concretions. The latter accumulate in the peripheral part of the cytoplasm, which thus develops a more or less striped appearance.

According to HIRSCHLER (1918) each nuchal cell contains one large spherical Golgi body adjacent to the nucleus. Rod-shaped mitochondria are found scattered throughout the cytoplasm.

The nuclei of the nuchal cells are at first rich in DNA. The cytoplasm and nucleoli are very rich in RNA. Both nucleic acids disappear, however, when degeneration of the cells begins. The cytoplasm is rather strongly PAS–positive (H. VAN DER HEIDE, unpublished observations). The alkaline phosphatase reaction is negative (MINGANTI, 1950).

There has been much speculation on the function of the nuchal cells. LEREBOULLET (1862) considered them as the rudiments of cerebral and pedal ganglia, WOLFSON (1880) as larval brains. According to BLOCH (1938) they are probably excretory cells.

FOL (1880) and VON ERLANGER (1891) think that the nuchal cells later disperse through the body but persist. It has been shown, however, that they degenerate towards the end of the larval period. According to BLOCH (1938) they are then extruded through gaps between the ectoderm cells in the nuchal region, and fall apart in the albumen. This is confirmed by MINGANTI (1950).

e. LARVAL MUSCULATURE

In forms with free-living trochophore and veliger larvae there is as a rule a complicated larval musculature. Besides isolated muscle fibres (e.g. from the stomodaeum towards the pretrochal region), it consists mainly of two groups, (1) *retractors* of the velum, (2) larval *adductors* between the valves of the shell in Lamellibranchiata.

The larval musculature is probably derived mainly from the larval mesenchyme, but the primary mesoderm may also contribute to its formation.

The retractors chiefly run in an anteroposterior direction through the body cavity. In the Lamellibranchiata they are paired and symmetrical. For instance, in *Dreissensia* (MEISENHEIMER, 1901) there are three muscles on both sides, viz. a dorsal, middle and ventral retractor. They all have their origin behind in the dorsal part of the shell, run divergently forwards, and insert on the velum and mantle folds. They are reduced before metamorphosis.

In gastropods the retractors are asymmetrically developed. For instance, in *Haliotis, Patella, Patina*, and *Calliostoma*, there is a powerful larval retractor muscle, derived from cells of the right mesoderm band arising from 4d (CROFTS, 1955). It consists of six spindle-shaped cells, all attached to the shell apex on the original right side (in *Calliostoma* this attachment lies somewhat more anteriorly, in the middle of the right side of the body). It runs forward on the right side of the midgut towards its anterior attachment on the mantle, velum and stomodaeum. Three of these cells curve in sickle fashion dorsally over the stomodaeum

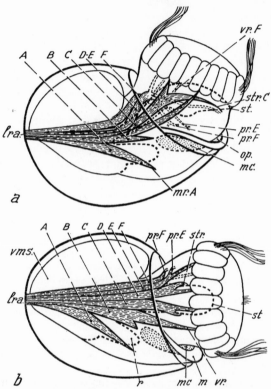

Fig. 48. Torsion in *Haliotis tuberculata*, (a) Veliger immediately before torsion, viewed from the right side. (b) Larva after first 90 degrees torsion in dorsal view in relation to the foot, showing half endogastric shell with mantle cavity and rectum on the right side. *A* to *F*, larval retractor cells; *lra*, shell attachment of larval retractor; *m*, mantle; *mc*, mantle cavity; *mr*, retractor termination to mantle; *op*, operculum; *pr*, pedal retractor termination; *r*, rectum; *st*, stomodaeum; *str*, retractor termination in wall of stomodaeum; *vr*, velum retractor termination; *vms*, visceral mass. After CROFTS, 1955.

behind the velum, and reach the left side, where two of them have attachments to the left side of the foot rudiment (Fig. 48a). This muscle probably plays an important part in torsion. After torsion has been accomplished, the posterior attachment has shifted to the left dorsal side. Now a second retractor is formed on the post-torsional right side.

The larval adductor of the Unionidae (LILLIE, 1895) is formed by a group of myocytes connecting the two valves. They have at first a granular cytoplasm and spherical nucleus with two nucleoli. Later the nuclei are drawn out according to the long axis of the cell, and a longitudinal fibrillation appears in the cytoplasm.

6. Asymmetry in gastropods

The asymmetric structure of the body is a characteristic of the gastropods. That this asymmetry is brought about during development by a *torsion* of the posterior part of the body, was first discovered by BOUTAN in 1885 in *Fissurella*.

Originally the mouth and anus of the embryo are both situated in the median plane. Then the whole visceral sac with the anus rotates about a longitudinal axis about 180° to the right. Thereby the anus is brought into an anterodorsal position. When the rotation is completed, externally the embryo once more looks symmetrical, but the internal organs, especially the nervous system, are twisted.

This torsion is preceded by a *ventral flexion*. By increased growth of the dorsal part of the embryo, the anus is shifted forwards, and approaches the mouth. The gut, which originally was straight, now bends into a loop. This is at first situated in the median plane, but when torsion begins it rotates away from this plane.

The primary cause of ventral flexion is probably the evagination of the shell gland, whereby the dorsal surface of the embryo greatly increases, and the anal region is displaced ventrad. This displacement may be enhanced by a stronger growth of the shell along its ventral margin, e.g. in *Acmaea* and *Haliotis* (BOUTAN, 1899).

As a rule the first indication of the commencing asymmetry is given by a displacement of the shell gland towards the left (in sinistral species, like *Planorbis*, towards the right), while at the same time the anal cells are shifted towards the other side (e.g. *Umbrella*: HEYMONS, 1893). The invagination at the margin of the mantle fold, which forms the first beginning of the mantle cavity, may at first lie ventromedially, and then be displaced towards the right (e.g. *Fulgur*: CONKLIN, 1907). Sometimes, however, the impending rotation is more or less anticipated, the right one of the two grooves, from which the mantle cavity develops, being larger than the left from the beginning (e.g. *Paludina*: DRUMMOND, 1902; *Pomatias*: CREEK, 1951). In still other cases the mantle fold at once develops asymmetrically on the right side (e.g. *Haliotis*: CROFTS, 1938).

The asymmetry may, moreover, be already visible before rotation in the structure of certain inner organs, e.g. a unilateral or asymmetric development of the larval retractor (*Patella*: SMITH, 1935; *Haliotis*: CROFTS, 1938) (Fig. 48a). As a rule, however, it is the gut which first becomes asymmetrical, e.g. by the unilateral or asymmetrical position of the larval liver (*Haliotis*: CROFTS; *Paludina*: DRUMMOND) or hindgut (*Littorina*: DELSMAN, 1912).

The asymmetry may even become visible at a much earlier stage, namely already during gastrulation. In *Crepidula* (CONKLIN, 1897) and *Trochus* (ROBERT, 1902) this occurs at the formation of the fifth quartette. In *Trochus* the right margin of the blastopore thus becomes longer than the left. In *Crepidula* 5c appears earlier, and lies more dorsally than 5d, whereby a certain degree of torsion in the posterior part of the archenteron is indicated. This displacement continues until 5d is situated medioventrally, and 5c dorsally. At the same time all ventral structures (e.g. hindgut) are shifted towards the right, whereas dorsal structures (e.g. shell gland) are displaced to the left. The ectodermal and mesodermal organs therefore follow the primary displacement of the endoderm. The distal end of the hindgut, which is shifted forwards on the ventral side by the simultaneous ventral flexion, is at the same time displaced upwards on the right side by this laeotropic torsion.

In the Prosobranchia, a rotation of about 180° of the visceral sac and shell with respect to velum and foot generally occurs (e.g. *Patella*, *Acmaea*, *Haliotis*, *Trochus*, *Paludina*, *Pomatias*). In *Paludina* this first rotation of 180° is followed by an apparent rotation of the posterior part of the visceral sac through a further 90° in the same direction, which is due to unequal growth (DRUMMOND, 1902). During rotation the stomach and liver are shifted along the left side in a ventral direction, whereas the mantle cavity and anus are displaced dorsally along the right side.

The pace at which torsion occurs is very different. In *Acmaea* the whole process takes place in two to three minutes (BOUTAN, 1899); in *Trochus* it lasts from six to eight hours (ROBERT, 1902), in *Pomatias* about ten days (CREEK, 1951); in *Ocinebra* it is also a very gradual process (FRANC, 1940). In *Haliotis*, *Patella*, *Patina*, and *Calliostoma*, torsion takes place in two phases (CROFTS, 1955). The first phase (90° in *Haliotis*, *Patella*, and *Patina*, and rather more in *Calliostoma*) takes place rapidly, occupying from three to six hours in *Haliotis* and *Calliostoma* to ten to fifteen hours in *Patella*. The second phase of rotation is slower, taking from thirty-two hours in *Calliostoma* to some two hundred hours in *Haliotis*.

Initially BOUTAN (1899) assumed that in Orthoneura no actual torsion takes place, but a 'déviation larvaire', in which the anus is gradually displaced through less than 180°, but the shell remains in place. Later (1902) he corrects this view in so far that he now assumes that at least in Opisthobranchia an incomplete rotation, through less than 180°, occurs, in which the shell takes part. For instance, in *Philine* the visceral sac rotates about 90°, whereby the larval shell is displaced toward the left, the anus and kidney toward the right. According to SAUNDERS and POOLE (1910), however, in *Aplysia* a rotation of more than 120° occurs, in which the gut, kidney and coelom take part, but the shell does not.

I must further mention here the view of PELSENEER and NAEF, who (mainly on comparative anatomical grounds) assume that in Orthoneura the torsion is followed by a de-torsion. As a matter of fact, in *Aeolidia* the anus first shifts to the right, but later returns to the median plane through a considerable extension of the hind margin of the mantle. A similar phenomenon has been observed in *Oncidium*, where the visceral mass and mantle after metamorphosis rotate back through about 90°, bringing the anus and kidney from the right side back to a ventro-median position (JOYEUX-LAFFUIE, 1882).

The asymmetrical *spiral coiling* of the shell must be sharply distinguished from the torsion of the visceral sac. Often the shell is still bowl-shaped when rotation occurs. In some cases, however, coiling by unequal growth of the shell already begins before torsion; it then takes place according to the plane of symmetry, however, and to the dorsal side (exogastric), e.g. in *Trochus* (ROBERT, 1902) (Fig. 48a). In those cases where torsion occurs rapidly (*Acmaea, Trochus*) the shell remains symmetrical during the process, but now it has become endogastric. Only then, e.g. in *Haliotis*, the unequal growth of the shell, mainly on the right side, begins, whereby the asymmetrically coiled shell is formed.

Many theories concerning the causes of torsion have been propounded. ROBERT (1902) gives a survey of these theories. As primary mechanical causes of torsion have been mentioned:

(1) The pulsation of the heart (GRANT).
(2) The rotatory movement of the larvae through the water by the action of the velar cilia (CARUS).
(3) The elongation of the gut (SARASIN).
(4) The weight of the shell (LANG).
(5) A conflict between the growth tendencies of the foot and the mantle (PELSENEER, BOUTAN, GROBBEN).
(6) The reduction of the right gonad (THIELE).
(7) A stronger growth of the left liver lobe (PLATE).
(8) An unequal growth of the body wall (SPENGEL, BÜTSCHLI).

With respect to the last-mentioned theories it can be said that in a slow rotation of the visceral sac differences in growth between the left and right side no doubt play a part. But these differences can never be considered as a primary cause, but must themselves be dependent on a preformed asymmetry. As a matter of fact, we have seen that often the first asymmetry becomes visible in the midgut complex, and has rather the character of asymmetrical cell shifting than of unequal growth. ROBERT in this connection further points to the asymmetry of cleavage, and to the fact that in sinistral forms also cleavage is reversed. We may further recall here STURTEVANT's hypothesis (cf. above, p. 104), according to which direction of cleavage is predetermined by a spiral structure of the cytoplasm in the oocyte, and the experimental data by which this hypothesis is supported.

As regards rapid torsion, it is evident that the asymmetrical development of the larval retractor muscle is the main cause of the process (CROFTS, 1955). Torsion begins as soon as the larval muscle cells are capable of retraction. The sickle-shaped curve of some of the retractor cells (cf. above, p. 170) is straightened out; after 90° of torsion have been accomplished, the muscles have a straight course, and their posterior attachment is now in the mediodorsal position relative to the head and foot (Fig. 48).

At the same time, the asymmetrical development of the retractors must itself be due to a preformed asymmetry of the early embryo.

7. Embryogenesis in cephalopods

Development in the cephalopods exhibits very special features because of the fact that the embryo arises from a flat germinal disc. However, comparison with the other molluscs is facilitated by taking into account the course of development in highly yolk-rich gastropods, as e.g. *Fulgur*, which in many respects form a transition to the relationships in the cephalopods (CONKLIN, 1907).

The germinal disc, which is originally situated at the animal pole of the egg, gradually extends over the yolk in the direction of the vegetative pole. In the Oigopsida, which are relatively poor in yolk, it finally envelops the whole yolk-mass. In other groups the yolk is at first only partly overgrown by the germinal disc, whereas its vegetative part remains covered only by the perivitelline membrane. Only at a much later stage is this part of the yolk covered by a flat ectodermal epithelium, greatly differing from the columnar epithelium of the germinal disc (Fig. 49). This extra-embryonic part then is separated by a groove from the embryo, and becomes the *outer yolk-sac*.

The whole surface of the ectoderm of the germinal disc becomes covered with fine cilia. Sometimes an annular zone along the free margin of the blastoderm develops a band of longer cilia (e.g. *Loligo pealii*, some Oigopsida).

The central gap in the endo-mesodermal layer is closed. Then the rudiments of various organs become visible, even before the extension

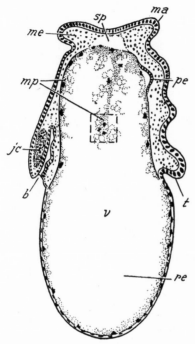

Fig. 49. Sagittal section of *Octopus* embryo. *b*, mouth; *jc*, cerebral ganglion; *ma*, mantle; *me*, mesoderm; *mp*, perivitelline membrane; *pe*, endoderm plate (rudiment of midgut); *re*, extra-embryonic region; *sp*, posterior sinus; *t*, arm primordium; *v*, yolk. After SACARRAO, 1945.

of the blastoderm is completed. A number of protuberances, folds and indentations are formed on the surface of the germinal disc, together forming a symmetrical pattern (Fig. 50).

At the place of the central gap in the endomesoderm the *shell gland* is formed from an area of highly columnar cells. It corresponds in its extension accurately with the central gap (NAEF, 1928). In some cases direct contact between this ectodermal area and the underlying yolk syncytium has been observed (*Tremoctopus*: SACARRAO, 1949). This area sinks in, but its margin, which forms the anlage of the *mantle*, rises above the surface. The central invagination closes to form a sac-like shell gland. This occurs also in those forms which have no shell in the adult stage. In *Tremoctopus* and *Argonauta* there is no true invagination of the shell gland, but an immigration of ectodermal cells, which then form a closed shell sac. In *Argonauta* this disappears at a later stage; in *Tremoctopus* it remains, and produces the shell, which consists of two chitinous rods in this form (SACARRAO, 1952c).

A broad area in the anterior part of the germinal disc forms the head rudiment. To left and right of the mid-line massive proliferations arise, the *cephalic lobes*. In their anterior part the eyes are formed. Behind and medially to them there is an extensive area of proliferation. Its medial part forms the cerebral ganglion, the lateral part the optic ganglion, while the remainder produces the so-called 'white body'. Somewhat later, between the cephalic lobes an ectodermal invagination forms the stomodaeum.

Behind and laterally, along the margin of the germinal disc, two semi-circular folds appear, which then divide into a series of isolated protuberances, the *arm primordia*. In Sepiadae (*Sepia, Sepiola*, etc.) each arm originates as a double primordium. In Decapoda the anterior arms appear later than the other ones, and at some distance from the latter. In Octopoda as a rule all arms appear simultaneously, but the fourth pair preponderates from the beginning.

On both sides of the mantle anlage semilunar folds occur, which are the rudiments of the *funnel sacs* (NAEF, 1928). Somewhat later behind the mantle a second pair of similar folds appear, which fuse to form the primordium of the *funnel*; they remain paired in *Nautilus*. The rudiments of the funnel sacs are overgrown by the mantle; in this way, they come to lie in the mantle cavity. They fuse only secondarily with the funnel folds.

The small endoderm plate, which was formed by delamination from the deep layer of the blastoderm (cf. above, p. 112) is situated behind the mantle anlage. At first it lies flat upon the perivitelline membrane (SACARRAO, 1945). Later it incurves, and its middle part is lifted from the perivitelline membrane, so that a primitive *gut* cavity is formed, which is bordered on one side by the yolk syncytium (Fig. 49). A small ectodermal invagination indicates the place where the anus will later break through.

Two symmetrical evaginations behind the mantle are the rudiments of the *gills*. The *statocysts* appear as deep invaginations in the posterior part of the blastoderm.

At the dorsal side along the line of closure of the shell gland a larval organ is formed, which is called HOYLE's *organ*. It consists of strips of glandular epithelium. Presumably it is a hatching-gland, which dissolves the egg shell. It disappears after the end of the embryonic period.

Once formed, the organ rudiments exhibit a strong growth, and are raised more and more above the surface. Sometimes the eyes are very large, occupying nearly half of the body of the embryo (*Loligo, Sepia,*

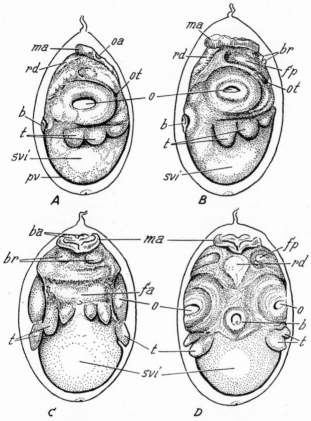

Fig. 50. Embryo of *Tremoctopus violaceus.* (A) From the left side. (B-D) older embryo; (B) from the left; (C) lower side; (D) upper side. *b*, mouth; *ba*, fin rudiments; *br*, gills; *fa, fp,* anterior and posterior funnel anlage; *ma,* mantle; *o*, eye; *oa*, aperture of shell gland; *ot*, statocyst; *pv*, perivitelline membrane; *svi*, yolk sac; *t*, arm primordia. After SACARRAO, 1949.

Argonauta). In *Octopus* the eyes are much smaller, in *Oithone* and the Oigopsida still more so.

On the outer side of the shell gland, to left and right of its last opening, the *fin primordia* are formed. The margins of the mantle turn down over the surrounding parts of the blastoderm, and extend in a vegetative direction, in this way forming the mantle cavity.

The arms remain for a long time concentrated at the posterior region of the embryo. Later they shift forwards, and surround the mouth.

The size of the yolk-sac varies a great deal. It is almost lacking in the Oigopsida; in *Sepia* and *Eledone*, on the other hand, it is so large that the blastoderm forms only a minute disc on its surface. Its size increases in the order Oigopsida $<$ *Argonauta* $<$ *Octopus* $<$ *Loligo* $<$ *Sepia*.

The mesoderm of the germinal disc extends into the extra-embryonic region. There it forms a provisional musculature of the yolk-sac, by which the latter undergoes regular contractions. Perhaps the perivitelline membrane has a contractility of its own. As the embryo develops, yolk is transported towards its interior (Fig. 63). Finally the external yolk-sac has entirely disappeared, but the inner yolk-sac may remain for a long time after that. Gradually the yolk becomes altogether resorbed.

When one tries to compare the cephalopod embryo with those of other molluscs, according to NAEF (1928) the connection of the outer yolk-sac with the embryo may be considered to correspond to the mid-line of the ventral surface, from the mouth to the anus. Hence, the foot is split, so to speak (the rudiments of the arms and funnel representing its two halves), and the halves are pushed apart by the big yolk-mass. In the course of development a kind of constriction of the brachial folds occurs, by which the connection between yolk-sac and embryo is reduced more and more, until finally only a very narrow stalk remains immediately behind the mouth (Fig. 63). The mouth is now surrounded on both sides by the arms.

B.   CAUSAL ANALYSIS

1. Mosaic development

According to the classical view the eggs of the Spiralia belong to the 'mosaic eggs', in which a very precocious determination of the cells takes place. Already at early cleavage stages, or even at the uncleaved stage, the fate of the various parts of the germ was supposed to be definitely and irrevocably determined.

This view has arisen especially from the results of experiments on the development of isolated blastomeres, like those of WILSON (1904b) with *Patella*.

Isolated blastomeres of *Patella* on further development form just those parts which would have been produced by them in normal development. For instance, isolated first micromeres form a cell group, consisting of four primary trochoblasts, two secondary trochoblasts, one quarter of the apical tuft, and a number of undifferentiated ectoderm cells. Isolated macromeres of the 8-cell stage each produce a second, third and fourth micromere, which further divide normally; after gastrulation, a minute 'larva' with two secondary trochoblasts is formed.

This and similar experiments led to the view that the cytoplasm of these eggs is a mosaic of different substances, the *organ-forming substances*. During cleavage, these substances are divided more or less passively among the blastomeres, which, in this way, differ from the beginning in their material composition and, hence, in their developmental potentialities.

However, such a view was difficult to reconcile with the results of centrifugation experiments, which showed that in many cases, when the egg structure was greatly modified by centrifuging at the uncleaved stage, a great percentage of normal embryos was nevertheless produced, even from eggs in which the distribution of the egg substances among the cleavage cells was quite abnormal (e.g. *Cumingia*: MORGAN, 1910; *Physa* and *Limnaea*: CONKLIN, 1910; RAVEN and BRETSCHNEIDER, 1942; *Aplysia*: PELTRERA, 1940). The fact that the displacement of visible egg inclusions did not prevent normal development, could only be explained by the assumption that these inclusions play no part in the determination of the cells, but are only indifferent building and food materials. The 'organ-forming substances' proper, on the other hand, would not be displaced by centrifugal force. As a matter of fact, it appeared that in *Limnaea* eggs, centrifuged immediately before first cleavage, a very abnormal distribution of the proteid yolk among the blastomeres was maintained during early cleavage stages, without preventing normal development to an early trochophore (Pl. VII, B). Apparently, therefore, this substance plays no part in the determination of the cells (RAVEN, 1946c).

One might imagine that the substances actually determining the fate of the cells are especially enzymes, vitamins, and similar substances important for cell metabolism, and that they are not displaced by centrifuging. However, it could be demonstrated by means of cytochemical methods that such substances are also heaped up in layers during centrifuging (*Aplysia*: RIES, 1938; PELTRERA, 1940; *Limnaea*: RAVEN and BRETSCHNEIDER, 1942) (Fig. 13, 16). Nevertheless these eggs may develop in a normal way. PELTRERA observed that in more or less normal *Aplysia* veligers from centrifuged eggs the vitamin C often still showed an abnormal localization.

An even greater difficulty for the hypothesis of mosaic development in its original form was presented by the fact that egg fragments, pro-

duced from uncleaved eggs by strong centrifugation (e.g. in *Physa*:
CLEMENT, 1938; *Diaulula*: COSTELLO, 1939b; *Aplysia*: PELTRERA, 1940)
in many cases may develop to more or less normal, harmoniously built
dwarf larvae. Such fragments may lack either proteid yolk, or fatty yolk,
or even both; fragments consisting only of hyaloplasm may produce
rather normal dwarf larvae. In centrifuged eggs of *Aplysia*, development
may be arrested in one or several of the blastomeres; the remainder of
the egg may then develop into a more or less normal dwarf larva,
irrespective of whether it represents an animal part, or a right or left half.

A related phenomenon is the development of double monsters. TYLER
(1930) produced them in *Cumingia* by compression of the eggs between
second maturation division and first cleavage. As a rule first cleavage
was equal, and in some cases double monsters with two pairs of shell
valves arose from such eggs. PELTRERA (1940) obtained double monsters
in *Aplysia* by centrifuging at the 2– or 4–cell stage; a 'physiological
blastotomy' might occur, after which each half cleaved and developed
as a whole egg. When the two halves were separated, each one of them
formed a more or less harmoniously built dwarf larva.

While these experiments suggest that the fate of the cells has not yet
been irrevocably determined at early cleavage stages, in other cases it
appears that no strict determination has been reached even at a much
later stage. Thus RAVEN and RIJVEN (1948) showed by means of lithium
treatment in *Limnaea* that the pattern of head organs in this species is
not definitely laid down before the 32–cell stage.

We may draw the conclusion from these experiments that the hypothesis of organ-forming substances in its original form is untenable.
The cells are not irrevocably determined from the beginning. Normal
development may follow upon an abnormal initial arrangement of cytoplasmic substances. Therefore, cellular determination is not merely due
to a passive distribution among the cells of a substance mosaic already
present in the uncleaved egg.

We must be careful, though, not to throw out the baby with the bath-
water. The view that the determination of the cells is ultimately dependent upon the material composition of the cytoplasm, and that this
becomes divergent in different parts of the germ by an unequal distribution of substances present in the egg (*germinal localizations*), need not
be rejected as such. But the assumption that this unequal distribution
is a mere passive process cannot be maintained. Apparently, the localization of the determining substances only takes place in the course of
early development by a complex of directed displacements. In other
words: the substances are (at least in part) preformed, but they are
not prelocalized.

2. Germinal localizations

We have seen in previous chapters that both at the uncleaved stage and during cleavage regular displacements and local accumulations of cytoplasmic substances take place (cf. p. 57 and 106). A number of experiments support the view that these processes are important for the determination of the cells.

In the first place we may mention here a number of experiments with eggs possessing a distinct polar lobe: *Ilyanassa* (CRAMPTON, 1896; CLEMENT, 1952, 1956), *Dentalium* (WILSON, 1904a) and *Mytilus* (RATTENBURY and BERG, 1954). As regards their normal development cf. p. 65 and 78.

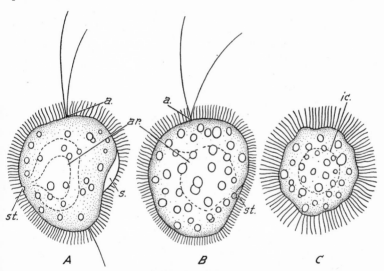

Fig. 51. Trochophore stages of *Mytilus edulis* at 24 hours. (A) From a whole egg. (B) From an isolated CD-blastomere. (C) From an isolated AB-blastomere. *a*, apical tuft; *ar*, archenteron; *ic*, internal cavity; *s*, shell; *st*, stomodaeum. After RATTENBURY and BERG, 1954.

A first group of experiments bears upon the development of isolated blastomeres. The larger blastomere CD, containing the whole of the polar lobe substance, may develop after isolation at the 2–cell stage to a more or less normal larva. In *Mytilus* at the trochophore stage only the dorsoposterior bristle, present in normal larvae, seems to be lacking (Fig. 51). A veliger with well-developed velum and mesoderm, but with only a fragmentary shell, develops; no further development occurs. In *Ilyanassa* the velum is not quite normal, often asymmetrical; a shell,

N

foot, operculum, enteron and heart are present, and there may be one or two eyes and one or two statocysts. In *Dentalium* the posttrochal region is relatively too large, the pretrochal region too small. The primary mesoderm is probably well-developed.

The smaller blastomere AB, which is devoid of polar lobe substance, in *Dentalium* and *Mytilus* becomes a partial trochophore lacking the apical tuft (Fig. 51). Moreover, in *Dentalium* the whole posttrochal region and the primary mesoderm are lacking; in *Mytilus* no shell gland and shell, no stomodaeum and primary mesoderm are present (in both species some mesenchyme cells, probably belonging to the larval mesenchyme, may be found). In *Ilyanassa* the velum is disorganized, and shell, foot, operculum, statocysts, heart and eyes are absent. Muscle fibres probably arising from ectomesenchyme may be present. The endoderm may contain a ciliated cavity.

After isolation at the 4–cell stage the cells A, B and C in *Dentalium* and *Ilyanassa* produce partial larvae resembling those from AB; in *Ilyanassa* each of them bears one group of velar cilia. In *Mytilus* these cells develop to spherical structures covered with uniform cilia, which show no further development.

D behaves in *Dentalium* like CD, forming a trochophore with apical tuft and too large posttrochal region. In *Mytilus* likewise a trochophore with apical tuft is produced; the veliger has well-developed velar cilia, but lacks a shell gland and mesoderm. In *Ilyanassa*, D may form a larva with velar cilia, one eye, a foot and a poorly formed shell.

Among the results of isolations established at later stages it may be mentioned that the isolated cell 1d of *Dentalium* produces a cell group bearing an apical tuft, whereas the structures derived from 1a, 1b and 1c lack this tuft.

Further interesting data were obtained in experiments in which the polar lobe was removed at first or second cleavage.

Removal of the first polar lobe in *Dentalium* gave rise to larvae lacking the apical plate and apical tuft (two lateral areas of proliferation in the pretrochal region, presumably the cephalic plates, were, however, present). The posttrochal region was wholly or nearly entirely lacking; no mesoderm bands were present. Later no outgrowth of the trunk region occurred, and the mouth, foot, shell gland, shell and mantle folds did not appear. After partial removal of the first polar lobe the posttrochal region was too small; the apical tuft might be present in these cases.

In *Mytilus*, removal of the first polar lobe produced trochophores without apical tuft and with a small thickened shell gland; no distinct mesoderm bands were present. Later the veligers had a well-developed velum and stomodaeum, but no shell.

'Lobeless' larvae of *Ilyanassa* have a disorganized velum and an indistinct dorsoventral polarity. There is no primary mesoderm, but mesenchyme and muscles, probably derived from the ectomesoderm, may be present. The endoderm may show some differentiation, but shell, foot, statocysts, eyes and heart do not develop (Fig. 52).

Removal of the second polar lobe in *Dentalium* results in larvae with-

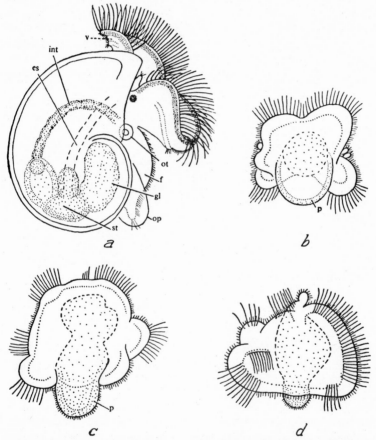

Fig. 52. Comparison of lobeless and normal larvae of *Ilyanassa obsoleta*. (a) Normal veliger about nine days old. (b) Six-day old lobeless larva. Posterior view. (c) Nine-day old lobeless larva. Posterior view. (d) Nine-day old lobeless larva. Anterior view. *es*, oesophagus; *f*, foot; *gl*, larval liver; *int*, hindgut; *op*, operculum; *ot*, statocyst; *p*, posterior protrusion of lobeless larvae; *st*, stomach; *v*, velum. The outline of the endoderm is indicated with a broken line in the lobeless larvae. After CLEMENT, 1952.

out posttrochal region, but as a rule possessing an apical tuft. In *Mytilus* likewise there is usually an apical tuft in these larvae; sometimes it is even reduplicated. The stomodaeum is present as a rule, but shell gland and shell are lacking.

The following conclusions may be drawn from these experiments. Some structures, like the velar cilia, depend for their development on a substance,* which is equally divided among the quadrants A, B, C and D. However, for a normal development of the velum, at least in *Ilyanassa* another factor must be present, which is bound to the polar lobe.

In *Dentalium* the development of the whole posttrochal body region depends on a substance, which is localized in the first polar lobe, passes with the latter into CD, is again present in the second lobe, and finally in D. In *Mytilus* and *Ilyanassa* shell and foot development is dependent on a substance which has a similar localization (although in *Mytilus* it is perhaps not wholly restricted to the lobe). However, other factors play a part in shell development too. In *Mytilus* normal differentiation of the shell never takes place in partial embryos; apparently, it is bound in some way or other to the totality of the embryo. The same holds for other posttrochal organs such as mantle and foot in this species.

The formation of the apical tuft in *Dentalium* and *Mytilus* is controlled by a substance present in the first polar lobe and CD, but not in the second lobe. Apparently, in the interval between first and second cleavage it has shifted towards a more animal part of the cell CD. At the next divisions it passes into D and (at least in *Dentalium*) into 1d. (In *Patella*, on the contrary, the substance for apical tuft formation is equally distributed among the cells 1a, 1b, 1c and 1d, cf. above, p. 178.)

Stomodaeum formation in *Mytilus* depends on a substance, which is present in CD to the exclusion of AB; it is not localized in either first or second polar lobe.

Finally, in all three species the formation of the primary mesoderm is dependent on a substance present in the first lobe and in CD. Its further fate has not been followed; presumably, it ultimately comes to lie in the second somatoblast 4d.

WILSON (1904a) has shown that the determining substances for apical tuft and posttrochal region in *Dentalium* are already localized in the vegetative half in unfertilized eggs. Animal fragments of such eggs develop into larvae without posttrochal region and (as a rule) without

---

* Strictly speaking, there is no proof that these factors are of the nature of 'substances'; they might be of another kind. On first approach, however, the assumption that these factors, which show a distinct localization in certain cells of the germ, are chemical substances, appears to be the simplest one.

apical tuft. Vegetative and meridional fragments form complete normal dwarf larvae.

The results of these experiments allow us to draw a fairly coherent picture of the processes of 'germinal localization' taking place during early cleavage in these eggs. A number of different cytoplasmic substances, preformed in the uncleaved egg, and showing already a certain degree of localization at this stage, are reshuffled during early development, partly by means of the mechanism of unequal cleavage with polar lobe formation, partly by secondary displacements in the interval between cleavages (cf. the behaviour of the 'apical tuft substance'); in this way the differential distribution of these substances among the cleavage cells is effected.

It must be emphasized that it follows clearly from the experiments that in many cases the presence of a certain substance is not in itself a sufficient cause for the differentiation of the organ in question, but that other factors, residing either in other cells or bound to the totality of the embryo, are involved. Therefore, the term 'organ-forming substances', which easily might give rise to an exaggerated view of their importance, can better be replaced by the more neutral expression 'morphogenic substances'.

Further data on morphogenic substances result from centrifugation experiments. As mentioned above (p. 179), as a rule normal embryos develop from eggs moderately centrifuged at the uncleaved stage. This is easy to understand if one takes into account that usually in a short time a rearrangement of substances occurs, by which the stratification caused by the centrifugal force is lost (cf. above, p. 58 and 108).

Centrifugation at later stages is often more injurious, however. According to CONKLIN (1910) and CLEMENT (1938), in *Physa* and *Limnaea* the effects of centrifuging become increasingly harmful during the uncleaved stage up to first cleavage. But this could not be confirmed by RAVEN and BRETSCHNEIDER (1942). If the eggs are centrifuged at the 2- or 4-cell stage, however, many abnormal embryos are produced. Especially centrifuging immediately prior to second and third cleavage is much more harmful than at earlier or later stages (CLEMENT, 1938; RAVEN and VAN EGMOND, 1951). This is probably due to increasing segregation and decreasing possibilities of readjustment of the egg substances.

The following deviations of development were found in *Physa* and *Limnaea* in such experiments: vesicular embryos (exogastrulae), bladder-like outgrowths at various places of the body, eversion of the stomodaeum, diverse malformations of the head (monophthalmia, eye reduplications, dislocations of eyes and tentacles), shell malformations (dislocations, reduplications), inverse asymmetry, median splitting of the foot (CLEMENT, 1938; RAVEN and VAN EGMOND, 1951; RAVEN and KOEVOETS, 1952; PARIS, 1953; RAVEN and BEENAKKERS, 1955).

The most characteristic effect, observed by RAVEN and BEENAKKERS in *Limnaea* after centrifuging at a late 4–cell stage consists in the formation of a supernumerary cephalic plate (cerebral ganglion, tentacle and eye) in an abnormal location, either in the pretrochal or the posttrochal region or on the boundary between the two (Pl. IX). According as it is situated nearer to one of the 'host' cephalic plates, the differentiation of the latter may be more or less suppressed. The most obvious explanation of these facts is given by the assumption that the differentiation of the cephalic plate depends on a morphogenic substance which is displaced by centrifugal force.

The notion of morphogenic substances should not be taken too strictly, as if there were a rectilinear relation between a single substance and the differentiation of a certain organ. PELTRERA (1940), who obtained dwarf larvae from egg fragments and isolated blastomeres of centrifuged *Aplysia* eggs, even when one or more of the egg substances were lacking, points out that these larvae show no definite defects, but only a slightly dysharmonic development with reduction of certain organs, e.g. underdevelopment of the foot, or failing anteroposterior elongation. A normal proportion of various cytoplasmic substances is required for normal development. If this 'histochemical equilibrium' is broken, the harmonic development of the larvae is disturbed.

The progressive localization of egg substances brings about the 'chemo-differentiation' (HUXLEY) of the embryo. It has been pointed out that this chemo-differentiation must be clearly distinguished from the 'chemical differentiation' which goes hand in hand with the histological differentiation (RAVEN, 1946b). In *Limnaea* a great difference in composition occurs between the cells of larval organs (larval ciliary cells, albumen cells, and protonephridium), on the one hand, and the small ectodermal, endodermal and mesodermal cells, destined to form the adult organs, on the other. The larval organs consist of large cells, which have lost the capacity to divide, often possess big albumen vacuoles, many Golgi bodies and mitochondria, and a great amount of fat, glycogen and iron, but are poor in RNA and DNA. The primordia of adult structures, on the other hand, have small cells which are actively dividing, possess no or only small albumen vacuoles, few Golgi bodies and mitochondria, little fat, glycogen and iron, but a great deal of RNA and DNA (Fig. 53). The two types represent opposite trends of cell life: on the one hand, functioning elements containing a great amount of fuel, and having a metabolism which is predominantly catabolic; on the

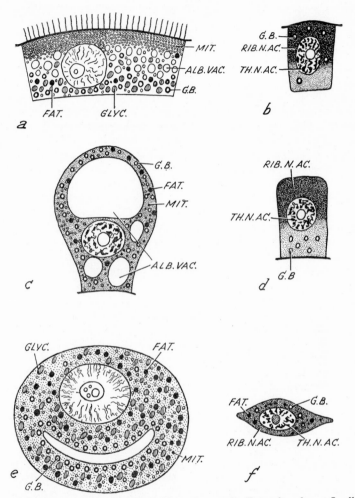

Fig. 53. Chemical differentiation in *Limnaea stagnalis*. Examples of type-I cells (larval differentiations, left) and type-II cells (imaginal primordia, right) in ectoderm (upper row), endoderm (middle row) and mesoderm (lower row). (a) Velum cell. (b) Ectodermal epithelium cell. (c) Albumen cell. (d) Gut epithelium cell. (e) Giant excretory cell. (f) Mesenchyme cell. *alb. vac.*, albumen vacuoles; *G.b.*, Golgi bodies; *glyc.*, glycogen; *mit*, mitochondria; *rib.n.ac.*, ribonucleic acid; *th.n.ac.*, desoxyribonucleic acid.

other hand formative cells, in which anabolism preponderates, leading to the synthesis of living protoplasm conditioned by a rich supply of nucleic acids.

3. The cortical field

The directed displacements of egg substances, taking place during early development, whereby a normal distribution of substances may ultimately be reached even in those cases where their initial arrangement was quite abnormal, are obviously controlled by a system of directing factors (cf. above, p. 60). The question of where these factors are located, how they are arranged, and what is their nature, forms the next step in the analysis of development. The centrifugation experiments have shown that this system of directing factors remains intact in moderately centrifuged eggs. Apparently, therefore, it is bound to some part of the egg which is not displaced during centrifugation. We know from cell-physiological investigations that the external limiting membrane of the egg cytoplasm and the layers situated immediately beneath it, together forming the so-called egg cortex, exhibit a considerable degree of rigidity. It is natural therefore to suppose that the above-mentioned system of directing factors is situated in the egg cortex. By local attractions and repulsions it may control the arrangement of substances in the more fluid inner cytoplasm (cf. above, p. 60 and p. 109). In this way, it forms, so to speak, a system of co-ordinates, in relation to which development takes place.

By very strong ultra-centrifugation, in which centrifugal forces up to more than 100,000 times gravity occur, which have, according to other data, a softening effect on the cortex, it appeared possible, in some cases, to deform the cortical field, and in this way to cause deviations in development. We have seen above (p. 49 and 91) that COSTELLO (1939b), PEASE (1940) and PELTRERA (1940) claim to have altered by this means the original polarity of the egg, as it expresses itself in maturation and cleavage. In COSTELLO's experiments many abnormal veligers developed from *Diaulula* eggs ultra-centrifuged at the uncleaved stage. PELTRERA obtained a number of double monsters from *Aplysia* eggs centrifuged at the 2– or 4–cell stage.

Moreover, some agents which may be supposed primarily to affect the egg cortex, like certain ions of the external medium, appeared to be able to cause definite deformations of the cortical system of co-ordinates. In this way very characteristic malformations of the embryo are produced.

RANZI (1928) studied the influence of lithium on the egg of *Loligo*. A great number of malformations of various kinds were produced. Among

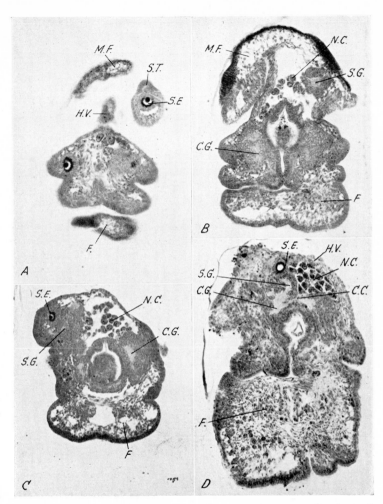

Plate IX. Effects of centrifuging at 4-cell stage on structure of embryos in *Limnaea stagnalis*. (A, B) Two transverse sections of head region of the same embryo. On the left side of the neck region there is an outgrowth with supernumerary eye (*S.E.*) and tentacle (*S.T.*). At the basis of the outgrowth lies a supernumerary cerebral ganglion (*S.G.*). (C) Transverse section through the head. Above right tentacle region an outgrowth with supernumerary eye (*S.E.*) and cerebral ganglion (*S.G.*). (D) Transverse section through the head. Above right tentacle region an outgrowth with supernumerary eye (*S.E.*) and cerebral ganglion (*S.G.*). The latter is in connection with cerebral commissure (*C.C.*). *C.G.*, cerebral ganglion; *F.*, foot; *H.V.*, head vesicle; *M.F.*, mantle fold; *N.C.*, nuchal cells.

[*Facing page* 188

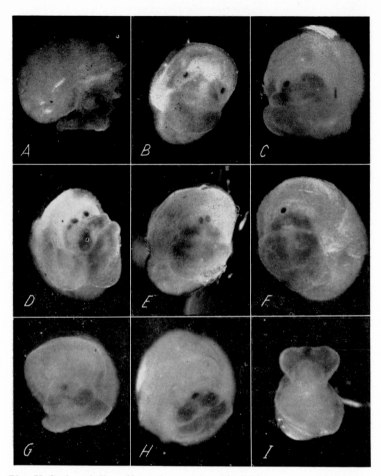

Plate X. Cyclocephalic malformations produced by lithium treatment in *Limnaea stagnalis*. (A) Normal embryo, nine days old, from the right side. (B) The same, front view. (C) Beginning synophthalmy, combined with reduction of left eye and tentacle. (D) Synophthalmy, combined with reduplication of right eye. (E) Synophthalmy. (F-H) Cyclopy. (I) Anophthalmy, viewed from above; head region much reduced.

them, the cyclocephalic malformations were the most characteristic. They may be arranged in the following order:

a. *Synophthalmia*: The eyes have approached each other. The cerebral ganglia as a rule are slightly reduced; the other ganglia are normal. The stomodaeum is usually everted, sometimes reduced; the more the eyes have approached the median plane, the more generally the stomodaeum is reduced. The ventromedian part of the embryo is broader than normally; consequently the fusion of the two halves of the funnel is delayed.

b. *Cyclopia*: The eyes have fused in the midline. Sometimes the resulting eye-ball is still clearly bipartite, but lens, cornea and eyelids are single; in other cases a single eye of double size has been formed. The optic ganglia are originally paired, but fuse during later development into a single ganglion. The cerebral ganglion is small and unpaired, or it is lacking altogether. The 'white bodies' tend to be displaced medially, but are never fused. The visceral ganglia are normally situated, the pedal ganglia are found on either side of the yolk-sac. The stomodaeum may be lacking altogether.

c. *Anophthalmia*. This may either be due to bilateral eye reduction, or belong to the cyclocephalic series. In the latter case the eyes, optic ganglia, cerebral ganglia, and stomodaeum, are lacking altogether. The statocysts are well-developed, and are displaced anteriorly. The visceral and pedal ganglia are well-developed.

d. *Acephaly*: The only organs which may still be formed are shell gland, pedal ganglia, Hoyle's organ, and endodermal gut, in decreasing order of frequency. The pedal ganglia are fused to an unpaired mass.

Similar malformations of the head region were obtained by RAVEN (1942) from *Limnaea* eggs treated with lithium (Pl. X). Besides synophthalmic, cyclopic, anophthalmic and acephalic embryos, other head malformations, not belonging to the cyclocephalic series (triophthalmia, monophthalmia asymmetrica, etc.) were also observed; some embryos showed still greater disturbances of the normal pattern of organization.

A study of forty-two embryos exhibiting cyclocephalic malformations (RAVEN, 1949) showed that, besides the displacement, reduplication, fusion or reduction of the eyes, a characteristic syndrome of malformations was present in these embryos. The cerebral commissure was often short, and the left and right cerebral ganglia were fused in the midline. The differentiation of apical plate, head vesicle and velum was suppressed. The cephalic plates had often fused in the midline (Fig. 54). The most constant of these deviations was the suppression of the posterior part of the apical plate; it had occurred in all cases studied. It was accompanied, in decreasing order of frequency, by the fusion of the cephalic plates, the shortening of the cerebral commissure, the suppression of velum and head vesicle, and the suppression of the anterior part of the apical plate. No characteristic defects in the mesodermal and endodermal organs could be observed. It was concluded that the effect of the treatment consisted in a suppression of the differentiation, being most pronounced at the animal pole, and decreasing with increasing distance from this pole.

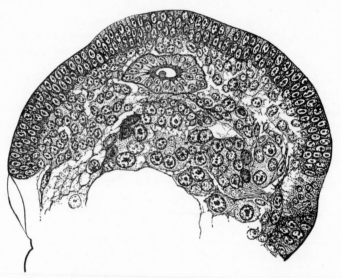

Fig. 54. Transverse section of cyclopic embryo of *Limnaea stagnalis*. Single median eye. Apical plate lacking. Cephalic plates fused in the middle.

This view was corroborated by a study of exogastrulae produced by lithium treatment (RAVEN, 1952). In the animal hemisphere of these structures as a rule a clear distinction could be made between the small-celled ectoderm, representing the cephalic plates, and the big-celled ectoderm of apical plate, head vesicle and velum. Three types of exogastrulae could be distinguished. In the first one, the small-celled ectoderm formed two cephalic plates, lying on either side of the animal pole, and surrounded by a cracknel-shaped area of large-celled ectoderm. This agrees with the arrangement found in normal embryos. In type II, the median band of large ectoderm cells had disappeared, and the cephalic plates had fused in the midline into a single area of small-celled ectoderm. This corresponds to the situation found in the cyclocephalic embryos studied previously. Finally, in a third group of exogastrulae the small-celled ectoderm of the animal hemisphere had disappeared altogether, this hemisphere consisting only of large ectoderm cells. Presumably, embryos of this type, provided that they could have pursued their development, would have formed totally acephalic monsters. Taken together, these three types of exogastrulae clearly demonstrate a progressive suppression of animal differentiation under the influence of lithium (Fig. 55).

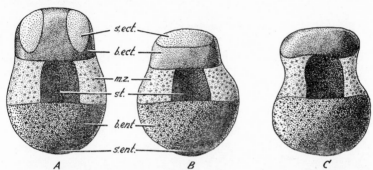

Fig. 55. Diagram of the topographical relationships in exogastrulae, produced by lithium treatment in *Limnaea stagnalis*. (A) Type I. (B) Type II. (C) Type III. *b.ect.*, big-celled ectoderm. *b.ent.*, big-celled endoderm. *m.z.*, marginal zone. *s.ect.*, small-celled ectoderm. *s.ent.*, small-celled endoderm. *st.*, stomodaeum.

It must be emphasized that, so far as could be made out, no displacement of the ecto-endodermal boundary had taken place in these embryos. The ectodermal area has therefore not been diminished in size, but its pattern of differentiation has been modified.

From these experiments the conclusion may be drawn that the cortical field is polarized. A certain property of the field attains its maximum value at the animal pole, and decreases gradually from this point. Therefore, the cortical field has the character of a *gradient-field* (RAVEN, 1943).

The pattern of differentiation is in some way or other dependent on this field. It may be assumed that each type of cellular differentiation corresponds to a certain range of values of the field factor. The disjunctive character of cell differentiation, compared with the continuous variation of the field, may be accounted for by assuming that certain critical values (thresholds) of the field factor decide between alternative differentiations.

Lithium treatment leads to a weakening of the field. The value of the field factor at each point now equals the value corresponding to a lower field level in normal embryos. Therefore, when differentiation occurs, the pattern is shifted towards the middle, while its median parts drop out (Fig. 56, a–b).

The action of lithium is phase-specific. In *Loligo* cyclopic embryos are only produced if the eggs are transferred to lithium solutions at or before the stage with 170 blastomeres; for synophthalmic embryos this stage arrives somewhat later (RANZI, 1928).

In *Limnaea*, the eggs are susceptible to lithium, as regards the production of cyclocephalic malformations, from immediately after laying until the 32–cell stage. In the middle part of this period, the effect is more or less obscured by the strong tendency of the eggs to exogastrulate (RAVEN, KLOEK, KUIPER and DE JONG, 1947; RAVEN and RIJVEN, 1948; RAVEN, 1952). The maximum susceptibility lies probably in the middle of the 4–cell stage (RAVEN and BURGERS, 1952). There are indications that susceptibility also fluctuates rhythmically with the cleavage cycles (RAVEN, KLOEK, KUIPER and DE JONG; E. D. NIJENHUIS, unpublished observations).

In an anaerobic medium lithium treatment produces no head malformations (GEILENKIRCHEN, 1952b). But the exogastrulae, produced by a strongly reduced oxygen pressure (cf. above, p. 124), belong in a large percentage of cases to the types II and III showing a suppression of animal differentiation (RAVEN and VAN RIJCKEVORSEL, 1953). Apparently, therefore, anaerobiosis in itself has a weakening effect on the animal gradient-field. It is true that hardly any embryos with head malformations are produced after treatment with a low oxygen pressure (RAVEN and MOOY, 1954) or with KCN (HAYE and RAVEN, 1953). This is probably due to the fact that after these treatments the great majority of the embryos with suppression of animal differentiations exogastrulate, and then never reach the stage of head differentiation.

MANCUSO (1955a) obtained head malformations in *Physa* by means of treatment of the eggs with sodium azide.

Besides lithium, other monovalent and bivalent cations (Na, K, Mg, Ca) may produce some head malformations in *Limnaea*; they are, however, much less effective than lithium (RAVEN and SIMONS, 1948). Potassium slightly enhances the lithium effect (ELBERS, 1952). Calcium (DE VRIES, 1953) and cyanide (HAYE and RAVEN, 1953), on the other hand, may suppress the effect of lithium.

An extensive investigation on the action of various ions (RAVEN, 1956) showed that the typical cyclocephalic malformations are almost specific lithium effects. Only sporadically can similar malformations be produced by CsCl and $CaCl_2$. With low calcium concentrations no distinct antagonistic effect to lithium was observed, but sodium and rubidium were strongly, caesium weakly antagonistic to lithium; potassium proved to be neutral or slightly synergistic. It was concluded from the 'action spectrum' of various cations that head malformations are caused by a direct action of the cations on a phosphate colloid. Although there is a strong parallelism with the action leading to exogastrulation, presumably the two effects are not strictly identical.

We may surmise also in this case that the colloid structure of the cortex is very important for the properties of the cortical field. One might even consider the possibility that the physical basis of the field is provided by local differences in colloid structure. Further experiments are needed to test this supposition.

That the animal gradient-field is located in the cortex is proved by the fact that it is not influenced by moderate centrifuging. Exogastrulae produced by centrifugation all belong to type I (PARIS, 1953). The pattern of head organs in embryos from centrifuged eggs is relatively undisturbed, apart from secondary interference by the neighbourhood of accessory organs (RAVEN and BEENAKKERS, 1955). A combination of centrifugation and lithium treatment gives only a summation, not an interaction between the effects of the two treatments (RAVEN and KOEVOETS, 1952).

The animal gradient-field proved to be affected by heat shock treatment (one to three hours at 37°) at the uncleaved, 4–cell or 24–cell stage. Head malformations were produced after such treatment (VISSCHEDIJK, 1953). However, they did not belong to the cyclocephalic series. Apart from local reductions and reduplications of eyes, the most characteristic effect of the treatment consisted in a reduplication of the posterior part of the apical plate, with the formation of a median cephalic plate bordered on either side by a row of apical plate cells, and which may give rise to an eye or tentacle (RAVEN, DE ROON and STADHOUDERS, 1955) (Pl. XI). Such malformations might have arisen from a very local depression of the field at the animal pole, in consequence of which part of the presumptive apical plate material would be transformed into structures corresponding to lower field levels (Fig. 56c). Since, however, the total number of apical plate cells had not been reduced but, on the contrary, in many cases was distinctly enlarged, it was concluded that a strengthening of the animal gradient-field had taken place. In consequence of this the pattern of head organs is, so to speak, drawn out toward the sides, and its median part has reduplicated by the formation of two new apices on either side of the midline (Fig. 56d).

The view that we are once more concerned here with an action on the cortex is corroborated by the fact that $CaCl_2$ diminishes the effect of a heat shock (RAVEN and VAN ERKEL, 1955).

Apparently, the cortical field controls development by exercising attractions and repulsions on the morphogenic substances, which thereby adjust themselves to certain levels of the gradient. For instance, the 'cephalic plate substance' in *Limnaea* (cf. p. 186) must accumulate in normal development beneath cortical areas in which the field factors vary between certain limits (RAVEN and BEENAKKERS, 1955). Other examples of such attractions have been mentioned in previous chapters (cf. p. 60). Since the displacements of nuclei and spindles apparently

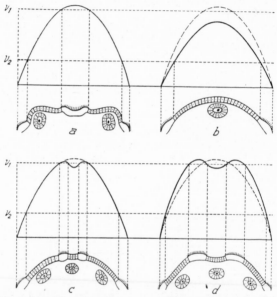

Fig. 56. Diagrammatic representation of the effect of the animal gradient field on the pattern of head organs in *Limnaea stagnalis*. (a) Normal embryo. (b) Cyclocephalic embryo after depression of gradient field. (c, d) Reduplication of apical plate, either after local depression (c), or strengthening (d) of gradient field.

are also controlled by the cortical field (cf. p. 49, 101, and 106), we may conclude that this field has a general co-ordinating and integrating function in development.

It must be assumed that the field not only has a polar structure, but is also organized in the dorsoventral and transverse directions. As we have seen above (p. 92), the dorsoventral field structure possibly comes into being only secondarily during early cleavage. In forms with a distinct polar lobe, the principle of dorsiventrality is probably bound to this lobe, and the arbitrary fusion of the latter with one of the blastomeres determines the dorsoventral character of the field. In this connection, the following observations (CLEMENT, 1952, 1956) are important.

In *Ilyanassa*, larvae from lobeless eggs show a disorganized velum (Fig. 52), although the germinal localizations for velum development, which are mainly found in the cells $1a^2$–$1d^2$, are probably present. Apparently, a 'lobe factor' is necessary for a normal structure of the velum.

Likewise, larvae from lobeless eggs, and from isolated blastomeres AB, A, B or C, lack eyes. On the contrary, larvae from D mostly have one eye, those from CD may even have two eyes. If, however, distinct germinal localizations for eye development are present, they are most likely located in $1a^1$ and $1c^1$, perhaps also in $1b^1$. In this case also a 'lobe factor' clearly is necessary for eye development.

It is an obvious assumption that this action of the lobe is due to its influence on the dorsoventral configuration of the cortical field. In the absence of this influence, the pattern of differentiation is disturbed, the structure of the velum is abnormal, and the eyes do not develop. The formation of eyes in CD– or D–larvae proves that with regard to this organ the epigenetic field action is even more decisive than the segregation of substances during early cleavages. Apparently, the definite localization of cephalic plate substances under the influence of the field takes place rather late in *Ilyanassa*, as it does in *Limnaea*.

With regard to the transverse structure of the field, which presents important problems especially in gastropods on account of their strongly marked asymmetry, the following observations may be mentioned.

Local eye reduction in *Limnaea* following lithium treatment at early cleavage stages occurs preferentially on the left side (RAVEN, 1942), but after a heat shock in the same period it is mainly found on the right side (RAVEN, DE ROON and STADHOUDERS, 1955). Apparently there exists already during early cleavage a physiological left-right asymmetry in the eggs.

In *Ilyanassa*, larvae from AD–halves show a strong tendency for unilateral development of velum and eye, these structures being confined for the most part to the left side. In CD–larvae there is a tendency for the velum to develop more often and more completely on the right side (CLEMENT, 1956).

4. Induction

Embryos of *Limnaea*, which have exogastrulated following lithium treatment at early stages, develop into vesicular, often dumb-bell-shaped structures. They may increase considerably in size by the accumulation of fluid, but show no further development, and eventually die.

A study of these exogastrulae at the height of their development (RAVEN, 1952) has shown that various tissues reach a certain degree of histological differentiation. In general, three regions may be distinguished: an ectodermal hemisphere, an endodermal hemisphere, and an intermediate 'marginal zone' forming an equatorial girdle (Fig. 55).

In the endodermal hemisphere, a clear distinction between a large-celled and a small-celled region has appeared. The large-celled endoderm, which occupies the greater part of this hemisphere, consists of big cells with large nuclei containing big nucleoli. The latter exhibit considerable activity. They have irregular outlines; nucleolar buds may be constricted off, or the whole nucleolus disintegrates into a number of granules. Although a certain degree of nucleolar activity is also found in the large-celled endoderm of normal trochophores, it is much more pronounced in the exogastrulae. The large-celled endoderm mostly forms a regular epithelium. In the peripheral parts of the cells large albumen vacuoles are found, which do not, however, attain such huge sizes as in the albumen cells of normal embryos. The cells often exhibit an apocrine secretion, whereby apical cell parts are constricted off at the surface of the exogastrula.

The small-celled endoderm, which occupies a small nearly circular area at the vegetative pole, exhibits a much less conspicuous differentiation. It forms either a one-layered epithelium or an irregular cell mass protruding more or less into the interior.

In the ectodermal hemisphere, likewise a large-celled and a small-celled part may be distinguished. The large-celled ectoderm, representing the cells of velum, head vesicle and apical plate of normal embryos, as a rule forms a one-layered epithelium of flattened cells with pale cytoplasm, and a large vesicular nucleus with big nucleolus. They may partly form well-differentiated ciliary cells. Sometimes, however, they show an aberrant differentiation, being filled with big watery vacuoles; this may represent an incipient degeneration of the cells.

The small-celled ectoderm, which represents the cephalic plates of normal embryos, forms either a one-layered epithelium or an irregular plug, often with a more or less concentric arrangement of cells.

As regards the topographical relationships between large-celled and small-celled ectoderm, cf. above, p. 190.

The marginal zone is covered externally by a layer of small cells with oval nuclei, often containing two small nucleoli. This layer represents the post-trochal ectoderm of normal embryos. Internally the zone contains a mass of mesodermal cells, partly differentiated into mesenchyme. Moreover, sometimes a more or less atypical protonephridium (mainly consisting of the giant nephroblast) has been formed.

Part of the surface of the marginal zone is occupied by the stomodaeum cells, recognizable by their dense darkly-stained ectoplasm layer. Sometimes a funnel-shaped invagination has been formed in this region. In its centre a few cells with pale watery cytoplasm and clear oval nuclei probably represent the oesophagoblasts.

Summarising, it may be said that a certain measure of histological differentiation of the cells has taken place, but it has stopped at an early stage. As regards their histogenetic potencies, the cells are, therefore, to a certain extent self-differentiating. This applies especially to larval differentiations (ciliary cells, albumen cells, protonephridium). The adult types of tissue differentiation do not occur, however. With respect to organogenetic potencies, moreover, we may only deduce the existence

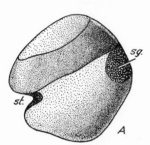 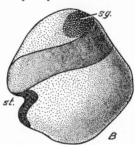

Fig. 57. Diagram of the position of the shell gland, induced by the invaginated archenteron in abnormal embryos of *Limnaea stagnalis*. (A) posttrochal. (B) pretrochal. *s.g.*, shell gland; *st.*, stomodaeum.

of a certain autonomous tendency for invagination of the stomodaeum cells. No gut, radular sac, shell gland, statocysts, ganglia or eyes have ever been found, however.

On the basis of these observations we may conjecture that the primary chemo-differentiation during early stages of development under the influence of the cortical field forms a sufficient cause for larval differentiation, and lays down the general pattern of the embryo in broad outline, but that both organogenesis and histogenesis of adult organs require the intervention of new causal factors, which make their appearance during gastrulation in consequence of the displacements of cells thereby taking place.

This is corroborated by the following observations. Occasionally, in *Limnaea* eggs treated with lithium the invagination of the archenteron is more or less defective. Part of the presumptive endoderm remains at the surface, the rest is invaginated, and forms either a solid cell mass incompletely filling the cleavage cavity, or a more or less reduced

o

archenteron. In these cases protonephridia are formed much more frequently than in true exogastrulae; sometimes paired protonephridia develop. Moreover, in a great number of cases a shell gland is formed. It is always situated at a place where the tip of the archenteron or the small-celled part of the invaginated endoderm mass touches the inner side of the ectoderm. In those cases where the archenteron has grown inwards in an abnormal direction, its tip may come into contact with the inner side of the pretrochal part of the ectoderm; then, a shell gland may develop even in the pretrochal ectoderm (Fig. 57). It was concluded from these observations that the formation of the shell gland is due to inductive action exerted by the tip of the archenteron on the ectoderm with which it makes contact (RAVEN, 1952).

It has been shown above (p. 147) that in gastropods generally the area of the shell gland in the ectoderm coincides with the position of the small-celled endoderm in the archenteron wall, and that there is a very close contact between the two during a certain period of development. We may presume, therefore, that the contact induction of the shell gland by the archenteron wall is a general phenomenon in gastropods. This is confirmed for *Bithynia* by the observations of HESS (1956a, 1956b).

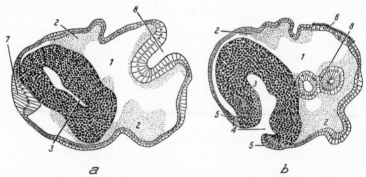

a   *b*

Fig. 58. Exogastrula of *Bithynia tentaculata* after lithium treatment; fourteen days old. (a) Section through shell gland anlage and invagination of stomodaeum. (b) Section through invagination of liver primordium and midgut epithelium. The oesophageal part of the stomodaeum reaches the endoderm. 1, ectodermal vesicle; 2, mesenchyme; 3, liver; 4, invagination aperture of liver primordium; 5, midgut epithelium; 6, trochal cells; 7, shell gland; 8, stomodaeum. After HESS, 1956b.

In *Bithynia*, exogastrulation may occur either in whole embryos after lithium treatment, lack of oxygen, or other injurious actions, or in half-embryos obtained by isolation of blastomeres at the 2- or 4-cell stage. In contrast to *Limnaea*, these *Bithynia* exogastrulae exhibit a belated invagination of part of the endoderm at the age of six or seven days. Apparently, this corresponds to the formation of the larval liver, which occurs in normal embryos of this age. The small-celled midgut epithelium remains for a large part at the surface. In most cases a stomodaeum is formed; it is deeply invaginated, but hardly ever makes contact with the endoderm. A clearly recognizable oesophagus may be formed, but no radular sac (Fig. 58). In embryos from isolated half-blastomeres (AB and CD) only one of the half-embryos from one egg has a stomodaeum, in half embryos isolated at the 4–cell stage (AD and BC) both may possess a stomodaeum. Apparently, the stomodaeum is formed by self-differentiation from a predetermined area, as in *Limnaea*.

After the invagination of part of the endoderm, a shell gland may be formed at the place of contact between endoderm and ectoderm (Fig. 58). In normal embryos of *Bithynia* it appears already after three days, but in exogastrulae only after six or seven days, when the endodermal invagination has occurred. Both AB– and CD–embryos are able to form a shell gland. It is concluded that shell gland formation is due to contact induction in *Bithynia* also.

We may conjecture that induction phenomena play an important part at later stages of development in the processes of organogenesis. Up to now, however, the experimental evidence in this field is very scanty

CHAPTER VI

Organogenesis

1. Skin

THE outer ectodermal layer of the embryo becomes the one-layered *epidermis* of the adult mollusc. The mesodermal layer lying beneath the ectoderm produces the *cutis* and *musculature* of the body wall.

The *chromatophores* of the Cephalopoda arise from mesoderm cells of the cutis. JOUBIN's (1891) view that they are derived from ectoderm cells which have sunk beneath the surface is probably erroneous. The formation of the chromatophores in *Bolitaena* was described by CHUN (1902) in the following way. Unbranched connective tissue cells in the cutis, possessing an eccentric nucleus and a centrosphere with centriole, begin to grow. A clear ectoplasm is separated from the endoplasm containing nucleus and centrosphere. From the ectoplasm about nine to fourteen radially directed and anastomizing pseudopodia are formed. A contractile substance is laid down in each of these outgrowths in two lateral zones; a ring of similar substance is produced at the base of the pseudopodia in the ectoplasm. The radial fibres now become connected with a nerve plexus in the cutis. Their anastomoses disappear. In the cell part turned towards the surface numerous refringent granules appear. Afterwards they are dissolved, and in their place a yellowish or reddish coarse pigment is formed, which later breaks up into fine granules. In the meantime, the nucleus of the chromatophore has repeatedly divided by amitosis. The resulting nuclei arrange themselves in a circle along the periphery of the cell, with the exception of one larger nucleus, containing from one to three nucleoli, which remains in the centre. The peripheral nuclei, varying in number from about eighteen to thirty-two, come to lie in the bases of the radial fibres.

The description given by SACARRAO (1954a) of the formation of chromatophores in *Tremoctopus* differs in important respects from the above. The future chromatophores are from the beginning connected by delicate protoplasmic fibres with the surrounding mesenchyme cells. When the central cell begins to grow, the mesenchyme cells arrange themselves radially around it, and their nuclei come to lie quite close to its membrane. They are then transformed into the radial muscle fibres. In the central cell pigment is accumulated in a large central vacuole. Its cytoplasm and nucleus are restricted to a marginal zone around the vacuole. The nucleus remains always undivided.

The *suckers* on the arms of the cephalopods arise as solid papillae. Originally they are situated in one row, as a rule in the form of transverse ridges. At the proximal end of the row a rearrangement occurs; the papillae are displaced in a zigzag manner, so that two alternating longitudinal rows are formed. This process may repeat itself a number of times, so that there are finally four, eight, sixteen or more rows. Since the arm grows terminally, and new sucker rudiments are formed throughout at the distal end of the row, the number of suckers increases with the age of the animal (NAEF, 1928).

In the epidermis numerous mucus-secreting *gland cells* may be formed. This is e.g. the case in *Acanthochiton* (HAMMARSTEN and RUNN-STRÖM, 1925). The secretion granules in these cells originate in or against the nucleus.

In *Loligo* likewise some epidermal cells become goblet cells, probably secreting mucus (FAUSSEK, 1901). Their number increases strongly during development, so that they even exceed the ordinary ciliated epidermis cells in number. Locally small groups of undifferentiated ectoderm cells remain, however. Finally nearly the whole epidermis consists of mucous cells; only in the head region ciliated cells remain, and the inner sides of the arms also consist of ordinary columnar epithelium. FAUSSEK assumes that at the end of embryonic life the greater part of the epidermis is cast, and is regenerated from the un-differentiated cell groups mentioned above.

According to RANZI (1931a) the secretion of the epidermal gland cells serves to dissolve the deeper layers of the egg capsule. If by operative intervention upon the embryo part of the glandular skin epithelium has been removed, regulation takes place, the remaining glands exhibiting a stronger secretion.

The *spicules* of Polyplacophora and Aplacophora are also epidermal secretions. According to KOWALEWSKY (1883a) the spines are formed in the larvae of *Chiton* within certain ectoderm cells containing a large vacuole. The spicule is secreted within this vacuole. Secondarily it breaks through towards the surface, and connects with the gelatinous cuticule covering the dorsal part of the larva.

In adult Amphineura a somewhat different mode of spicule formation has been described, however (e.g. BLUMRICH, 1891). Here the spines are formed in ectodermal papillae, in which an invagination occurs. At the base of this invagination there is a broadened cell, which plays the main role in spine formation. As the spine increases in size, it pushes the cells of the papilla apart, and protrudes with its tip above the surface. The chitinous spine basis is secreted by the surrounding cells of the papilla. By continuous secretion of cuticular substance by these cells the spine is pushed upwards and the basal cell is pulled out in a thread-like manner. The main body of the spine consists in *Acanthochiton*, according to HAMMARSTEN and RUNSTRÖM (1925), of aragonite crystals, oriented in a longitudinal direction.

The formation of the *operculum* of gastropods was studied by FISCHER (1940) in *Purpura*. The whole epithelium of the dorsal side of the foot contributes to the secretion of the larval operculum, which may be considered as the cuticule of these cells. When the columellar muscle is formed, its fibres connect with some of these cells, which then differentiate into myo-epithelial cells. On further development, the cells along the margin of the opercular area become specialized, and produce the definitive operculum by secretion of new layers externally to the first-formed layer. The area of insertion of the musculus columellaris does not take part in this secretion.

2. Pedal glands

As regards the larval foot gland of Polyplacophora, cf. above, p. 154.

The *byssus gland* of Lamellibranchiata originates as a pitlike invagination ventrally in the midline of the foot, at the level of or immediately behind the pedal ganglia. The first invagination is unpaired in *Dreissensia* (MEISENHEIMER, 1901), *Nucula* (DREW, 1901) and *Anodonta* according to HERBERS (1913); it is paired in *Sphaerium* (OKADA, 1936) and in *Anodonta* according to HARMS (1909). The epithelial cells grow inwards and backwards as paired strands of glandular cells, which may extend nearly to the tip of the foot. In most cases the gland remains connected with the surface at the place of its first invagination. In *Anodonta*, however, according to HERBERS this invagination is pinched off as a closed sac with one-layered wall, consisting of ciliated and glandular epithelium, and innervated by a prominent nerve from the pedal ganglion.

The cells of the foot gland of *Anodonta* have a granular protoplasm. In *Nucula* they are strongly swollen and vacuolated. The byssus gland of *Dreissensia* secretes numerous byssus threads at the time of spatfall. In *Nucula* no byssus is formed; the gland lumen certainly contains traces of secretion, but this does not pass out. In *Anodonta* the strands of gland cells probably become a subepithelial mucus gland.

In gastropods pedal glands mostly occur in the anterior part of the foot (propodium); in *Vermetus* there is in addition a posterior pedal gland (SALENSKY, 1887).

As a rule the pedal glands originate as an ectodermal invagination, either tubular or sac-like, which is situated at the anterior border of the foot or in the propodium. The posterior pedal gland of *Vermetus* arises in a similar manner from an invagination situated further backwards. The floor of the invagination thickens, and glandular tubules arise from it, sometimes forming paired lappets. The place of invagination as a rule remains as gland orifice.

In other cases, however, the formation of pedal glands from the mesenchyme of the foot has been described, e.g. in *Littorina* (DELSMAN, 1912), *Patella* (SMITH, 1935) and *Haliotis* (CROFTS, 1938). Since, however, in many cases mesenchyme formation at the expense of the pedal ectoderm at earlier stages has been observed (a.o. also in *Littorina*), it seems most likely that these glands are ectodermal in origin too. They have no true duct, but discharge between the epithelial cells of the sole of the foot, partly into a small pit in the anterior part of the foot (*Haliotis, Littorina*).

The secretion of the pedal glands in Gastropoda is probably mucous. In *Littorina* there are two kinds of gland cells, which probably have different secretions.

3. Shell

The early development of the shell has been described above, p. 146. As regards later stages, the following points may be added.

The thin pellicle, forming the first rudiment of the larval shell of the Lamellibranchiata, represents the *periostracum*. The remaining part of the shell is formed by the secretion of granular calcareous substance beneath the cuticular membrane, first in two symmetrical patches, which by further growth produce the shell valves. They grow towards the dorsal side, where they meet.

The shape of the larval shell valves as a rule differs from that in the adult shell. Initially the hinge line, along which the shell valves meet, is nearly straight. Then the valves begin to vault, and the umbo is formed; this is the *prodissoconch* stage. Still later the specific shapes of the shells appear, brought about by differential growth processes.

The median part of the original shell pellicle, situated between the valve rudiments, which does not calcify, forms the first part of the *hinge ligament*. In the glochidium larva of *Anodonta* this lies at first internally. Later it divides into an inner and outer layer; finally, only the outer ligament remains (HERBERS, 1913). In *Ostrea* an inner layer is added secondarily to the original ligament, and extends mainly in a ventral direction. The original dorsal part of the ligament degenerates, so that the pivotal axis is displaced ventrally between the valves (TRUEMAN, 1951).

The *hinge teeth* are formed by protrusions of the mantle. In *Nucula* (DREW, 1901) first a small knob of cartilage is formed near the middle of the hinge line. The teeth only appear at a much later stage. The first teeth to be formed appear just in front of the cartilage pit, somewhat later also behind. New teeth are added anteriorly and posteriorly as long as the shell grows.

In *Macoma* the first tooth appears at the anterior end of the hinge line on the left shell; it fits into a notch of the right shell. In front of this notch the first tooth of the right side is then formed, soon followed by a second tooth nearer the middle of the hinge line. In *Mytilus, Cultellus* and *Zirphaea*, hinge teeth in characteristic arrangement are already formed in the larval shell of the veliger; they disappear at metamorphosis, and are then replaced by the definitive hinge teeth (WERNER, 1939).

The molluscan shell grows by apposition, new shell substance being secreted by epithelial cells. At first this secretion takes place both on the inner side and at the margin, whereby the shell gets a lamellar and zonal structure. Later the main growth takes place in the peripheral parts of the mantle. In consequence of this, the shell often shows fine more or less parallel growth lines. By more rapid growth in certain regions, indicated by a greater distance between successive growth lines, the shape of the shell changes and approaches the adult shape.

In some Prosobranchia (e.g. *Fissurella, Haliotis*) at an early stage in the development of the adult shell a slit appears at the rim of the mantle, which leads to the formation of a similar slit in the edge of the shell. Afterwards the margins of the mantle slit approach each other, and the fissure in the shell is closed to a hole. In *Fissurella* during later growth this hole is relatively displaced towards the apex of the shell. In *Haliotis* the process is repeated periodically, so that a row of shell perforations is formed.

The adult shell is therefore for the most part a product of the mantle edge. The superficial sculpture of the shell may be due to irregularities of the mantle edge, or to local differences or periodic variations in the rate of lime secretion. In *Crepidula* the shell consists in young individuals of two layers only, the periostracum and the later *nacreous layer*. Soon after hatching, however, the middle, *prismatic layer* is formed by secretion at the mantle edge (MORITZ, 1939). In *Buliminus* the periostracum is secreted by the epithelial cells of the mantle furrow. Beneath this furrow there follows a zone with very tall narrow epithelial cells with basal nuclei, which produces the upper layer of the *ostracum*. The following cell rows gradually become lower; they secrete the deeper part of the ostracum. Finally the *hypostracum* is formed by the ordinary epithelium of mantle and visceral sac (BECK, 1912),

In various Lamellibranchiata the mantle breaks up distally into tentacle-like folds, usually three in number. During the process of shell formation these folds undulate back and forth in the region of the free margin of the shell. The elaboration of the organic matrix of the shell (conchin) is brought about by the activity of a layer of cuboidal cells occupying the outer surface of the middle fold of the mantle.* This substance gives a positive test for protein and reducing sugars (BEVE-LANDER and BENZER, 1948).

Often special glands are found at the mantle edge, which take part in shell formation. In *Malletia* and *Solemya* there are oval goblet cells, filled with strongly refringent granules, which probably represent specific lime-secreting gland cells (STEMPELL, 1900). The granules give a positive test for calcium phosphate (BEVELANDER and BENZER, 1948). In *Crepidula* alveolar invaginations occur at the inner side of the mantle edge; they are at first unicellular, but then enlarge to form compound alveolar glands, which open at the place of invagination at the shell periphery (MORITZ, 1939). In *Oncidium* it has been observed that the mantle edge secretes small highly refringent spherules, which coalesce to irregular platelets, uniting in their turn to the shell substance (JOYEUX LAFFUIE, 1882). BEVELANDER and BENZER (1948) showed that in *Pinna* the organic matrix of the shell is first secreted as a thin layer, which in later stages becomes arranged into prisms and striae. Granules of calcium phosphate from the gland cells are deposited upon this matrix, and undergo crystal growth. Finally the crystals, enclosed in a thin layer of organic matrix, assume a polyhedral shape. The final calcified product is composed of calcium carbonate (calcite).

Pigment in the shell is sometimes secreted by special pigment glands; in other cases it is formed by ordinary epithelium cells, however.

In the areas where muscles are attached to the shell the epithelium remains, but the epithelial cells often show a fibrillar striation in the direction of tension. Presumably these fibrillae extend continuously into the shell. Similar relationships are found at the attachment of the hinge ligament. It is probable that in these places, besides the extrusion of a fluid secretion, a direct transformation of apical cell parts into shell substance takes place.

The architectonics of the shell is not due to mere processes of crystallization, but is attributable to the structure and activity of the shell-forming cells. Periodic differences in rate of secretion cause a horizontal stratification. The prismatic structure of certain shell layers is due to

---

* According to E. KESSEL (*Zschr. Morph. Ökol. Tiere* **40**, 348, 1943), however, the middle fold does not take part in shell secretion, the periostracum being exclusively produced by the inner surface of the outer fold of the mantle.

local differences in secretion, whereby the mantle epithelium is sub-divided into a number of cell groups, each corresponding to a prism. When these complexes are shifted during development with respect to the formed parts of the shell, then the prisms are not perpendicular to the surface, but oblique or bent.

As regards the cytochemistry of shell gland and mantle fold, cf. above, p. 151.

The mineral substances for shell formation are for the greater part extracted from the medium. During shell formation the ash content of embryo and yolk of the cephalopods increases three times (RANZI, 1931b). For the uptake of these substances the integrity of the animal is not a necessary condition: an isolated visceral sac with the mantle of *Loligo* is able to absorb them from the perivitelline fluid. Likewise, in a mantle-shell preparation of *Crassostrea* typical shell substance is deposited, although at a slower rate than in the intact animal (HIRATA, 1953).

The physiology of shell secretion was studied by JODREY (1953) in a mantle-shell preparation of *Crassostrea*, by means of Ca^{45}. The mantle takes up calcium from the seawater and deposits it in the shell. The greater part of the calcium contained in the mantle is inert, however; only 2·4 per cent takes part in turnover, and is renewed every twenty-four minutes. The calcium turnover rate in the mantle edge is about twice as large as in the inner part of the mantle, but the turnover time of the renewing fraction is equal in the two cases. Since the amount of calcium renewed per unit of time equals the amount deposited in the shell, apparently the fraction undergoing rapid turnover is responsible for shell formation.

Shell secretion is not dependent on a normal morphogenesis of the shell gland; it may take place in abnormal cephalopod embryos, in which the shell gland has remained open and evaginated, and also in small isolated fragments of a shell gland (RANZI, 1928a, 1931a, 1931b).

In the morphogenesis of mantle and shell some enzymes, which reach a high concentration in the cells of the mantle fold, play an important part (cf. p. 151). If *Physa* embryos are kept from the early trochophore stage in a solution of KCN, which inhibits the stable M-nadi oxidase in the mantle fold, a specific action upon the system shell gland-shell becomes evident. Although the shell gland primordium is formed, it develops in an irregular way, and the shell is rudimentary or lacking altogether. The mantle does not develop; the visceral sac remains naked, but nevertheless shows a normal spiral coiling (MANCUSO, 1955c). Similar deviations were obtained in *Bithynia* by a treatment at early cleavage stages with NaN_3, which is a specific inhibitor of cytochrome oxidase (ATTARDO, 1955b).

When the eggs of *Limnaea* are treated at the uncleaved stage with beryllium salts, the most characteristic deviations are shell malformations due to disturbances in the morphogenesis of the shell gland

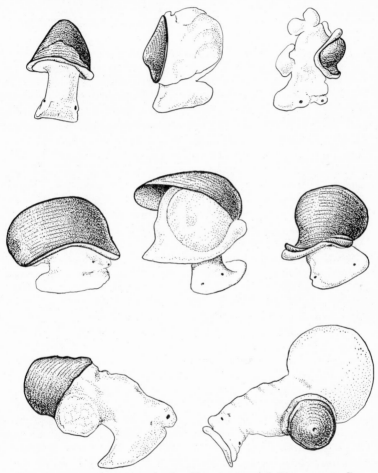

Fig. 59. Shell malformations after beryllium treatment in *Limnaea stagnalis*.

(RAVEN and SPRONK, 1952) (Fig. 59). The secretion of shell substance is not impeded. The effects were attributed to an inhibition of alkaline phosphatase in the shell gland by beryllium ions. However, later investigations have shown that in embryos from eggs treated with beryllium the intensity of the alkaline phosphatase reaction is not perceptibly diminished. Inactivation of the enzyme was only observed when the beryllium ions were present during the execution of the reaction (E. KLIPHUIS, unpublished observations). Therefore, the explanation of the beryllium effects on the egg remains uncertain for the present.

4. Mantle cavity and lung

The genesis of the mantle cavity has been described, p. 150.

The mantle cavity, once formed, may enlarge secondarily by in-growth into the body. For example, in *Littorina* the connection of the visceral sac with head and foot is reduced in this way to a narrow stalk, only traversed by the columellar muscle and the oesophagus (DELSMAN, 1912). Posteriorly, the mantle cavity may extend beneath the heart and kidney, so that these organs come to lie secondarily in the roof of the mantle cavity (e.g. *Patella*: SMITH, 1935; *Pomatias*: CREEK, 1951).

In the Lamellibranchiata the mantle folds may come together behind the foot. By local fusion of their edges in this region the dorsal mantle slit in *Anodonta* is delimited (HERBERS, 1913). Further ventrally the *funnels* are formed by foldings of the mantle edges.

This process has been extensively studied in *Cyclas* by WASSERLOOS (1911). First the mantle edges unite behind the foot to form the *inter-siphonal septum*, by the fusion of a small outgrowth on either side. The opening above this septum, the *cloacal funnel*, is narrowed by further union of the mantle edges. A second fusion further down delimits the *branchial funnel*. The margins of both siphons grow out into tubes. Later the two funnels grow together along their entire length.

The formation of the *lung* in the pulmonates was studied by MEISEN-HEIMER (1898) in *Limax* and by HEYDER (1909) in *Arion*. In both cases the lung primordium arises very early as an ectodermal invagination. In *Limax* this at first lies ventrally, but is then displaced to the right side in consequence of the rotation of the visceral sac. In *Arion* it appears immediately on the right side. The mantle cavity is formed slightly later, in *Arion* as a wide shallow groove situated in front of the lung primor-dium. By rolling-in of the mantle fold the original lung invagination is displaced into the depth; it now opens into the mantle cavity. The lung primordium penetrates deeper into the body, its epithelium at the same time becoming greatly flattened. The lung cavity enwraps the whole heart-kidney complex from the anterior and ventral side, with two lateral wings, which in *Arion* unite again behind the pericardium. In the wall of the cavity protruding folds appear, enclosing blood vessels; in this way the vascular reticulum of the lung is formed. In the edge of the mantle near the anus a slit occurs, which then closes to a hole, the *pneumostome*. As the margins of the pneumostome then grow together with the margins of the lung opening into the mantle cavity, the pneumostome ultimately leads directly into the lung.

The wall of the mantle cavity often bears cilia, either as isolated ciliary cells or small groups of such cells (e.g. *Acanthochiton*, Basommatophora), or as strips of ciliated epithelium near the gills or the anus (*Haliotis*, *Pomatias*). The edge of the mantle may also bear cilia (Basommatophora) and glands.

Often mucous glands are found in the mantle cavity. In *Acanthochiton* there are strips of columnar gland cells on both sides near the gills, which extend from the level of the mouth to the anus, and unite posteriorly near the anus into a broad field of gland cells. The secretion of these mucous cells is formed as a basophil substance, which swells after extrusion (HAMMARSTEN and RUNNSTRÖM, 1925). In Gastropoda *hypobranchial glands* are often formed in the roof of the mantle cavity, between the gill base and the rectum. In *Pomatias* they contain, beside mucous cells, a second kind of gland cell, perhaps serous cells (CREEK, 1951). Further the so-called *endostyle* of *Crepidula* may be mentioned here, which forms already at a very early stage, together with the gill rudiment, at the surface of the body, and is only secondarily overgrown by the mantle (MORITZ, 1939).

After lithium treatment of *Loligo* embryos the mantle is often reduced (RANZI, 1928a). There is no clear correlation between the abnormalities of the shell gland and the mantle. A very characteristic malformation occurs as a result of a strong hydropia of the sinus posterior. The mantle folds begin to grow out in the wrong direction, whereby the mantle turns inside out as an inverted umbrella. In such cases the shell gland, fin, Hoyle's organ, and the musculature may be differentiated in the normal way; the epithelium of the mantle is also cytologically normal. The visceral sac, though not now surrounded by the mantle, nevertheless shows a normal development. Apparently, therefore, the mantle does not influence the shape of the visceral sac. The same has been shown to hold in gastropods (*Physa*: MANCUSO, 1955c).

After cutting away portions of the mantle in cephalopod embryos no regeneration takes place. The isolated fragments pursue their development, and give rise to just those parts which they would have formed in normal development, without any signs of regulation occurring (RANZI, 1931a).

5. Gills

The first rudiments of the gills of Gastropoda sometimes appear at a very early stage, prior to the formation of the mantle cavity, on the surface of the body, and are only secondarily taken up in the mantle cavity (e.g. *Crepidula, Fulgur, Fasciolaria*). In most cases, however, they are formed from the first in the mantle cavity, either in its floor or its roof.

The mode of formation of the gills is somewhat different. For instance, in *Haliotis* at first a thickened epithelial ridge appears in the roof of the mantle cavity. After some time new ridges occur on either side of it, the rudiments of the *gill filaments*, whereas the first ridge forms the *rhachis* of the gill (CROFTS, 1938). In Pteropoda (FOL, 1875) and *Littorina* (DELSMAN, 1912) the gills are likewise formed by a process of folding. In *Fulgur* (CONKLIN, 1907) and *Crepidula* (MORITZ, 1939) the edge of the original thickening becomes scalloped. Each prominence later grows out to a small nipple, which then becomes finger-shaped and forms a gill filament; new lobes may later be added at one end. Finally, a row of knob-like projections, one behind the other, may directly grow out from the wall of the mantle cavity, and by further growth produce the gill filaments.

The early gill anlage is usually lined by powerful cilia. The gill filaments are afterwards penetrated by mesoderm cells, which form their axis. Later, supporting rods may differentiate in this mesodermal axis, e.g. in *Crepidula*.

In the Cephalopoda the gills originate as papillate elevations on either side of the anal region (Fig. 50), which are only secondarily overgrown by the mantle. On two opposite sides a longitudinal ridge appears, in which the gill vessels are formed, the afferent vessel in the lateral, and the efferent one in the medial ridge. The gill primordium has in the meantime flattened, and developed a pointed triangular shape, bordered by the two vascular ridges. The blade of the gill now begins to fold in a transverse direction. The edges of these folds, projecting alternately towards either side, are the rudiments of the gill filaments. Each of these filaments grows out again into a triangular plate, with afferent and efferent vessels along its sides. Now each filament undergoes a similar folding process as formerly the whole gill rudiment did, whereby gill filaments of the second order are formed. This process may repeat itself a third or even a fourth time, the gill structure each time becoming more complex. The afferent and efferent vessels connect secondarily with the main vessels of the body (NAEF, 1928).

In the Lamellibranchiata gill development exhibits various degrees of complication. The most simple condition is found in the Protobranchia (*Nucula, Yoldia*: DREW, 1899; 1901). Here the gills arise as thickenings of the posterior part of the mantle. They grow in an anterior direction, and develop a strong lining of cilia. A constriction occurs in the middle, and both halves grow out to lobes. The dorsal lobe elongates into a finger-like outgrowth. The ventral lobe broadens, and divides. In this way new lobes are formed successively by unequal growth of the ventral-most lobe. When four lobes are formed, prolongations at the base of the lobes grow out to the outer gill filaments, whereas the lobes themselves give rise to the inner filaments. Each filament develops into a flattened triangular plate. The chitinous supporting elements of the gill appear at an early stage, when the gill rudiment is bilobed. At first a thin sheet is formed just beneath the epithelium at the anterior margin of the gill, extending continuously from one lobe into the other. As new lobes are formed, it also extends into those. When the lobes grow out into filaments, the chitinous sheets become trough-shaped. Later their margins fuse, so that they become nearly tubular. The tubules of different filaments are united at their bases. When the outer filaments form at the base of the inner ones, this supporting structure also extends into the former.

The typical lamelliform gill of the other Lamellibranchiata develops in two fundamentally different ways. The first one is the 'papillary type', in which a row of papillae is formed on either side of the foot in an anteroposterior sequence. They grow out to gill filaments, which unite secondarily to the inner gill. The outer gill arises somewhat later from a similar row of papillae. This type is found in *Mytilus*, *Arca*, *Pecten*, *Dreissensia*, *Ostrea*, *Modiola*, *Anomia* and the Unionidae.

In the second type the gills are formed as a fold, arising from behind forwards on either side of the foot, and in which perforations appear secondarily. This occurs in *Teredo*, *Zirphaea*, *Cyclas*, *Calyculina* and *Pisidium*.

Gill formation according to the *papillary type* has been studied the most extensively by HERBERS (1913) in *Anodonta* (cf. also HARMS, 1909, and WASSERLOOS, 1911). The first rudiment of the gills consists in an epithelial thickening on the inner side of the mantle fold, laterally to the foot. This divides in an antero-posterior direction into papillae, covered with a dense lining of cilia. They grow out to gill filaments. At their ends knob-like thickenings occur. They fuse in a longitudinal direction into a narrow membrane, connecting all papillae with each other. These membranes of the left and right inner gill fuse with each other behind the foot, forming in this way the floor of the cloacal cavity. Now all filaments bend inwards and upwards, whereby the membrane is lifted on their tips. In this way the inner lamella of the inner gill is formed, which therefore is fenestrated from the beginning in the Unionidae. In *Dreissensia*, on the other hand, the inner lamella is at first continuous, and fenestration occurs secondarily, the membrane separating into filaments, except for its dorsal- and ventralmost edges, which remain uninterrupted (WASSERLOOS, 1911). Between the outer and inner lamella interlamellar bridges are formed in a ventrodorsal sequence. In *Dreissensia* this takes place in every second filament, the intermediate ones remaining free. Later in the Unionidae also interfilamentar bridges are formed between successive filaments. In the Filibranchia (*Mytilus, Pecten, Arca*), however, the filaments remain separated. The development of the outer gill, which appears much later, takes place in a similar manner; the tips of the filaments, though, bend upwards at a relatively much earlier stage, and that outwards, to form the outer lamella of the outer gill. Ultimately, they fuse by their tips with the inner side of the mantle.

Gill formation according to the *fold type* has been studied accurately by WASSERLOOS (1911) in *Cyclas*. The origin of the inner gill is here likewise due to an ectodermal proliferation, giving rise to a ridge on the ventral side of the mantle fold. It grows out to a fold, with a high columnar epithelium, and filled with mesenchyme. Beginning at its lower edge, indentations of the epithelium occur at regular distances on the outer side of the fold. Similar furrows appear on the inner side, and then perforation takes place, beginning some distance above the lower edge, and progressing upwards. In this way the gill fold is divided into filaments, which remain connected along its lower margin. Behind the foot the gill folds from either side come together, and unite first by interlacing crests of cilia, later by epithelial fusion. Ciliary cells differentiate among the margins of the gill slits. Within the filaments supporting rods are formed, secreted by mesenchyme cells; they are at first double, but then fuse. The marginal bridge, connecting the filaments along their ventral ends, extends medially towards the foot, and then grows upwards. The filaments of the outer lamella become connected along their inner sides with the inner lamella formed in this way. On the inner side of the latter furrows appear, corresponding to the perforations of the outer lamella, and finally break through. Now the gill perforations extend into the marginal bridge, so that the whole gill becomes divided into single segments. Later interfilamentar connections appear secondarily by fusion of adjacent filaments, at certain levels, progressing in anteroposterior direction. Since the supporting skeleton also develops in these bridges, a grid is formed in this way. The inner lamella does not extend towards the base of the outer lamella. As soon as it has reached about one third of the height of the outer lamella, its growth upwards stops, and the two lamellae of the inner gill now grow together in a ventral direction along their lower edges. The outer gill does not appear until the inner one possesses thirteen or fourteen filaments, and arises as a fold, beginning in the middle and extending both forwards and backwards. It grows dorsally towards the body wall, and fuses anteriorly with the visceral sac, posteriorly with the intersiphonal septum. Furrows appear on either side, and then it separates into filaments, except its dorsal edge. Later the filaments of the outer gill at their base extend somewhat over the inner gill; here over a small distance an inner and outer lamella are formed (this does not occur in *Pisidium*).

According to RANZI (1930, 1931a) there is in *Loligo* under experimental circumstances a correlation between the development of the gill and branchial heart of the same side. If in an isolated fragment of an embryo there is little blood, the gills remain small. It is concluded that the growth of the gills depends on blood pressure. Reduction of the branchial heart causes a diminution in blood pressure in the gill, which brings about its reduced growth. In the formation of the first gill rudiments the blood vessels apparently play no part.

6. Labial vela

The formation of the labial vela of Lamellibranchiata was studied by DREW (1901) in *Nucula*, by HARMS (1909) and HERBERS (1913) in the Unionidae, and by WASSERLOOS (1911) in *Cyclas*.

They arise from an area around the mouth, which is lined with cilia in *Nucula* and *Cyclas*. In *Dreissensia* (MEISENHEIMER, 1901) and *Ostrea* (COLE, 1938) this originates at least partly from the apical plate, which sinks in at metamorphosis when the velum is cast, and connects secondarily with the epidermis above the mouth. It divides by furrows on either side of the mouth into a dorsal and ventral part, forming the upper and lower lip. The upper lip grows out laterally and forms the outer labial vela. The lower lip somewhat later produces in a similar way the inner vela. These vela are densely lined with cilia, especially on their adjacent sides. In *Cyclas* a row of cilia runs from the velar field to the anterior end of the gills, where it is connected with a strip of ciliary epithelium on the marginal edge of the gill. Later a transverse folding of the adjacent surfaces of the velar lobes occurs. In *Nucula* the outer velum grows out into two *palp appendages*, each consisting of a pair of ridges with intervening furrow.

7. Nervous system

For the early development of the cerebral ganglia from the cephalic plates of the larva, cf. above, p. 145.

The development of the nervous system in the Polyplacophora has been studied most extensively by HAMMARSTEN and RUNNSTRÖM (1925) in *Acanthochiton*. The nervous system originates here from derivatives

P

of the rosette cells $1a^{11}$–$1d^{11}$, occupying an H-shaped area in the trochophore. From the arms of the H, cells are released which are arranged in two lateral groups. They differentiate into ganglionic masses, with peripherally located ganglion cells and a central neuropileme. They are connected by a commissure running beneath the apical organ.

According to KOWALEWSKY (1883a) the pedal and lateral nerve trunks in *Chiton* arise from local ectodermal thickenings along the entire length

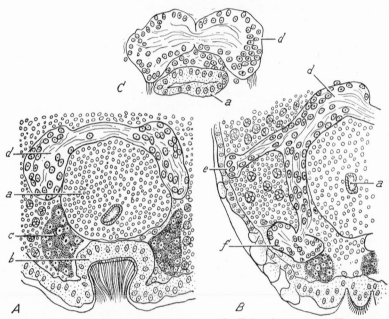

Fig. 60. Development of nervous system in *Epimenia verrucosa*. Transverse sections of (A) Early trochophore. (B) Slightly advanced trochophore. (C) Older larva. *a*, stomodaeum; *b*, prepedal cavity; *c*, pedal glands; *d*, cerebral ganglion; *e*, lateral nerve cord; *f*, pedal nerve cord. After BABA, 1938.

of the body, which split off from the outer ectoderm. According to HAMMARSTEN and RUNNSTRÖM, however, they originate from the cerebral region; no other part of the ectoderm produces nerve cells. Isolated cells from the cerebral ganglion masses migrate backwards along the inner side of the ectoderm, dividing mitotically on the way. First the rudiments of the lateral trunks grow out, then the pedal trunks are formed as buds directed inwards and backwards from the anterior ends of the lateral trunks. The pedal trunks are connected by anterior and posterior commissures, to which later several smaller ones are added.

The lateral trunks have at their posterior end a commissure above the gut. In front of the anterior pedal commissure a subcerebral commissure is formed. Two strands originating from the latter and growing dorsad along the lateral walls of the pharynx give rise to the buccal commissure. The cells forming the buccal ganglia have probably also migrated from the cerebral ganglia; they show no connection with the pharynx epithelium. Nerves supplying the gut grow backwards from the buccal ganglia. Finally a subradular commissure with paired ganglia is formed dorsoposteriorly to the subradular organ.

The development of the nervous system in Aplacophora, according to BABA (1938: *Epimenia*) shows considerable resemblance to that in *Acanthochiton*. The cerebral ganglia arise by a paired proliferation in the pretrochal region. The cells migrate towards the stomodaeum, and give rise to a pair of cerebral ganglia connected by a fairly long commissure (Fig. 60a). Two well-marked ganglia split off on either side from the cerebral ganglion, one situated laterally and the other ventrally (Fig. 60b). They extend backwards, and turn into four longitudinal nerve cords connected by interpedal commissures and latero-pedal connectives.

In the Lamellibranchiata the cerebral, pedal and visceroparietal ganglia arise from independent paired ectodermal thickenings, which split off from the epithelium, and then connect by commissures and connectives. The cerebral ganglia originate from the cephalic plates, either by invagination (*Yoldia*, *Dreissensia*) or delamination (*Nucula*, *Sphaerium*, Unionidae). The ectoderm thickens, becomes pluristratified by repeated division, and then its deeper parts split off as paired cell groups, which form the cerebral ganglia. They are connected in front of the stomodaeum by the cerebral commissure. This commissure sometimes arises very precociously, even before the cerebral ganglia have become free from the ectoderm, in which case the intervening ectoderm probably contributes to its formation (e.g. *Dreissensia*: MEISENHEIMER, 1901; Unionidae: HARMS, 1909). In these cases the commissure is already fibrous when the cerebral ganglia are set free.

In most adult Lamellibranchiata there are no separate pleural ganglia, but these are united with the cerebral ganglia into common cerebropleural ganglia. As a rule, however, during development separate pleural ganglia are formed, by ectodermal proliferation of the lateral body wall behind the cerebral ganglia; they fuse with the cerebral ganglia at an early stage, however (e.g. Unionidae, *Sphaerium*, *Dreissensia*, *Modiolaria*, *Xylotria*, *Teredo*). In the Protobranchia they remain separated even in the adult.

The pedal ganglia arise from ectodermal thickenings on the lateral sides of the foot rudiment (in *Teredo* these thickenings are present even before the delimitation of the foot). The pedal ganglia, formed by splitting-off of cells from these thickenings, approach each other, and connect by the formation of the pedal commissure. In *Teredo* they are said to be connected from the outset.

The visceral ganglia develop from paired ectodermal thickenings, situated closely behind the rudiments of the pedal ganglia at the level of the posterior end of the foot. By the appearance of the posterior pedal furrow they are separated from the pedal ganglia, and come to lie in the posterior part of the body, ventrally to the gut and posterior adductor. The ganglia of the two sides connect at an early stage by a commissure.

The connectives between the ganglia lie at first immediately beneath the ectoderm, later more deeply. Presumably they develop by out-growth of nerve fibres from the ganglia. In *Dreissensia* the cerebro-visceral connective, according to MEISENHEIMER (1901), arises partly by direct splitting-off from the ectoderm.

In Scaphopoda the cerebral ganglia originate by paired invaginations from the cephalic plates of the trochophore, and the pedal ganglia by ectodermal proliferation from the sides of the foot (KOWALEWSKY, 1883b).

The ganglia of Gastropoda arise by proliferation and later delamination from the ectoderm. In the formation of the cerebral ganglia invagination sometimes takes place. As a rule there are six kinds of independent primordia, viz. the cerebral, pedal, pleural, parietal, visceral and buccal ganglia. The anlage of the visceral ganglion is mostly unpaired, the other primordia are paired. The commissures and connectives are formed by secondary outgrowth from the ganglia. Both the formation of the ganglia and of the commissures and connectives as a rule progresses craniocaudally.

The cerebral ganglia originate from the cephalic plates, either by proliferation and delamination or by invagination (e.g. *Patella, Cavolinia, Vermetus*). In the pulmonates the main body of the ganglia may arise by proliferation. When it has already become partly separated from the ectoderm, a local invagination of the ectoderm occurs at the base of the tentacle, which becomes a tubular ingrowth, the *cerebral tube* (in *Helix Waltoni* there are two such tubes on either side). The tips of these become closely applied to the cerebral ganglia, and are constricted off, giving the lobus accessorius of the ganglion. The cerebral ganglia are separated at first, but later connect through the commissura cerebralis, elongated cells from the two ganglia growing towards each other and uniting in the middle. In *Crepidula* the cerebral commissure is connected from the outset with the apical sense organ (CONKLIN, 1897). The cerebral ganglia then shift in a ventrocaudal direction, and come to lie with the commissure astride the stomodaeum (Pl. IX; Pl. XI, D). An anterior prolongation remains as the optic nerve. From dorsal outgrowths of the cerebral ganglia separate tentacular ganglia may arise (e.g. *Pomatias*: CREEK, 1951). Finally a connection with the statocyst arises.

The pedal ganglia arise from paired cell proliferations laterally or ventrally on the foot. At first the two ganglia are some distance apart, but later they approach each other and connect by means of a commissure. In *Haliotis* the pedal ganglia later grow out forwards and backwards to long trunks (CROFTS, 1938). In their neighbourhood, by separate local proliferations of the epithelium of the sole of the foot, small propodial (*Crepidula*: MORITZ, 1939) or infra- and postpedal ganglia (*Littorina*: DELSMAN, 1912) may arise, which connect secondarily with the pedal ganglion of the same side by short connectives.

The pleural ganglia arise from two lateral cell proliferations, mostly of small size, immediately behind the velum and near the pleural groove. According to DELSMAN (1912), in *Littorina* the pleural ganglia have no separate primordium, but are derived from posterior prolongations of the cerebral ganglia; presumably, however, the pleural ganglion primordia have been overlooked. In primitive Prosobranchia, like *Patella* and *Haliotis*, the pleural ganglia soon after their formation are closely connected with the pedal ganglia (SMITH, 1935; CROFTS, 1938). In higher gastropods, however, their connection with the cerebral ganglia becomes increasingly close.

The parietal ganglia are formed behind the pleural ganglia, likewise from or immediately above the pleural groove between foot and visceral sac. In those forms in which they arise early, so that torsion has not yet taken place, they lie at first symmetrically on the left and right (e.g. *Paludina, Bithynia*: VON ERLANGER, 1891, 1892). In *Pomatias* the ganglia do not appear, however, until torsion has progressed to an angle of about 90°. They arise from the floor of the mantle cavity, which is situated on the right side of the body. The morphological right parietal ganglion now lies above (supraoesophageal ganglion), the morphological left one (infraoesophageal ganglion) immediately ventral to it (CREEK, 1951). In *Littorina* the ganglia only arise from the floor of the mantle cavity after torsion has been completed; the relations of left and right are now reversed, the supraoesophageal ganglion lying on the left, the infraoesophageal on the right (DELSMAN, 1912).

Similar relationships hold for the visceral ganglion. This arises from an unpaired ectodermal thickening in the floor at the posterior end of the mantle cavity, either ventrally prior to torsion (*Paludina, Bithynia*), on the right side of the body during torsion (*Pomatias*), or dorsally after torsion (*Patella, Littorina*). Later it may come to lie in the roof of the mantle cavity in front of the heart (*Littorina*).

The buccal ganglia are formed by delamination from the wall of the stomodaeum, notably from the region of the suboesophageal clefts in the angle between radular sac and oesophagus. Only in *Haliotis* are they said to originate from prolongations of the cerebral ganglia, which recalls the relationships in Polyplacophora (CROFTS, 1938). They are soon united by a commissure, and connect with the cerebral ganglia by a connective.

Besides these ganglia, special ganglia may be formed in other places, e.g. an olfactory ganglion in *Limax* in the margin of the lung (MEISENHEIMER, 1898).

Once the ganglia have been formed, they connect by commissures and connectives. In the formation of the commissures as a rule cellular contact occurs at first, the ganglia either approaching each other until they touch, or becoming united by a strand of migrated cells. According to SMITH (1935) and MORITZ (1939) these cell strands in *Patella* and *Crepidula* arise by delamination from the ectodermal epithelium between the ganglion rudiments. Later the commissures become fibrous by the ingrowth of fibres from the ganglia. In *Haliotis* the cerebral ganglia connect, not only by the cerebral commissure, but also by a ventrally situated labial commissure (CROFTS, 1938). Of the connectives, the cerebropedal connective as a rule is the first to appear, sometimes even before the pedal ganglia are clearly delimited (e.g. *Crepidula*: CONKLIN, 1897). This connective is often entirely lined with ganglion cells. As a rule the other connectives are formed by the free outgrowth of a bundle of nerve fibres from the ganglia. In *Crepidula*, however, according to MORITZ this is preceded by cell strands split off from the overlying ectoderm; the same is described for the pleurovisceral connective of *Haliotis* by CROFTS. In the Pulmonata the connectives subsequently shorten considerably, so that all ganglia are drawn closely together around the oesophagus.

Chiastoneury in Prosobranchia is connected with torsion. This is most clearly shown in those forms, where the ganglia and connectives develop early, before torsion begins. In *Paludina* and *Bithynia* (VON ERLANGER, 1891, 1892) the parietal ganglia are lying symmetrically at first. During rotation the right ganglion shifts dorsally and to the left, and becomes the supraoesophageal ganglion, whereas the left parietal ganglion is displaced via the ventral side to the right, and comes to lie, as the infraoesophageal ganglion, first below, then to the right of the supraoesophageal ganglion. In *Fulgur* likewise all ganglion primordia are present before torsion begins; the occurrence of chiastoneury can be followed with diagrammatic clearness in this form (CONKLIN, 1907). On the other hand, there are cases in which the parietal and visceral ganglia are formed only after torsion, as in *Acmaea, Haliotis, Trochus* and *Littorina*. Here the supra- and infraoesophageal ganglion are situated from the beginning in their definitive places, and connect at once with the pleural ganglia of the contralateral side. For instance, in *Haliotis* a pleurovisceral connective grows out from the right pleural ganglion towards the left in the roof of the mantle cavity, where the supraoesophageal ganglion is formed near the definitive left gill. The left pleurovisceral connective, on the contrary, grows ventrally to the right, in front of the columellar muscle, beneath the oesophagus, towards the right side of the mantle cavity. Here the infraoesophageal ganglion is formed late, simultaneously with the definitive right gill, from the epithelium of the right part of the mantle cavity. Both pleurovisceral connectives continue beyond the parietal ganglia, beneath the floor of the mantle cavity, and unite to the visceral part of the loop (CROFTS, 1938).

In the Cephalopoda the ganglia likewise originate from ectodermal thickenings by proliferation and delamination. The cerebral ganglia arise from the ectoderm of the cephalic lobes, which becomes many-layered by proliferation and then splits off a two to three layers thick cell mass from its deeper part in front of the eye anlage. By proliferation of the ectoderm behind the eye, cells are added secondarily to this mass (*Loligo*: FAUSSEK, 1901). The cerebral ganglia shift forwards, and connect above the stomodaeum by a cerebral commissure. The lower part of each cerebral ganglion becomes constricted off as optic ganglion. Cells are added to this ganglion from a sac-like solid ingrowth of the posterior wall of the eye-stalk, which is considered homologous to the cerebral tubes in pulmonates by FAUSSEK. The optic ganglia shift beneath the eye vesicles and connect with them.

The pedal ganglia arise by delamination from paired ectodermal thickenings situated behind the eye and in front of the statocyst; the visceral ganglia from similar thickenings behind the statocyst. The pedal and visceral ganglia approach one another, and with the disappearance of the inner yolk sac shift towards the foregut, where they fuse with each other to form the suboesophageal ganglion, which is connected by a broad posterior and a narrow anterior connective with the cerebral ganglion. The anterior part of the suboesophageal ganglion, where the narrow connective ends, differentiates into the brachial ganglion at an early stage. In later stages the visceral nerves, the nervus posterior infundibuli and the nervus pallialis grow out from the visceral ganglion.

In all molluscs at an early stage differentiation takes place in the ganglia into a central fibre mass (neuropileme) and a peripheral zone of ganglion cells (Fig. 60c; Pl. IX). The neuropileme continues into the commissures and connectives. The ganglion cells have a vesicular clear nucleus and a lightly staining cytoplasm. The nerves to peripheral organs (eyes, tentacles, statocysts, mantle and visceral sac) arise by outgrowth from the ganglia.

According to RANZI's (1931b) experiments parts of ganglia of cephalopods separated by dissection may differentiate in a normal way. In considerably deformed ganglia likewise a normal differentiation of nerve fibres occurs. In an embryo of *Limnaea* showing a longitudinal splitting of the foot, with a pedal ganglion in each half, and the pedal commissure lacking, normal differentiation of the pedal ganglia had nevertheless taken place (RAVEN and BEENAKKERS, 1955). In other cases a dislocation of the cerebral ganglia had taken place in consequence of an asymmetric eversion of the stomodaeum. The cerebral ganglion on one side was situated at a considerable distance from the pedal ganglion, and was not connected with it; yet both the cerebral and the pedal ganglion were well differentiated (RAVEN, DE ROON and STADHOUDERS, 1955). It is remarkable that in such cases the pleural extremity of the visceral loop on the abnormal side is not connected with the cerebral ganglion, but with the pedal ganglion. This recalls the relationships in primitive Prosobranchia (cf. above, p. 217).

On the other hand, according to RANZI (1928a, 1928b) there is in cephalopods an obvious dependence of the optic ganglion on the eye. If the eye is reduced, the optic ganglion is reduced too. If the eye is lacking, there is no optic ganglion either. Cases with reduced ganglion and normal eye do occur, but the reverse has never been met with. However, if the eye is removed at the time when fibre formation is beginning in the ganglion, differentiation in the latter proceeds normally.

The statocyst of cephalopods seems to influence the pedal ganglion in a similar way. When the statocyst is lacking on one side, the corresponding part of the chiasma in the pedal ganglion is not differentiated.

8. Eyes

Three kinds of eyes occur in molluscs:

(1) Cephalic eyes in Gastropoda and Cephalopoda.
(2) Posttrochal larval eyes in Polyplacophora and Lamellibranchiata.
(3) Accessory eyes situated in various places.

The *cephalic eyes* of gastropods arise from the cephalic plates (cf. above, p. 145), and that from their dorsolateral parts. As a rule a small invagination occurs, which constricts off from the surface as a small vesicle with one-layered wall (Fig. 61). In some cases, though, the eye rudiment seems to appear as a solid cell plug, arising by delamination from the deeper layers of the ectoderm, in which only afterwards a lumen occurs (e.g. *Vermetus*: SALENSKY, 1887; *Littorina*: DELSMAN, 1912).

Soon differentiation begins in the eye vesicle. Its inner wall thickens by elongation of cells, and becomes the retina. Pigment appears in its

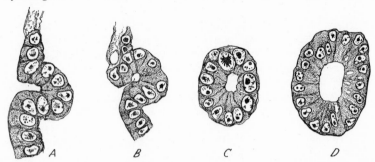

Fig. 61. Eye development in *Limnaea stagnalis*. (A, B) invagination; (C, D) growth and beginning differentiation of eye vesicle.

cells, first in the apical cell parts, then also along the cell walls. Pigment formation begins in the middle, and progresses towards the periphery; it does not extend into the outer wall, however (Pl. IX, XI). In *Patella* (SMITH, 1935) and *Haliotis* (CROFTS, 1938) pigment formation in the cells of the eye anlage begins even before invagination takes place. The outer wall of the eye vesicle, where the cells possess a clear cytoplasm and basal nuclei, becomes the inner part of the cornea. The overlying ectoderm also remains transparent, and forms the outer layer of the cornea. Between the two layers often a delicate layer of connective tissue cells occurs.

In the cavity of the eye vesicle a lens and vitreous body are formed, probably by the extrusion of cuticular substances by the cells lining the cavity (Pl. IX, XI). The lens is a spherical body. In *Limax* a number of small droplets are first secreted; these coalesce into the lens (MEISEN-HEIMER, 1898). The lens grows by the deposition of layers upon its surface, so that it later exhibits a concentric striation. In the vitreous body delicate fibrils run from the retina to the lens (Pl. XI, D).

The eyes are innervated by a nerve from the cerebral ganglion. Sometimes this forms a separate ganglion opticum against the inner side of the eye (*Limax*). In the Stylommatophora the eyes are carried upwards with the growth of the tentacles.

In some cases the eyes remain in the shape of open grooves (*Patella*) or cups (*Haliotis*, *Trochus*) in connection with the surface. In the latter case the mouth of the cup is filled by the lens, which protrudes partly outside.

The eyes of the cephalopods commence as oval plates of highly columnar ectoderm. An annular fold of the ectoderm appears, which partly overgrows this plate, so that a cup is formed with thick floor and thin roof, connected by a narrow opening with the outer world. In *Nautilus* the eyes remain at this stage. In the dibranchiate Cephalopoda, however, the eye vesicle closes, and is constricted off from the ectoderm. Mesodermal cells intrude between the eye vesicle and the overlying ectoderm.

The inner wall of the eye cup gives rise to the retina. This consists initially of a single-layered highly columnar epithelium. Rodlets are formed at the free end of the cells. On their basal side the cells are lined by a membrana limitans externa. According to FAUSSEK (1901) in *Loligo* part of the nuclei secondarily pass through the membrane, and form at its external side a layer of visual cells. Pigment first appears on the surface of the rodlets; afterwards it is especially found between the rodlets and the underlying nuclei. The pigment is yellowish at first, but then changes via orange and red into black.

The outer wall of the eye vesicle and the overlying ectoderm form the lens and the surrounding ciliary body. According to FAUSSEK (1901) the central part of the outer eye vesicle wall in *Loligo* consists at first of large cells with big nuclei. They are secondarily pushed aside towards the periphery, and are replaced by smaller cells from neighbouring regions. On the inner side of the outer wall of the eye vesicle a conical prominence of cuticular substance appears. This enlarges by the deposition of concentric layers, and gives rise to the inner segment of the lens. The smaller outer segment forms somewhat later in a similar way from the overlying ectoderm. At first mesodermal cells are found between the two segments, but later they disappear. The large cells displaced towards the periphery develop into the ciliary body; its musculature is probably derived from the mesoderm.

Meanwhile an annular fold bordering an ectodermal pit has arisen upon the eye. Mesodermal elements penetrate between its two layers. The anterior and outer part of this fold produces the iris; its inner surface is heavily pigmented.

Once more an annular fold is formed. This time it arises from the body surface surrounding the eye; its various parts have a very different origin, and have only secondarily come together (NAEF, 1928). This so-called primary lid fold remains open in the middle in the Oigopsida, but it closes entirely or nearly entirely in Myopsida, in this way forming the cornea; the enclosed cavity is the anterior eye chamber. By a final folding process the eyelids are formed.

In the Octopoda, the cornea forms in a slightly different way, from secondary folds arising on the inner side of the eyelids (SACARRAO, 1954b).

The *larval eyes* of the Polyplacophora differ in many respects from the cephalic eyes of Gastropoda and Cephalopoda, with which they are certainly not homologous. They are situated in the posttrochal region, close behind the velum at the level of the lateral nerve trunks. At early stages each ocellus consists of a single cell, embedded in the skin epithelium, and surrounded by pigment. According to KOWALEWSKY (1883a) they later come to lie beneath the skin in *Chiton*, and the overlying epidermis cells, which are narrower and more elongated than elsewhere, form a kind of cornea. HEATH (1904) found, however, that they remain in the epithelial layer in *Ischnochiton*, *Trachydermon*, *Nuttalina*, *Katharina* and *Tonicella*, though they may sink in a little; no lens or cornea is formed here. These larval eyes remain in existence for a considerable time after metamorphosis.

The larval eyes, which have been described by PELSENEER (1900) in *Mytilus*, *Modiolaria*, *Lithodomus* and *Avicula*, are probably homologous with those of the Polyplacophora. In the larvae they are situated in the posttrochal region. They persist in adults, and are then situated at the base of the first inner gill filament, immediately above the cerebral ganglion. They are cup-shaped with pigmented epithelial cells, and a cavity filled by a lens, which is connected with the cuticle of the surrounding epidermis.

As regards *accessory visual organs*, which may occur in various regions, in the first place the eyes at the mantle edge of Lamellibranchiata may be mentioned. They belong to various types. Partly they are compound eyes, derived from thickenings of the mantle epithelium. Their cells differentiate partly into sense cells, which develop a crystalline cone and a cornea-like peripheral part. In between pigment and supporting cells develop. The sense cells connect with nerve fibres.

In addition, eyes of a different structure occur, of which the development is mostly unknown. The highest degree of differentiation is exhibited by the mantle eyes in *Pecten* and the related genera *Spondylus*, *Chlamys* and *Amussium* (DAKIN, 1928). In *Pecten* eyes are continually formed along the mantle edge as the animal grows. They arise at the base of a tentacle as an ingrowing bud or invagination, which develops to a vesicle. The retina differentiates from the anterior wall of the vesicle, the tapetum and argentea from the posterior wall. The lens originates from connective tissue cells (BUTCHER, 1929).

Further we may mention here the accessory eyes of *Oncidium*, which are formed on the dorsal tubercules of the mantle. According to LABBÉ (1933) they are derived from cells emigrated from the epidermis ('opto-blasts'). These cells arise by mitotic division of epidermal cells in in-vaginations or in the ducts of unicellular tegumental glands. They form clusters of cells, from which one or more eyes may develop. The lens cells secrete silica, so that these eyes have a glass lens. Eye formation continues in the adult.

In *Limnaea* unilateral eye reductions and eye reduplications occur after various interventions (lithium treatment, heat shock, centrifuga-tion) (RAVEN, 1942; RAVEN, DE ROON and STADHOUDERS, 1955; RAVEN and BEENAKKERS, 1955). Eye reductions after lithium treatment are mainly localized on the left side, after heat shock treatment on the right. Apparently, eye development is easily disturbed by abnormal circum-stances. Unilateral eye reductions after centrifugation are often accom-panied by reduction of the tentacle and cerebral ganglion of the same side, but the frequency of reduction diminishes in the sequence eye> tentacle>cerebral ganglion. From this result it was concluded that the eye probably corresponds to the highest gradient level within the cephalic plate.

In the cephalopods histogenesis of the eye proves to be independent of organogenesis; in abnormal embryos pigment and sense cells may develop in eyes, which have remained at an open plate stage (RANZI, 1931b). An eye fragment of sufficient size may regulate to a closed vesicle. A lens also develops in greatly deformed eyes; if the eye has remained open it develops along the margin of the opening. In cyclopic eyes showing a partial duplicity of the retina there is only one lens, hence some regulation takes place. If an eye is cut in two fragments, each regulating to a vesicle, only one of the two develops a lens.

The size of the cephalopod eye is greatly dependent on the environ-ment. If the amount of blood has been diminished, or blood circulation is disturbed, the volume of the eye is reduced and its wall often folded. The same occurs in isolated eyes, and after premature hatching from the capsule. It is concluded that the walls of the eye are distended by the pressure of the ocular liquor, which is in active exchange with the blood and the perivitelline fluid (RANZI, 1931a).

A remarkable phenomenon was found by NAEF (1928) in *Sepia*. If embryos are transferred to seawater prematurely, the primary lid fold remains open and behaves as an eyelid; it contracts upon stimulation, as occurs normally e.g. in *Spirula*.

The mantle eyes of *Pecten* regenerate after removal. The nervous system influences the rate of regeneration, but removal of the visceral ganglion or the pallial nerves does not prevent regeneration. Eyes in various stages of development can be grafted on the edge of the gonad, after which their development continues. A nerve grows out in the direction of the visceral ganglion (BUTCHER, 1929).

9. Statocysts

The statocysts originate on the sides of the foot primordium, near the boundary between foot and body; in the Lamellibranchiata and Scaphopoda this corresponds to the boundary between foot and mantle fold, in the depth of the invaginating mantle cavity.

As a rule statocysts arise as ectodermal invaginations, which close to vesicles and then constrict off from the ectoderm. In *Littorina* (DELSMAN, 1912), the Basommatophora (RABL, 1879; FOL, 1880; WIERZEJSKI, 1905; RAVEN, 1952) and *Limax* (MEISENHEIMER, 1898), there is no invagination, but a delamination of a solid cell cluster from the ectoderm, in which a lumen appears only secondarily.

In the Cephalopoda the mouth of the invagination does not close immediately, but is drawn out into a tubular channel, which is called KÖLLIKER's *duct*. This may be compared with the endolymphatic duct in vertebrates. Later it is constricted off from the surface.

The cavity of the statocyst is very narrow at first; the cells lining it are columnar or cubical. Soon the cavity widens, however, and the cells of the wall flatten. Fine sensory hairs or cilia appear on their surface. In the cephalopods, the duct especially is strongly ciliated; in the opposite wall an epithelial thickening appears, the *crista acustica*. Here the cells are elongated, and bear a lining of delicate sensory hairs.

At an early stage a large spherical *statolith* is formed, from substances secreted by the cells. As it does not entirely dissolve in acids, it apparently has an organic matrix. In the Pteropoda it is formed, according to FOL (1875), in the thickened anterior part of the wall, and comes to lie in the lumen only secondarily. In Basommatophora it forms against the outer or anterior wall of the statocyst (FOL, 1880), in Cephalopoda on the crista acustica. At first it is immobile, being connected with the wall; in *Anodonta* even by a little stalk (HERBERS, 1913). When it has reached the centre of the vesicle, however, it becomes entirely free, and begins to vibrate, set in motion by cilia. It does not fill the whole cavity. The statolith increases in size, concentric growth zones being deposited on its surface. Later a number of small statoliths are often formed around the big central one, entirely surrounding the latter, e.g. in *Haliotis*, Pteropoda, Basommatophora, *Oncidium*.

In the Lamellibranchiata and the Gastropoda the statocysts lie close to the pedal ganglia or the cerebropedal connectives; they are however innervated from the cerebral ganglia. In the Cephalopoda they gradually move beneath the funnel, and finally come to lie in cavities of the head cartilage. They thus come closely together, and flatten against each other.

In *Nucula delphinodonta* the statocysts are later connected with the surface, at first by a solid strand, which then becomes a channel opening on the side of the foot (DREW, 1901).

The statocysts of *Limnaea* at an early stage exhibit a positive alkaline phosphatase reaction; the statolith remains unstained, however (MINGANTI, 1950).

RANZI (1928a) often obtained malformations of the statocyst in *Loligo* embryos after lithium treatment. Sometimes KÖLLIKER's duct remained open; in other instances the whole statocyst even remained open on the surface. In such cases the presumptive epithelium of KÖLLIKER's duct showed normal differentiation; apparently histogenesis is independent of organogenesis also in this case.

The differentiation of the statocyst in *Limnaea* proved to be independent of the presence of a normal cerebropedal connective on the same side (RAVEN, DE ROON and STADHOUDERS, 1955).

Like the eye, the statocyst of cephalopods is dependent, as regards its normal shape, on the pressure of the internal fluid, which is in active exchange with the blood. If the amount of blood is diminished after experimental interventions, the statocyst remains small, and its walls are folded and thickened (RANZI, 1931a).

10. Olfactory organs

In some molluscs organs have been described to which an olfactory function has been attributed.

In Basommatophora there is, according to FOL (1880), in older larvae a groove in front of the mantle edge. It becomes funnel-shaped, but then shows no further increase in size.

In the Cephalopoda at a rather late stage an epithelial thickening is formed behind the eye. Later it develops to a shallow groove with thickened floor and thin roof, connected through a wide opening with the outer world. Some of the cells develop to spindle-shaped sensory cells, provided with a stiff sensory sensilla. The other cells bear cilia in *Sepia* and *Loligo*. Later the organ deepens and becomes saccular.

The sense organs near the gills, probably serving for testing the water passing the gills, the so-called *osphradia*, also belong to this category.

In *Acanthochiton* there are, according to HAMMARSTEN and RUNNSTRÖM (1925), strips of sensory epithelium on the external side of the gills and the adjoining roof of the mantle cavity. They are innervated by a special ganglion, split off from the lateral nerve trunk, lying close behind the nephric duct. There is also an arc of sensory epithelium behind the anus, in direct connection with the posterior part of the lateral nerve trunk.

In *Anodonta* (HERBERS, 1913) there are ridges of sensory epithelium on the inner side of the outer lamella of the inner gill, along its dorsal margin. Later they are found on the partition-wall between inner and outer gill duct. They are continued on the ventral wall of the visceral sac, where they connect with the abdominal sense organ (cf. below).

The osphradium of gastropods originates as an ectodermal thickening of the wall of the mantle cavity, which grows into a fold, more or less parallel to the gill rudiment. Furrows may be formed in this fold (*Paludina, Pomatias*), or hillocks may appear on its surface (*Crepidula*). In the furrows the epithelium is lined with cilia, in the intervening areas there is a sensory epithelium. The organ is innervated by a nerve from the supraoesophageal ganglion.

11. Integumental sense organs

In the first place, the *aesthetes* of Polyplacophora belong to this category. According to HAMMARSTEN and RUNNSTRÖM (1925), the calcareous plates of *Acanthochiton* are pierced from the beginning by aesthetes, which initially are rooted diffusely in the underlying epithelium. Presumably part of the original aesthetes are lost with the formation of the articulamenta, so that they later only take rise from the areas near the intersegmenta.

HERBERS (1913) described a system of ectodermal sensory ridges in *Anodonta*. The *abdominal sense organ* forms a paired ectodermal thickening in front of the anus, innervated from the visceral ganglion. It is connected with the osphradium, and is continuous anteriorly with the *lateral sense organ*, forming on either side of the foot paired ridges, which end in front with a pronounced swelling between the nephric and genital pores. Moreover, there are *oral sensory ridges* between the basis of the labial vela and the mantle on the one side, the foot on the other; the outer one bears a swelling, the *adoral sense organ*, innervated from the cerebral ganglion.

CREEK (1951) described in *Pomatias* a strip of nervous tissue immediately beneath the epithelium of the anterior edge of the mantle, connected through the pallial nerves with the pleural ganglia. It contains sense cells with stiff prolongations extending above the surface, and is probably tactile in function.

Finally in Stylommatophora during a certain embryonic period sense buds are found in the skin. They were first described by P. and F. SARASIN in *Helix Waltoni*, later by MEISENHEIMER (1898) in *Limax*. They are dispersed over the body, especially the foot and the cephalic plates, but also e.g. on the mantle edge. They have a little pit on the surface, at the bottom of which there is a central pear-shaped cell, surrounded by a number of flattened cells with disk-shaped nuclei. Sensory rodlets projecting into the pit are probably in part connected with the peripheral cells too. Later these buds are said to sink in completely and join the ganglia.

12. Tentacles

The tentacular apparatus of scaphopods originates from a knob behind the mouth, which elongates and becomes trilobate.

The tentacles of gastropods arise from the cephalic plates, part of which bulge out. The epithelium is highly columnar (Pl. IX); the interior is filled by mesodermal cells, later forming a network of muscle fibres, between which clusters of vesicular supporting cells may appear. In *Limax* the lateral part of the cephalic plate produces the first tentacle, after which the second and third tentacle arise from more medially situated parts, at first as a single outgrowth, which soon divides. The eye is carried upwards with the growth of the tentacle in Stylommatophora.

In *Haliotis* papillae are formed on the cephalic tentacles, the larger of which bear terminal tufts of cells with stiff sensillae. The number of papillae gradually increases, until the whole surface of the tentacle is covered by them. On the epipodial tentacles, arising during metamorphosis, similar sensory papillae are formed (CROFTS, 1938).

13. Foregut

For the early development of the stomodaeum, cf. above, p. 155.

The entrance to the stomodaeum generally becomes the mouth. In the cephalopods, however, the stomodaeum appears to elongate forwards secondarily by fusion of the margins of a furrow formed in front of the primitive mouth (RANZI, 1928a; 1931b).

The ciliary lining to the stomodaeum is as a rule lost at the end of the embryonic period. Instead a cuticule of chitinous substance on the surface of the cells of the buccal cavity is often already formed at an early stage. Near the mouth opening in Scaphopoda, Prosobranchia, Pulmonata and Cephalopoda, epithelial thickenings occur in one or more places by considerable elongation of the cells (Pl. XII, A). By rapid secretion of cuticular substance by the cells, and lateral fusion of the vertical bars of chitin produced in this way, the *jaws* are formed. In

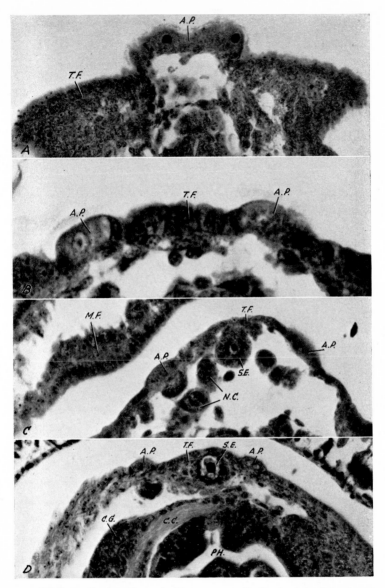

Plate XI. Reduplication of apex in *Limnaea stagnalis* after heat shock treatment.
(A) Transverse section of dorsal region of head. Normal pattern: the median
apical plate (*A.P.*) separates the two tentacle fields (*T.F.*). (B) Reduplication of
apical plate; between the two rows of apical plate cells (*A.P.*) a supernumerary
median tentacle field (*T.F.*). (C) Supernumerary eye (*S.E.*) in median tentacle
field, bordered by the two halves of the reduplicated apical plate. (D) Similar
section in somewhat older embryo. *C.C.*, cerebral commissure; *C.G.*, cerebral
ganglion; *M.F.*, mantle fold; *N.C.*, nuchal cells; *PH.*, pharynx.

[*Facing page* 228

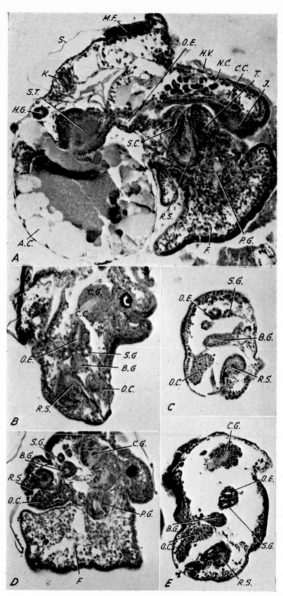

Plate XII. Normal and abnormal development of the stomodaeum in *Limnaea stagnalis*. (A) Mediosagittal section of normal embryo. (B-E) Transverse sections of embryos with everted stomodaeum. Mouth cavity and pharynx are lacking. The radular sac, a tubular oesophagus, and the salivary glands open directly on the surface. Normal differentiation of radula, odontophore cartilage, salivary glands, and buccal ganglion. *A.C.*, albumen cells; *B.G.*, buccal ganglion; *C.C.*, cerebral commissure; *C.G.*, cerebral ganglion; *F.*, foot; *H.G.*, hind gut; *H.V.*, head vesicle; *J.*, jaw; *K.*, kidney; *M.F.*, mantle fold; *N.C.*, nuchal cells; *O.C.*, odontophore cartilage; *O.E.*, oesophagus; *P.G.*, pedal ganglion; *R.S.*, radular sac; *S.*, shell; *S.C.*, suboesophageal cleft; *S.G.*, salivary gland; *S.T.*, stomach; *T.*, tongue.

Limnaea this region exhibits a distinct positive alkaline phosphatase reaction (MINGANTI, 1950).

In Polyplacophora a small backwardly directed pouch arises from the floor of the stomodaeum in front of the radular sac; it is the rudiment of the *subradular organ*. A papilla lined with cilia forms at its bottom.

The stomodaeum is surrounded by mesodermal cells at an early stage (Fig. 45a, c). This mesodermal envelope thickens greatly against the ventral side of the stomodaeum immediately in front of the radular sac. Here, the primordium of the tongue (*odontophore*) is formed by bulging upwards of the anterior lip of the radular sac. Thereby this part of the foregut is more or less flattened in a dorso-ventral direction; it becomes the *pharynx*. The tongue is bounded in front by the paired *sublingual clefts*, which demarcate the tongue from the floor of the stomodaeum (Pl. IX, C). It is entirely filled with a dense mass of mesoderm. In this mass a pair of *odontophore cartilages* is formed. Their formation is described by DELSMAN (1912) in *Littorina* as follows. A layer of cells immediately beneath the epithelium of the tongue arrange themselves perpendicularly to the epithelium. The cells lengthen, and become highly columnar with elongated nuclei. The rudiments of the odontophore cartilages, which become delimited from the rest of the mesoderm, are thus one-layered at first, but become two-layered, finally multi-layered, by division of the cells. The cells become vacuolated, and in this way form a 'chordoid' tissue. Later a pair of accessory cartilages are formed more laterally. From the rest of the tongue mesoderm the musculature is formed, which shows a regular arrangement.

The *salivary glands* appear in Polyplacophora, Aplacophora and Gastropoda rather late as paired diverticula in the dorsolateral angles of the pharynx (Pl. IX, B). They lengthen considerably, and grow backwards along the oesophagus. Later they branch. In the terminal ramifications mucous cells, and serous cells containing protein granules, differentiate. The proximal part forms a collecting duct without cilia, surrounded by a thin layer of circular muscle fibres.

In the cephalopods the primordium of the posterior salivary glands appears as an independent invagination in front of the primitive mouth, which is secondarily taken up in the stomodaeum. It is at first unpaired, but soon divides into two branches, which grow backwards and form diverticula. The unpaired part of the duct lengthens considerably. The anterior salivary glands appear somewhat later as evaginations of the stomodaeum.

The *sugar glands* of Polyplacophora arise likewise as lateral outgrowths of the stomodaeum.

The inner part of the stomodaeum gives rise to the *oesophagus*. This

Q

part lengthens considerably, and becomes tubular. It is delimited by the *suboesophageal cleft* from the posterior side of the radular sac (Pl. XII, A). During the larval period the oesophagus is usually lined with cilia, either over its whole circumference, or in the form of a dorsal or ventral row of cilia. Gland cells may also appear in its wall. The mesodermal envelope of the oesophagus differentiates into a thin inner layer of circular muscle fibres and an outer layer of longitudinal muscles.

The *radular sac* initially has a rather wide lumen. As it grows out, it narrows proximally, whereas its distal end widens, so that it becomes more or less pear-shaped. By the occurrence of a bend in its anterior portion, the distal end is lifted dorsally (Pl. XII, A). The whole sac flattens dorsoventrally, then its lateral edges bend upwards, so that it forms a double-walled gutter with a lumen, which is crescent-shaped in transverse section (Fig. 45d). This lumen gradually narrows by the opposite walls coming together, until it finally disappears altogether. The dorsal cavity of the gutter is filled with a mass of connective tissue. In some Prosobranchia (e.g. *Littorina*) the radular sac grows to a considerable length. Its extremity thereby pushes against the mantle cavity, then the radular sac rolls together to a spiral coil to the right of the median plane (DELSMAN, 1912).

The formation of the *radula* begins at an early stage with the secretion of a thin cuticular lamella on the ventral wall of the radular sac (Fig. 45d). This is crescent-shaped in transverse section, in accordance with the shape of the radular sac, and extends over the tongue in front. This *radular membrane* is formed simultaneously along the whole length of the radular sac; apparently, it is secreted by all cells of the ventral wall together. These cells readily take up stains at this stage. Tooth formation does not begin until the radular membrane has been formed. It occurs at the posterior end, ventrally near the blind end of the radular sac.

Here special cells are differentiated, which play the main role in tooth formation: the *odontoblasts*. They belong to two types. In the Placophora, Prosobranchia and Cephalopoda there are numerous small narrow odontoblasts, not always exceeding the cells of the surrounding epithelium in length, which form a common hemispherical cushion, divided into as many parts as there are teeth in a transverse row. They have a strongly staining, granular cytoplasm, and dark nuclei. They are not very different from the surrounding cells, into which they merge gradually.

In Opisthobranchia and Pulmonata, however, the odontoblast cushions consist of a small number of large cells with big spherical nuclei. The anterior row of odontoblasts is very different in shape from those situated behind, which form a hemispherical cushion together. In the

Pteropoda the nuclei of the odontoblasts are rich in chromatin, and the cytoplasm stains darkly (SCHNABEL, 1903). In the Pulmonata, on the contrary, the nuclei are clear and poor in chromatin, while the cytoplasm stains lightly with acid and basic dyes. Presumably, it is very watery and turgescent (SPEK, 1921). According to MINGANTI (1950), the odontoblasts in *Limnaea* contain less RNA than the other cells of the ventral wall of the radular sac. On the other hand, they exhibit a clear positive alkaline phosphatase reaction.

The odontoblasts of pulmonates differentiate at a very early stage. Even at the first evagination of the radular sac, cells with rounded nuclei containing distinct nucleoli occur at its terminal end. Somewhat later these nuclei are clearer than their neighbours, and their chromatin is less finely dispersed. At first the odontoblasts lie terminally, later more ventrally (SCHNABEL, 1903).

Very peculiar views are upheld by PRUVOT-FOL (1925, 1926). It is claimed by this author that the odontoblasts arise by fusion of smaller cells originally situated further backwards. These cells lose their membranes, and coalesce into a large vesicular granulated nucleus (!), which swells and rounds off. The odontoblast cushions in Opisthobranchia and Pulmonata are said to become syncytial by disappearance of the cell boundaries. On the contrary, nearly all other authors depict distinct cell boundaries, and HOFFMANN (1932) and GABE and PRENANT (1952) explicitly oppose the view that the cushions form a syncytium.

Tooth formation is described by ROTTMANN (1901: *Loligo*) and SCHNABEL (1903: pulmonates) in the following way. The first anlage of a tooth is a thin membrane on the odontoblast cushion, as a direct continuation of the radular membrane. New substance is secreted beneath it, staining more lightly, whereby the first lamella becomes the back of the tooth. When the upper part of the tooth is completely formed, it rises from its cushion and turns from a horizontal into a vertical position, so that it comes to rest upon the radular membrane. Now the foot plate of the tooth is formed, which fuses with the radular membrane and with a prolongation of the basal part of the preceding tooth. Hence, each tooth partly sits upon the prolonged foot plate of its predecessor. Then the whole tooth withdraws from the odontoblast cushion, and the formation of a new tooth begins. According to BLOCH (1896) this is due to the fact that chitin secretion in the odontoblast cushion takes place at a slower rate than more ventrally, so that every now and then a part of the secreted substance is taken along with the radular membrane in its forward movement.

Again PRUVOT-FOL's view (1926) stands quite apart, according to which the teeth are formed in closed follicles, formed by cells from the roof epithelium of the radular sac. Somewhat related to this view is MORITZ's contention (1939) that the teeth in *Crepidula* are formed by the dorsal wall of the radular sac, whereas the odontoblasts only serve for the formation of the radular membrane. These assertions can hardly be accepted without further proof.

According to PRUVOT-FOL, the teeth arise by direct chitinization of apical cell parts. Most other authors, however (especially BLOCH, 1896; HOFFMANN, 1932; GABE and PRENANT, 1952) assume a true secretion process. GABE and PRENANT point out that the cytoplasm of the odonto-blasts often contains inclusions, corresponding in their staining pro-perties to the substance of newly-formed teeth. For instance, the odonto-blasts in *Acera*, *Philine* and *Runcina* contain a Hotchkiss-positive poly-saccharide, also occurring in the young tooth. Futhermore, the odonto-blasts have a Golgi apparatus greatly resembling that in gland cells. The mitochondria are heaped up in the apical cell part. The Feulgen reaction indicates that the nuclei play a part in secretion.

The older authors, basing themselves mainly on sagittal sections, assumed that there are in Opisthobranchia and Pulmonata only four or five odontoblasts per tooth (e.g. RÖSSLER, 1885; MEISENHEIMER, 1898). As a matter of fact, in such a section the odontoblast cushion as a rule consists of four or five cells, the foremost being lower than the others. BECK (1912) was the first to show by means of tangential sections and surface views of the radula of *Buliminus* that the relationships are actually quite different. The anterior cells (called by BECK ε–cells, by HOFFMANN, 1932, however, δ–cells) form a transverse row of big rectangular cells. Presumably these cells contribute to the formation of the radular membrane only. Behind each ε–cell there is in *Buliminus* a group of fourteen smaller cells, together forming the matrix of a tooth. The cells δ, situated immediately behind the ε–cells, produce the foot plate of the tooth; the cells lying still further posteriorly form the upper part of the tooth (according to HOFFMANN, the relationships are somewhat more complicated in *Limnaea*). The median tooth in *Buliminus* is an excep-tional case; it has sixteen instead of fourteen odontoblasts in its matrix.

In *Vitrina* there are two ε–cells in front of the median tooth, one in front of each lateral tooth (ECKARDT, 1914). In *Vitrina brevis* the matrix of the median tooth consists of twelve odontoblasts, ε–cells in-cluded; those of the lateral teeth have ten cells. In *V. elongata* these numbers are fourteen and thirteen, respectively. In *Limnaea stagnalis* (HOFFMANN, 1932) the median tooth has about seven, the lateral teeth eleven, the marginal teeth five odontoblasts (exclusive of ε–cells).

ROTTMANN (1901), SCHNABEL (1903) and PRUVOT-FOL (1925, 1926) assume that each group of odontoblasts functions only once, and is then replaced by the cells lying behind it. The matrix cells are supposed to move forwards together with the tooth produced by them, and pass into the low cells of the basal epithelium. PRUVOT-FOL even speaks about an exhaustion and degeneration of the odontoblasts. According to this author several odontoblast cushions function simultaneously, new 'follicles' arising behind the old ones. According to BLOCH (1896) a single odontoblast group produces several teeth consecutively, but is then gradually replaced and passes into the basal epithelium. A similar gradual replacement is also held possible in pulmonates by SCHNABEL.

On the contrary, RÖSSLER (1885), BECK (1912), SPEK (1921), HOFFMANN (1932) and GABE and PRENANT (1952) assume that a single odontoblast cushion produces consecutively all the teeth of a longitudinal row. There are no signs of exhaustion or degeneration of odontoblasts. Sometimes all teeth of a longitudinal row exhibit the same deviation from the normal shape. Especially HOFFMANN advances very convincing arguments in favour of this view, which is probably the correct one.

The radular membrane is produced, as stated above, in first instance by all cells of the ventral wall. Later its matrix cells are confined to the posterior part of the ventral wall, and the lengthening of the membrane takes place by addition at its posterior end. In Placophora, Prosobranchia and Cephalopoda the membrane is formed by the lower part of the odontoblast cushion. In Opisthobranchia and Pulmonata it is especially the first row ϵ (or δ), which produces the membrane. Beneath the radular membrane a thin *subradular membrane* is secreted by the basal epithelium; it is only weakly connected with the radula. The subradular membrane sometimes shows a perpendicular striation, which is continued into the cytoplasm of the cells.

The cells of the dorsal wall of the radular sac also play a part in tooth formation. This is a columnar epithelium, which intrudes between successive teeth, and almost entirely fills the intervening spaces. The cells have large nuclei, sometimes as big as the odontoblasts. The tips of the cells are often not clearly delimited, more or less fibrous. Threads of secretion reaching to the surface of the teeth, and covering the latter with a continuous layer, have been described.

The older authors (RÖSSLER, 1885; BLOCH, 1896) assumed that this secretion hardens on the surface of the teeth to a resistant enamel substance. The outer layer of older teeth is often brown (chitons) or black (Docoglossa). According to RÖSSLER this part of the tooth is optically isotropic, whereas the part formed by the odontoblasts is birefringent. However, this is contested by SPEK (1921), according to whom all parts of the radula are isotropic in *Helix*. ROTTMANN (1901) and SCHNABEL

(1903) deny that the roof epithelium plays any part whatsoever in tooth formation.

Later it has been shown that this epithelium does indeed take part. However, enamel formation does not occur by apposition, but by intussusception. The chitin produced by the odontoblasts is secondarily impregnated with various substances, secreted by the roof epithelium. This appears from the fact that the structure and stainability of the teeth change from behind forwards, and from the tip to the base of each tooth. The newly-formed teeth are soft, often not sharply outlined, homogeneous and structureless, colourless and difficult to stain. As they move forwards, their stainability increases; later it spreads also into the radular membrane (SOLLAS, 1907; SPEK, 1921). Still further in front the stainability of the peripheral parts of the teeth decreases again; finally, they hardly stain at all. Similar changes occur with respect to the natural yellow or brown colours, which are due to ferri-compounds. For instance, SPEK found in *Helix* a weak brown coloration of the points of the teeth and the inner parts of the foot plates, beginning at the seventh to tenth row from behind. It becomes stronger in front of this, but from about the thirty-eighth row the teeth are colourless again. The Prussian blue reaction shows that this is not due to a loss of ferri-compounds, for this reaction becomes even stronger as one advances forwards, and extends also to the marginal parts of the foot plates. Only still further in front do the points of the teeth become colourless again. Lime salts are not found in the youngest teeth, but begin to appear farther in front in a zone, where the roof cells also contain these salts. In *Bulla* and *Haminea* a certain zone of the roof epithelium is very rich in Hotchkiss-positive polysaccharides; opposite these cells the same substances occur in the teeth (GABE and PRENANT, 1952). Finally, SPEK showed by means of Millon's reagent that the teeth of *Helix* are impregnated with protein. This occurs beginning with the seventh row, and further parallels more or less the impregnation with ferri-compounds.

The mechanism by which the radular teeth move forward is not yet fully understood. The older authors (RÖSSLER, 1885; BLOCH, 1896) assume that the radula shifts forward with respect to the underlying epithelium, partly by the growth of surrounding tissues, partly as a result of pull exerted by the muscles. According to ROTTMANN (1901) and SCHNABEL (1903) the teeth are displaced together with the underlying epithelium. SCHNABEL observed in *Spongiobranchaea* and *Pneumoderma* that the basal epithelium is divided into separate hillocks, each bearing a tooth, and apparently shifting forwards together with it. PRUVOT-FOL (1925, 1926) also thinks that each tooth remains connected with its matrix cells. The forward shift of the radula is only apparent, and is due to the growth of the radular sac behind, and its unfurling in front. HOFFMANN (1932) comes to a similar view. If it is true, however, that all teeth of a longitudinal row are produced by the same odonto-blast cushion, it must be assumed that at least at the posterior part a real shift of the radula with respect to the epithelium takes place.

The observations by CARRIKER (1943) on the rapid replacement of the radular teeth likewise speak in favour of a real displacement of the radula. This author showed that the anterior teeth in *Limnaea* are strongly worn down; finally they come off and are swallowed. In one specimen 613 teeth were lost in 23 days. Hence, the 'turnover' of teeth is very considerable.

The number of teeth to a transverse row corresponds to the number of odontoblast cushions in function. The longitudinal rows do not all appear at the same time. In *Oncidium* (JOYEUX-LAFFUIE, 1882) and *Loligo* (ROTTMANN, 1901) the median row appears first, then the lateral rows in mediolateral order. In *Paludina* and the Pulmonates the first rows to appear are paired, and the median row is formed only later (SCHNABEL, 1903). In *Paludina* first three pairs of lateral rows appear, in mediolateral order, then the median row; the number of seven rows is not further increased even in postembryonic stages. In *Planorbis* two pairs of lateral rows are formed first, then the median row; afterwards the number of lateral rows increases continually both during embryonic and postembryonic life. In *Patella* the median row is one of the first to appear, but some time after metamorphosis this row disappears, so that the adult animal has twelve teeth per transverse row (SMITH, 1935).

The first formed radular teeth are small, and often have not yet the shapes of the later ones. The dental formula of the adult is only gradu-ally reached. For instance, in *Limnaea* in the youngest snails the lateral teeth still have the shapes of marginals; presumably, they are formed by relatively few odontoblasts. With increasing age the odontoblast cushion extends laterally, and produces an increasing number of longi-tudinal rows of teeth. Each part of the odontoblast cushion undergoes progressive differentiation, and produces successively the various types, which in the adult snail are found in a transverse direction in one row: marginals, intermediates and laterals (CARRIKER, 1943).

The radular sac is surrounded at an early stage by mesodermal cells, especially against its anterior side. This mesodermal envelope gives rise to the connective tissue sheath and the musculature of the radula.

In exogastrulae of *Limnaea* (RAVEN, 1952) and *Bithynia* (HESS, 1956a, 1956b) the stomodaeum may invaginate independently of the endoderm. It is obviously not induced by the endodermal gut. In half-embryos of *Bithynia* produced at the 2–cell stage (AB– and CD–embryos) only one partner develops a stomodaeum, in those formed by isolation at the 4–cell stage (AD and BC) in both a stomodaeum may be formed. Apparently the capacity for stomodaeum formation is distributed unequally in the egg already at an early stage. In these exogastrulae with invaginated stomodaeum the formation of a radular sac has in no case been observed, however.

If in cephalopods the endodermal gut is reduced, the stomodaeum may develop in a normal way; the oesophagus ends blindly in these cases (RANZI, 1931b). The stomodaeum may also show a normal development in the absence of an inner yolk-sac.

If the posterior part of the body, including the posterior portion of the oesophagus rudiment, is cut away in cephalopods, the anterior part of the rudiment regulates and grows out forming a complete oesophages (RANZI, 1931a). This does not occur if the whole oesophagus rudiment has been removed.

The normal invagination of the stomodaeum is not a necessary condition for the development of the tongue, salivary glands and radular sac. In *Loligo* malformations of the stomodaeum often occur under the influence of LiCl (RANZI, 1928a). Sometimes its invagination fails entirely. In such embryos a cylindrical or conical outgrowth may be present which represents the tongue. Near its apex the abdominal salivary gland forms an invagination with tubular lumen and cubic epithelium. At its caudal slope there is a radular sac, normally developed and with the beginning of the formation of radular teeth. Within the tongue often buccal ganglia have been formed.

A nearly identical malformation may occur in *Limnaea* under the influence of beryllium (RAVEN and SPRONK, 1952), lithium (RAVEN, 1952), heat shock (RAVEN, DE ROON and STADHOUDERS, 1955) or centrifugation (RAVEN and BEENAKKERS, 1955). The buccal cavity and pharynx are entirely everted and their epithelia have spread over the surface. The salivary glands and radular sac open independently towards the exterior in this area. The radular sac shows a normal morphogenesis, and has formed a well-developed radula with several rows of teeth (Pl. XII). The only important difference from the relationships in *Loligo* is provided by the fact that, while in the latter the oesophagus is lacking in such embryos, in *Limnaea* there is a narrow tubular oesophagus, debouching directly upon the surface.

14. Midgut and hindgut

As regards the early development of the endodermal gut, cf. above, p. 159.

The primitive gut primordium of cephalopods (cf. p. 176) enlarges, and divides by a constriction into the rudiment of the ink-sac and the gut proper. This grows towards the tip of the yolk-sac, where it finally connects with the foregut. The anterior part of the gut widens into stomach and caecum. The opening of the gut lumen towards the yolk narrows (Fig. 62), and is finally closed.

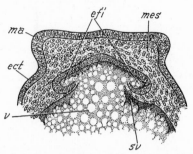

Fig. 62. Frontal section of embryo of *Tremoctopus violaceus*, showing closure of gut and liver rudiments (*efi.*). *ect.*, ectoderm; *ma*, mantle; *mes*, mesoderm; *sv*, yolk syncytium; *v*, yolk. After SACARRAO, 1949.

The *stomach* primordium has a one-layered epithelium, covered externally by a layer of mesodermal cells, which gives rise to the muscular wall of the stomach (Pl. XII, A). The epithelium initially is columnar, and often bears cilia at early stages. These cilia may in places be lacking, or be replaced by stiff hairs, as in *Aplysia* (SAUNDERS and POOLE, 1910). Later this ciliary lining may disappear; the stomach epithelium flattens, and is often lined by a distinct cuticule (e.g. *Dreissensia*, Unionidae, *Crepidula*).

In the Lamellibranchiata (*Dreissensia*, Unionidae) the connection between stomach and hindgut, which at first lies in the median plane, is later displaced to the right. In *Pomatias* a caecum develops as a wide evagination of the anteroventral wall of the stomach (CREEK, 1951).

Various local differentiations may appear in the wall of the stomach. In the pteropods (FOL, 1875) a number of *gastric teeth* are formed from folds of the stomach wall, which become covered with a horny layer. In *Crepidula* (MORITZ, 1939) and *Pomatias* (CREEK, 1951) a leaf-like ridge of chitin is formed on the posterior wall of the stomach, the so-called *gastric shield*. Other folds, covered with cilia, give rise to a food-sifting mechanism in *Pomatias*. Finally a *style sac* develops near the entrance to the hindgut in *Crepidula* and *Pomatias* (Fig. 37).

In the Lamellibranchiata an evagination lined by cilia is formed at the right side of the stomach. It becomes a deep pouch, which extends in a posterior direction. In its lumen a highly refringent homogeneous substance is secreted, which projects into the stomach, the *crystalline style*.

The formation of the *larval livers* has been described above (p. 100). In some instances they are supposed to pass directly into the adult liver, e.g. in Opisthobranchia. In other cases, however, the larval livers are broken down at the end of the larval period, and replaced by the definitive liver. For instance, in the Protobranchia *Nucula* and *Yoldia* the liver pouches break down after metamorphosis, their cells round off and are dispersed throughout the schizocoel. Later the liver cells arrange themselves anew. The liver pouches become hollow, and lose most of the round cells; some of these cells go to pieces and are perhaps digested (DREW, 1899, 1901). In the pteropods *Creseis* and *Styliola* the larval livers, after a temporary enlargement, degenerate, and are replaced by the adult livers, which arise at the end of larval life from two finger-like processes at the ventroposterior wall of the stomach (FOL, 1875). In *Limnaea, Planorbis* and *Physa* the albumen cells are broken down towards the end of the embryonic period. Their cell membranes break up, the nuclei atrophy. The stomach epithelium begins to grow around the albumen sac, starting from the place where the larval livers are connected with the stomach (Pl. XII, A). Even before this process has been completed, the epithelium begins to differentiate into glandular tissue. Sac-like invaginations and evaginations occur. When the albumen sac has been completely enwrapped, in this way a complicated gland, divided into several lobes of glandular tissue, has been formed. Remnants of the albumen cells may be found in its lumina for some time (BLOCH, 1938).

The *adult livers* as a rule appear as two lateral evaginations of the stomach. The left lobe is often larger than the right (e.g. *Acanthochiton, Nucula, Anodonta, Aplysia, Oncidium*). Initially they are rounded, but soon secondary evaginations give rise to separate lobules. Progressive subdivision of the latter leads to the formation of a great number of follicles. The originally broad connections of the liver pouches with the stomach later become narrower, and form the collecting ducts. The small-celled epithelium of the stomach may extend a short distance into these ducts, and give rise to the columnar epithelium lining them (e.g. *Littorina*: DELSMAN, 1912; Basommatophora: FOL, 1880).

The hepatopancreas of the cephalopods is formed as a pair of finger-like diverticula near the boundary between foregut and midgut (Fig. 62). According to SACARRAO (1945) in *Octopus* an unpaired evagination is first formed. The diverticula protrude into the blood sinus surrounding the inner yolk-sac. Their wall consists of a one-layered columnar epithelium showing many mitoses, surrounded by two or three layers of mesoderm cells. When the inner yolk-sac increases in size, the hepato-pancreas rudiments likewise enlarge; they grow forward between the yolk-sac and the body wall (Fig. 63). The anterior part becomes flattened, and elliptical in transverse section. According to RANZI (1928a, 1931b) the flattening is due to the pressure exerted by the inner yolk-sac; when the latter is lacking or reduced, the liver lobes have a rounded shape. The posterior part of the primordium extends in all directions, and opens with a wide aperture in the caecum rudiment. This portion gives rise to the pancreas, whereas the anterior part becomes the liver; the two parts are connected by a narrow channel (PORTMANN and BIDDER, 1928).

The liver as a rule consists of large cells with big nuclei. Vacuoles appear at an early stage in the cytoplasm; further secretion granules appear, often being yellowish or brown in colour. In *Acanthochiton* the nucleus seems to play a part in secretion; acidophil substances and basophil granules pass from the nucleus into the cytoplasm (HAMMAR-STEN and RUNNSTRÖM, 1925). BLOCH (1938) described various cell types in the liver of freshwater pulmonates, which probably represent different functional states of a same cell type, however.

As stated above (p. 178), in the cephalopods yolk is transported during development from the outer yolk-sac towards the interior of the embryo, where an inner yolk-sac is formed. This is small at first, but then increases greatly in size (Fig. 63); with the resorption of the yolk it then decreases again, and finally disappears completely. Conveyance of the yolk from the outer to the inner yolk-sac is an active process, caused by contractions of the circumoral musculature (PORTMANN and BIDDER, 1928; SACARRAO, 1945). This is confirmed by the experiments of RANZI (1931a, 1931b). If the visceral sac and mantle are cut away, a kind of inner yolk-sac is still formed behind the level of the statocysts; it is filled with material from the outer yolk-sac. If, however, the anterior part of the embryo is injured by an oblique direction of the cut, this does not occur. In *Eledone* no inner yolk-sac is formed, according to SACARRAO (1943).

The perivitelline membrane of the cephalopods plays an important part in yolk resorption (*Loligo*: PORTMANN and BIDDER, 1928; Octopoda: SACARRAO, 1945). It functions as a trophic organ. Liquefaction of the yolk begins in the intra-embryonic part of the yolk-sac. The perivitelline membrane thickens; the nuclei of the yolk syncytium are enlarged, and possess one or two big nucleoli. The yolk syncytium penetrates deeply into the yolk, especially in the region of the sinus posterior (Fig. 49). Here digested food substances pass directly into the circulation.

According to KONOPACKI (1933) accumulations of lipids occur already at early stages near the nuclei of the perivitelline membrane; presumably a degradation of lipoproteins takes place under the influence of enzymes secreted by the cells. This occurs especially immediately beneath the germinal disc. The liberated lipids are passed on to the embryo, in which they are first found in the intercellular spaces. At a later stage, lipids and proteins are found in the blood sinuses. Glycogen also appears in the perivitelline membrane, especially near the vena cava; it is passed on to the blood in this vein. Near the shell gland glycogen passes directly from the yolk into the neighbouring tissue. Towards the end of the embryonic period the breakdown of the yolk is greatly increased in the regressing outer yolk-sac.

According to PORTMANN and BIDDER and SACARRAO, the liver plays an important part in the passage of the digested yolk substances to the embryo. With the enlargement of the inner yolk-sac, and the disappearance of the surrounding blood sinus, the liver cells come in direct contact with the perivitelline membrane. The intervening mesoderm cells disappear. The liver now covers as a pair of large thin lobes the sides of the anterior part of the inner yolk-sac (Fig. 63d). The perivitelline membrane here differs in structure from elsewhere. It shows considerable activity, and an active digestion of the yolk occurs in this region. When the inner yolk-sac diminishes in size, the space becoming available is taken up by the liver, which grows considerably, and at last almost entirely surrounds the rest of the yolk-sac. Blood vessels have been formed, from the aorta to the liver, and from the liver to the vena cava. The liver cells exhibit great activity; granules and droplets appear in the apical cell parts. Presumably yolk substances are passed through the liver cells, and taken up in the lumen. Since the pancreas is completely surrounded by a sinus pancreaticus, it is probable that the yolk substances are transmitted to the blood at this place.

In *Eledone*, where there is no inner yolk-sac, presumably the digested yolk substances pass directly from the outer yolk-sac into the circulation in the region of the sinus cephalicus. This is also in this case accompanied by a great activity of the perivitelline membrane in this area (SACARRAO, 1945).

The *hindgut* rudiment exhibits a considerable growth in length, whereby it begins to coil. The muscle coat and connective tissue of the gut arise from the mesoderm. As a rule the hindgut has a ciliary lining. These cilia may be so long that they project outside the anus at early stages (e.g. *Dreissensia*). In *Anodonta* a typhlosole is formed as a longitudinal furrow in the outer wall, which becomes filled with fibrous connective tissue (HERBERS, 1913). The hindgut of *Pomatias* differentiates into three regions: (1) a glandular part, in which elongated columnar cells containing protein spherules alternate with ciliated supporting cells; (2) a second part, which is also glandular, but in which the gland cells are still more elongated; (3) a third region, which is the longest one, consisting of low non-glandular cells without cilia, apart from a longitudinal strip of longer ciliated cells, and a few mucous cells (CREEK, 1951).

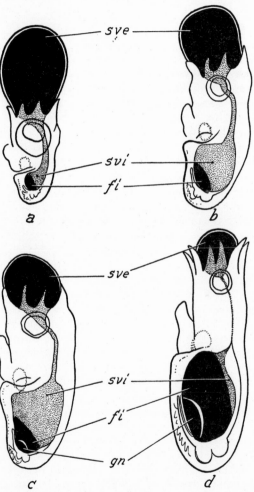

Fig. 63. Diagrammatic drawings of embryonic stages of *Octopus*, showing transfer of yolk from outer (*sve*) to inner yolk sac (*svi*), and replacement of the latter by the liver (*fi*). *gn*, ink sac. The inner yolk is indicated by stippling, the outer yolk and the liver in black. After SACARRAO, 1945.

The rudiment of the *ink sac* of cephalopods constricts off from the hindgut, and grows out into a tube surrounded by mesoderm cells. Its proximal part develops a wide lumen with one-layered wall; the distal part becomes more or less solid by folding of the wall. This becomes the secreting region, whereas the proximal part gives rise to the ink bladder and the duct.

15. Musculature

The adult musculature of the molluscs generally develops from the mesoderm independently of the larval musculature.

In *Acanthochiton* (HAMMARSTEN and RUNNSTRÖM, 1925) several dorsoventral and longitudinal muscles arise from the lateral mesoderm bands already at a free-swimming stage. The dorsoventral muscles develop even before the formation of the shell plates.

In *Epimenia* (BABA, 1938) an inner longitudinal and an outer circular hypodermic muscle layer develop from the mesoderm. Moreover, there are transverse muscle fibres running from above the foot obliquely to the lateral walls of the body.

In some Lamellibranchiata the larval musculature seems not to atrophy completely at metamorphosis; part of it persists in the adult musculature, e.g. in the adductors. However, in the Unionidae the larval adductors disappear completely, and are replaced by the adult ones. The adult musculature develops from scattered mesenchyme cells, which arrange themselves into strands, then become fibrillar and differentiate into muscle cells.

As a rule the anterior adductor develops first; but in *Anodonta* (though not in *Unio*) the posterior one is the first to appear (HARMS, 1909). The anterior adductor lies far in front and dorsally; at metamorphosis it comes to lie near the mouth. The posterior adductor is situated behind the visceral ganglion and above the hindgut. Both adductors may later break up into several bundles.

The posterior retractor originates from paired groups of myocytes, forming strands which run ventrally on either side of the hindgut, enclosing it between them and uniting below it, but dividing again in the foot into two branches, which become applied to the sides of the foot. The anterior retractor develops in a similar way. Finally transverse musculature is formed in the foot, connecting its two sides.

In some gastropods likewise a part of the larval musculature is included into the adult musculature. In *Haliotis* the larval retractor muscle, which lies dorsally after torsion, is displaced a little to the left by the extension of the mantle cavity on its right side. A further shift of the muscle attachment at the shell, towards the left and forwards, takes place by migration and by the addition of new muscle cells from the mesoderm. It thereby comes to lie ever nearer the left margin of the shell. Its muscle cells extend into the left side of the foot; they also insert upon the buccal mass. The adult *columellar muscle* arises from two mesoderm cells, belonging to the original left side of the body, which are displaced towards the right side during torsion. They begin to multiply after torsion, and give rise to muscle cells penetrating into the right side of the foot. They attach to the shell at the right of the umbo. The muscle grows by the addition of muscle cells from the mesenchyme. At first it is much smaller than the larval retractor, but as the latter does not grow any more, the columellar muscle soon begins to preponderate. It gradually shifts towards the centre of the shell. The larval retractor persists as an insignificant muscle at the left margin of the shell (CROFTS, 1938).

In *Patella* and *Calliostoma* the pedal musculature of the definitive right side develops during the second phase of torsion from the mesoderm of the post-torsional right side. For some time, when torsion is complete, the larval retractor and the definitive right shell muscle are equal in size and bilaterally situated; it is probable that they form a pair. In *Calliostoma* the right muscle persists as a typical columellar muscle, whereas the left one, the larval retractor, is reduced and lost as it is in the majority of prosobranchs (CROFTS, 1955). In *Patella* both muscles are lost in the adult, according to SMITH (1935), and replaced by adult shell retractors having a different origin.

In *Littorina* the musculus columellaris develops from a group of mesoderm cells at the base of the foot, lying in the median plane against the opercular epithelium. It attaches to this epithelium, bends sharply at the base of the foot, and inserts to the ectoderm beneath the mantle fold on the left side. Then differentiation to muscle cells takes place (DELSMAN, 1912). The intrinsic musculature of the foot arises in *Littorina* by outgrowth of muscle cells from the columellar muscle, according to DELSMAN.

16. Vascular system

In most molluscs (except the cephalopods) the heart, pericardium, kidney, and often also the reproductive organs, arise from a common anlage. According to some authors, this cell group is of ectodermal origin, and arises by a paired or unpaired proliferation of cells from the ectoderm near the hindgut; this is asserted by MEISENHEIMER (1898: *Limax*; 1901a: *Dreissensia*; 1901b: *Cyclas*), OTTO and TÖNNIGES (1906: *Paludina*), HARMS (1909: Unionidae) and MORITZ (1939: *Crepidula*). Nearly all authors agree, however, that it is mesodermal, and originates from the mesoderm bands of the embryo, e.g. PÖTZSCH (1904: *Planorbis*), WIERZEJSKI (1905: *Physa*), HEYDER (1909: *Arion*), HERBERS (1913: *Anodonta*), FERNANDO (1931a: *Ostrea*), SMITH (1935: *Patella*), CARRICK (1939: *Agriolimax*), OKADA (1939: *Sphaerium*) and CREEK (1951: *Pomatias*). As a matter of fact, it may for a certain time be closely applied to the ectoderm, but presumably no passage of ectodermal cells into the anlage takes place.

In *Dreissensia* this cell group lies at first mediodorsally above the hindgut. Later it extends symmetrically on either side of the gut. In many cases it is paired from the beginning, e.g. in *Cyclas*, *Sphaerium*, Unionidae, *Patella*, *Paludina*, *Planorbis* (Fig. 65). In *Planorbis* the left of these paired rudiments gives rise to pericardium, heart and kidney, whereas the right one disintegrates into mesenchyme. In *Bithynia* (VON ERLANGER, 1892), *Littorina* (DELSMAN, 1912), *Pomatias*, *Limax*, and *Arion*, the anlage is unpaired from the beginning, and is situated on the right alongside the hindgut.

Part of the cells of the common anlage in the Lamellibranchiata may differentiate into primordial germ cells, e.g. in *Cyclas* (MEISENHEIMER, 1901b; WASSERLOOS, 1911) (Fig. 65). In addition, it gives rise, as a rule from its lateral parts, to the left and right nephric vesicles. After the separation of the latter the remaining elements begin to spread medially, and apply themselves against the hindgut. They unite dorsally and ventrally, so that a ring of cells around the gut is formed. This gives rise to the pericardium and heart.

The cavity of the *pericardium* occurs as a cleft in this cell mass; at first it has irregular boundaries, but later it is bordered by a regular epithelial wall. It may appear earlier or later. Sometimes it makes its appearance when the pericardium rudiments are still paired, as cavities on either side of the gut (e.g. *Anodonta*, *Sphaerium*). These pericardial vesicles become crescent-shaped, and close in upon the hindgut; then they unite above and below the gut. In *Cyclas* at first a dorsal and ventral pericardial vesicle is formed on either side. The ventral vesicles fuse below the gut, the dorsal ones above the gut. Then the dorsal and ventral vesicles of each side unite, except in the middle, where a cell cluster remains, which is the rudiment of the atrium (MEISENHEIMER, 1901b; WASSERLOOS, 1911). In *Sphaerium* the course of events is slightly different, according to OKADA (1939). The paired pericardial vesicles extend backwards at their dorsal and ventral extremities (Fig. 64, a–b); these prolongations then fuse, so that a ring-shaped vesicle is formed on either side (Fig. 64, c–d). At the same time the two pericardial cavities unite above and below the rectum. Finally, in some instances the pericardial cavity does not appear until a closed cell ring around the hindgut has been formed. This splits into an inner and outer layer, e.g. in *Dreissensia*. In *Unio*, according to HARMS (1909), only the pericardial cavity ventrally to the gut appears in this way; the dorsal one is formed by the lateral ends of the dorsal cell mass turning dorsally and then medially, and growing together in the median plane, enclosing a cavity.

Between the inner wall of the pericardium and the gut a space remains, which becomes the *ventricle* of the heart. This is therefore bounded externally by the splanchnic layer of the pericardium, and internally by the gut. A few mesodermal cells, lying externally upon the endoderm of the gut, now spread out, and give rise to the endothelial inner wall of the heart (AHTING, 1902: *Mytilus*; HERBERS, 1913: *Anodonta*; OKADA, 1939: *Sphaerium*). The inner and outer wall pass into each other in front and behind where the gut enters into the heart.

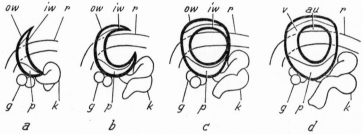

Fig. 64. Diagram of the development of the left pericardial vesicle, kidney and heart in *Sphaerium japonicum*. *au*, rudiment of atrium; *g*, germ cells; *iw*, inner and posterior wall of pericardial vesicle; *k*, kidney; *ow*, outer and anterior wall of pericardial vesicle; *p*, pericardial cavity; *r*, rectum; *v*, ventricle of heart. After OKADA, 1939.

Adjacent to the ventricle on the left and right is a mass of tissue, which has either been left in place during the formation of the pericardial cavity (*Cyclas*, *Sphaerium*), or has arisen by invagination of the lateral wall of the pericardial vesicles. In these cell clusters a haemocoelic space appears, which becomes the *atrial cavity*. The atria unite secondarily with the ventricle; at the place of junction the atrioventricular valves are formed. The heart now forms a transverse tube across the pericardial cavity, pierced by the hindgut; its lateral parts, separated by a constriction, represent the atria; its median part is the ventricle. The ends of the heart tube communicate with the blood cavities at the base of the gill rudiment. In *Nucula* the heart is later pushed dorsally by the development of the kidneys; in this way the gut becomes free, and now lies ventral to the heart (DREW, 1901).

R

The wall of the heart becomes multi-layered. The inner elements differentiate into muscle fibres, chiefly circular, but also longitudinal fibres. The muscle fibres also invade the cavity, both in the ventricle and the atria; they run right across the heart lumen.

The dorsal part of the pericardium expands more strongly than the ventral one, so that the atria are shifted somewhat ventrally in *Cyclas*. In *Mytilus* they even unite along the posterior margin of the pericardium, below the gut (AHTING, 1902).

The arteries and veins arise separately from the heart rudiment as cavities between the mesoderm cells. WASSERLOOS (1911) studied the development of the blood vessels in *Cyclas*. The *anterior aorta* originates by the joining together of mesenchyme cells dorsal to the foregut. It gives rise, above the middle of the liver, to the *arteria pedalis*, which supplies the stomach and liver and penetrates into the foot. The aorta divides in front in two *cephalic arteries*. The *posterior aorta* arises in a similar way to the anterior, ventral to the hindgut. It gives off the *visceral arteries*, and divides posteriorly in two arteries to the siphons. As regards the *venous system*, a longitudinal sinus is formed from the foot to the kidneys. The veins of the kidney empty into the dorsal part of the gill fold, where the *afferent gill vessel* is formed. Similar vessels arise in the edge of the inner lamella of the inner gill, and in the edge of the outer gill.

From cells of the walls of atrium and pericardium, swelling greatly, a *pericardial gland* may be formed. In *Mytilus* these cells project with rounded heads, filled with yellow and black concretions, into the cavity (AHTING, 1902).

In the gastropods the formation of heart and pericardium exhibits various modifications, according as the anlage is paired or unpaired. In *Paludina* the pericardial cavities arise as paired vesicles on the left and right of the hindgut (VON ERLANGER, 1891; OTTO and TÖNNIGES, 1906). The right one is larger than the left from the beginning. They fuse below the gut, but their cavities remain separated at first by a median septum. The left half remains behind in its development; the right expands strongly in a dorsal direction, and increases in size while its wall becomes thinner. A ventral evagination of the right pericardium forms the primordium of the right kidney; a rudimentary left kidney arises in a similar way from the left pericardium. Now the septum between the right and left pericardial cavities disappears. During torsion the whole pericardium is displaced to the dorsal side, then to the left side of the body. The pericardium of *Ampullaria* develops in a similar way (FERNANDO, 1931b).

In *Patella* the original mesodermal cell groups, which give rise to the pericardium, are paired, lying on either side of the hindgut; afterwards they are connected by a median cell mass below the gut, though. The lateral parts now give rise to the nephric primordia, while the pericardium arises as a small cleft in the median cell mass (SMITH, 1935).

In those cases, where the original cell mass is unilateral from the beginning, it divides in two parts. The posterior and more laterally situated part gives rise to the kidney, the antero-medial portion to heart and pericardium (Fig. 46). A small pericardial cavity arises by splitting; at first it has a multi-layered wall, but then it becomes wider, and its wall becomes thinner.

The formation of the *heart* begins, as a rule, with the appearance of a local thickening in the postero-dorsal wall of the pericardium. In *Paludina* and *Bithynia* (VON ERLANGER, 1891, 1892; OTTO and TÖNNIGES, 1906) the wall here invaginates to a furrow, which then closes in its middle part. So a tube is formed, running across the cavity of the pericardium, and opening at both ends into the primary body cavity. This tube divides by a constriction in the middle into the atrium and the ventricle.

In *Arion* (HEYDER, 1909) and *Patella* (SMITH, 1935) the heart originates likewise as an invagination of the wall of the pericardium; this is rather cup-shaped in *Patella*. In *Planorbis* two indentations, one behind the other, are formed in the solid pericardium rudiment; the posterior one is the anlage of the atrium, the anterior gives rise to the ventricle. The lumen of the pericardium appears at one side of these indentations. After both have closed and have united to a tube, the cavity of the pericardium also extends towards the other side, and finally surrounds the heart tube entirely (PÖTZSCH, 1904).

In *Pomatias* (CREEK, 1951) the course of events is slightly different. The invaginated part of the pericardium wall forms at first a solid fold, in which haemocoelic spaces appear, which then coalesce to form the heart tube; this is then constricted off from the wall of the pericardium in its middle part. Heart formation in *Crepidula* seems to take place in a similar way (MORITZ, 1939).

A further modification is found in *Limax* (MEISENHEIMER, 1898), where the cavity of the heart tube appears first in a solid pericardium anlage. The pericardial cavity then arises as a cleft on either side of the heart tube, whereby the outer cell layer is lifted off as the pericardium. This process begins at the level of the ventricle, and extends only gradually into the atrial region. Atrium and ventricle are separated by a thickening of the wall of the heart tube, forming the atrioventricular septum.

The end is in all cases the formation of a tubular heart, running through the pericardium, and connected at both ends with the primary body cavity. Dependent upon the degree of torsion, the heart tube may lie more transversely, with the atrium on the right and the ventricle on the left (Pteropoda, *Limax*), or longitudinally, with the atrium in front and the ventricle behind (*Bithynia, Pomatias, Crepidula*). In *Planorbis* the atrium lies behind at first, but during the development of the heart the whole anlage turns through 180°, so that in the end the atrium is situated in front, the ventricle behind it.

The wall of the heart tube is thin at first, and consists of flat cells. Soon it begins to thicken, and becomes multi-layered. It differentiates into endothelium and muscle cells. The muscle layer consists of crossing and anastomosing fibres. The lumen is traversed from the beginning by irregular strands of mesodermal cells; some of these differentiate perhaps into blood corpuscles, but others into muscle cells. Consequently the cavity of atrium and ventricle is later traversed by muscle trabeculae, attaching with fine branched prolongations to the walls.

The *blood vessels* originate as clefts in the mesoderm of the primary body cavity, which are at first independent of the heart. They connect secondarily with the ends of the heart tube, the ventricle communicating with the aorta, and the atrium with the efferent vein of the gill or lung. The arterial system generally appears earlier than the venous system. Often a blood sinus in the foot, which may function as a larval heart, is the first vessel to appear (e.g. in *Paludina*). Later this sinus becomes narrower and narrower in *Paludina*, and gives rise to the anterior portion of the aorta. The remaining part of the aorta arises, according to VON ERLANGER (1891), from a sinus surrounding the stomach and liver. The definitive venous sinuses appear only much later as cavities around the gut.

The development of the heart in the Cephalopoda differs considerably from that in other molluscs. It is true that heart formation in *Sepia*, as described by DISTASO (1908), shows some resemblance to its development in gastropods. The heart originates here as a part of the peri-intestinal sinus, bulging into the coelom (pericardial cavity); the wall of this part later differentiates into heart musculature. The heart remains connected with the gut through the mesocardium.

Heart development is much more different in *Loligo*, where the peri-intestinal sinus is lacking, according to NAEF (1909). It takes place quite independently from the pericardium, which connects only secondarily with the heart. The *ventricle* arises from paired cavities in the meso-derm. At first they form a pair of parallel tubes, not connected with other vessels. Later, they fuse in the median plane in their posterior parts. Each gives rise to a ventricle with its own aorta cephalica. On further development the left aorta cephalica obliterates. The left ventricle remains behind in its growth; in the adult heart it forms only an appendage taking up the left branchial vein. The *atria* are not morphological parts of the heart. They arise from the branchial veins, secondarily joining the heart, and are not taken up in the pericardium.

The *pericardium* originates as a pair of clefts in the mesoderm in the posterior part of the embryo, on either side of the gut. They have an irregular boundary at first, but are later lined by a distinct epithelium. According to FAUSSEK (1901) both the pericardium and the kidneys take origin from these cavities. This is contested by DISTASO and NAEF, however; according to these authors there is no primary connection between pericardium and kidney. The pericardial cavities increase in size, and envelop the gonad and certain parts of the vascular system. They unite in the median plane, temporarily forming a mesentery which soon disappears for the greater part; in this way the unpaired pericardium is formed. This lies above the heart, and occupies the upper part of the visceral sac as a spacious cavity. When the ventricle has been formed, the unpaired pericardium in *Loligo* grows with four flaps from above round the heart, on either side extending before and behind the atrium. Beneath the atria the suspensory of the heart remains, the sagittal part of which forms the mesocardium.

The *blood vessels* arise as lacunar cavities in the mesoderm. The lining mesoderm cells form pseudo-epithelial walls. At first two large sinuses appear, the *sinus posterior* and the *sinus cephalicus*. Besides these, in the extra-embryonic region a large *perivitelline sinus* occurs between the ectoderm and the perivitelline membrane; it plays an important part in yolk resorption. The perivitelline sinus is connected with the cephalic sinus by a dorsal and ventral *median yolk vessel*. The sinus cephalicus surrounds the inner yolk-sac at the level of the eyes. The sinus posterior lies as a large lacuna behind the midgut, between the inner yolk-sac and the shell gland (Fig. 49). On either side it takes up the *mantle vein*. Its lateral parts are continuous with the paired *venae cavae*. These veins arise in *Sepia* from the posterior sinus, according to DISTASO, portions of the latter being separated during the median fusion of the coelomic cavities. They have no proper wall. The paired venae cavae run forwards on either side of the hindgut, and join in front of it to form the *unpaired vena cava*, connecting with the sinus cephalicus. On either side the *afferent vein of the gill* is connected with the paired vena cava.

Blood circulation in *Loligo* is, according to PORTMANN (1926), in this first period exclusively due to contractions of the outer yolk-sac. Mesodermal muscle cells, lying between the ectoderm and the perivitelline membrane, contract. The blood between the two layers is squeezed out, in a dorsoventral direction. The blood, laden with food substances from the yolk, is pressed through the lower yolk vessel to the cephalic sinus. From here it runs through the head lacunae and the upper yolk vessel back to the perivitelline sinus. Part of it passes through the caval vein backwards into the posterior sinus. This circulation provides at the same time for respiration.

In a second period the central organs of blood circulation appear in the region of the posterior sinus. The arteries arise as channels in the mesoderm, around which the cells arrange themselves regularly. The *aorta cephalica* runs from the heart to the cephalic sinus, whereas the unpaired *aorta posterior* extends from the median part of the ventricle to the sinus posterior.

The sinus posterior is pushed upwards by the development of the heart and pericardium. At first it loses its connection both with the venae cavae and the mantle veins, but later the mantle veins again connect with it. The *branchial veins*, communicating at one end with the venae cavae, connect at their other extremity with the heart; in this way they form a loop at the base of each gill. A part of this loop begins to widen, bulges sac-like into the pericardium, and becomes the *branchial heart*. The remaining part of the loop grows out into the gill. However, the branchial hearts for a long time keep a direct connection with the ventricle; the gill circulation is only later inserted between the two. The cephalic sinus is narrowed by the strong development of the head organs to a system of lacunae between the organs.

Blood circulation now occurs as follows: The lower yolk vessel from the perivitelline sinus now ends in a sinus surrounding the statocysts. From this cavity there is a direct connection with the sinus posterior. The blood runs backwards through the vena cava, which divides in its two branches, each of which debouches in a branchial heart. From the latter, the blood passes (at first directly, later by way of the gills) to the ventricle; then either through the aorta posterior to the sinus posterior and mantle, or through the aorta anterior to the cephalic sinus, and from here through the upper yolk vessel back to the perivitelline sinus.

In the third period first the lower, then the upper yolk vessel is interrupted. Now there is no connection left between the outer yolk sinus and the embryo. The sinus posterior is still more reduced; ultimately, it becomes the unpaired *abdominal vein*. In this way the blood circulation of the adult animal is established.

From proliferations of the wall of the pericardium, surrounding the branchial hearts, the *pericardial glands* are formed, which invaginate partly into the branchial hearts.

From RANZI's experiments (1928a, 1931a, 1931b) it appears that the development of the sinus posterior is independent of the inner yolk-sac: it may be developed in a normal way, while the inner yolk-sac is lacking. A well-developed pericardial cavity is a prerequisite for a normal development of the heart; if the former is reduced, the heart is always reduced too. The walls of the vessels and of the heart may differentiate irrespective of the presence of blood.

17. Kidney

The kidneys of *Acanthochiton* originate as ventrolateral outgrowths of the pericardium, extending laterad on the dorsal side of the lateral nerve trunks. They end blindly at first, but then they grow out further, and open to the outside by way of the nephric pores. The original connection with the pericardium remains as the renopericardial funnel.

In the Lamellibranchiata the kidneys arise, as described above (p. 244), from the posterolateral parts of the common mesodermal cell mass, which round off forming the left and right nephric vesicle. In the Unionidae the first anlage of the kidney is formed on either side by one large cell with a clear vesicular nucleus (HARMS, 1909). This gives rise by division to a small group of four or five cells, in which a lumen appears. The nephric vesicles lie at first on either side of the hindgut. They elongate into tubules, and shift beneath the pericardium. They then bend forming a loop, consisting of an inner and outer arm connected dorsally. Both arms grow considerably in length. One of them fuses at its extremity with the ectoderm, and breaks through into the mantle cavity. In *Dreissensia* (MEISENHEIMER, 1901a) and the Unionidae (HARMS, 1909; HERBERS, 1913) the inner arms of the two kidneys first connect beneath the gut. Then the lateral angles of the common part grow out in a lateral direction, and connect with the mantle cavity. In *Dreissensia* and *Mytilus* (AHTING, 1902) a small invagination of the ectodermal epithelium of the mantle cavity contributes to the formation of the nephric pore. The other arm of the kidney grows forwards, then bends dorsally, and opens at its tip into the pericardium. Here a funnel-shaped renopericardial duct, provided with a ciliary flame, is formed. Afterwards the kidney may be thrown into coils by considerable growth in length. In the Unionidae an increase in surface occurs by folding inwards of its walls. In *Mytilus* the kidney does not become loop-shaped, but remains a straight tube, which forms numerous lateral outgrowths. Similar side-branches are also formed in *Nucula* (DREW, 1901).

The cells of the kidney are often strongly vacuolated at an early stage. They have large nuclei with big nucleoli, and a weakly-staining cytoplasm. In later stages the cells may be laden with concretions.

Among the Gastropoda, the kidneys are paired in some Prosobranchia, e.g. *Patella* and *Haliotis*. In *Haliotis* the left kidney remains much smaller than the right. In *Paludina, Ampullaria* and *Pomatias*, the kidney primordia are at first paired, but the development of the left one is arrested at an early stage. In the other gastropods the kidney is unpaired from the beginning; it is situated on the right side, as a rule, but on the left in sinistral forms, like *Physa*.

In *Paludina* (VON ERLANGER, 1891; OTTO and TÖNNIGES, 1906) and *Ampullaria* (FERNANDO, 1931b) a thickening appears in the ventral wall of the pericardial vesicles, even before their complete fusion. These thickenings then evaginate, forming paired renal primordia. The left one soon shows an arrest of development. According to DRUMMOND (1902) and OTTO and TÖNNIGES, it is taken up, together with the anlage of its excretory duct, into the efferent parts of the reproductive organs. The right kidney retains its original connection with the pericardium. It is tubular at first, then extends forwards and backwards, and becomes saccular.

In other gastropods the kidney arises from the postero-lateral part of the common mesodermal cell mass (cf. above, p. 247). It is solid at first, but then the cells arrange themselves radially, and a lumen is formed. In this way a thick-walled nephric vesicle is formed, closely applied to the ectoderm (Fig. 46). This vesicle now begins to elongate, and becomes tubular. In *Planorbis* (PÖTZSCH, 1904) and *Physa* (WIERZEJSKI, 1905) the sequence of events is slightly different, the kidney primordium first elongating to a solid strand, which then becomes hollow.

One end of the renal tubule remains in touch with the ectoderm, the other end lies against the pericardium. In *Haliotis* (CROFTS, 1938) and *Pomatias* (CREEK, 1951) the kidney and pericardium communicate from the outset through a wide renopericardial opening (Fig. 46). In most cases, however, the lumina are separated at first, and the kidney breaks through only secondarily into the pericardium. In *Bithynia* (VON ERLANGER, 1892) and *Limax* (MEISENHEIMER, 1898) the lumen of the kidney is T-shaped. The right arm connects with the ectoderm of the mantle cavity, the left with the pericardium, while the vertical part becomes the renal sac. In *Patella* (SMITH, 1935) and *Crepidula* (MORITZ, 1939) no renopericardial communication has been observed.

The outer end of the renal tubule lies against the ectoderm in the region of the mantle cavity. Here its lumen breaks through to the outside. At this point a distinct invagination of the ectoderm occurs, giving rise to the *primary ureter*. In *Paludina* this invagination is paired at first, opposite each primary nephric primordium. The left one remains rudimentary, however, and is taken up in the efferent duct of the reproductive organs (DRUMMOND, 1902; OTTO and TÖNNIGES, 1906). The right one gives rise to the definitive kidney duct, in which, however, the whole right horn of the mantle cavity is also included, which is separated from the remaining part of this cavity by a constriction, and then elongates considerably (OTTO and TÖNNIGES; JOHANSSON, 1951). The same holds for *Ampullaria* (FERNANDO, 1931b). In *Planorbis* (PÖTZSCH, 1904) and *Pomatias* (CREEK, 1951) the greater part of the efferent kidney duct is mesodermal, and takes rise from the nephric vesicle, only a small part near the orifice being ectodermal. Eventually the ureter opens into the mantle cavity on the right side (on the left in sinistral species), near the anus. In the land pulmonates it is supplemented by a *secondary ureter*. This arises as a groove in the outer wall of the mantle cavity, which closes to a tube from behind forwards. The primary ureter opens into the posterior end of this groove, so that it is prolonged by the secondary ureter to the anterior edge of the mantle. In a similar way a secondary ureter is formed in *Paludina*, according to JOHANSSON (1951).

On further development the kidney begins to extend. Its cavity widens, and its wall becomes thinner, so that it becomes sac-like. A great increase in surface occurs by folds growing inwards, at first especially from its outer (dorsal) wall. These folds are lined by a cuboidal epithelium, while the interior is occupied by connective tissue and blood vessels. Later a considerable increase in size and number of these folds may occur, whereby the whole organ develops a more or less spongy structure (e.g. *Paludina*). The ureter may elongate strongly, and be thrown into several coils (e.g. *Planorbis*). Folds may also appear in the ureter (*Ampullaria, Arion*).

During torsion the kidney is shifted from ventrally on the right to dorsally on the left side. By further ingrowth of the mantle cavity it may come to lie secondarily in its roof (e.g. *Crepidula*). In *Arion* the kidney embraces the pericardium in front and behind, so that it becomes crescent-shaped; finally its two ends meet, the kidney now forming a complete ring around the pericardium. In its turn it is surrounded in a similar way by the lung (HEYDER, 1909).

The wall of the renal sac consists of a single-layered epithelium, lined externally by a tunica propria. The cells of the epithelium possess numerous excretion vacuoles, which may later coalesce into one big vacuole. Yellowish concretions are often found in the vacuoles. The apical part of the cells is sometimes filled with granules. Here the Golgi bodies also lie in *Limnaea*, whereas the mitochondria are scattered throughout the cytoplasm (HIRSCHLER, 1918). In the renopericardial funnel there are large columnar cells, bearing long cilia. Ciliary cells may also occur in the ureter or near the nephric pore (e.g. *Patella, Haliotis, Arion*).

In the Cephalopoda the kidneys arise from paired mesodermal rudiments. According to Faussek (1901) they have a common anlage with the pericardium on either side. This is denied by Distaso (1908: *Sepia*) and Naef (1909: *Loligo*). According to these authors the kidneys differentiate from the mesoderm, simultaneously with the pericardium, as solid primordia. They develop a lumen, and are transformed in this way into pouches with an epithelial wall. They exhibit a close relationship to the venae cavae from the beginning. Their wall adjacent to these vessels consists of a tall columnar epithelium, whereas a flat epithelium is found elsewhere. The renopericardial connection arises secondarily, subsequent to the formation of the pericardium, as a short channel with cuboidal epithelium. At the end of the embryonic period the partition between the two kidneys disappears medioventrally, so that they form an unpaired sac. In *Sepia* there is in addition a dorsal connection, an evagination arising from the dorsal side of the right kidney, which connects with the left kidney, and applies itself against the hindgut. Where the wall of the kidney lies against the veins, venal appendices are formed by folding; they are lined with tall glandular cells.

According to Ranzi (1931a, 1931b) the renal epithelium in *Loligo* shows a normal differentiation when the blood is absent (e.g. in embryos cut away from the yolk).

18. Reproductive organs

The gonad of *Acanthochiton* originates as a solid proliferation of the pericardium, forming a cell strand extending cranially, which becomes hollow only later. Primordial germ cells with large nuclei, and a network of chromatic substance in the cytoplasm, lie against this strand. In *Trachydermon* and *Nuttalina* the gonad primordium is paired at first. The gonoducts arise as paired outgrowths, opening into the mantle cavity.

In the Lamellibranchiata the gonad primordium becomes recognizable at an earlier or later stage, according as the primordial germ cells differentiate earlier or later. The latter are generally large round cells with big clear vesicular nuclei, containing one or two distinct nucleoli and peripherally arranged chromatin, and a clear cytoplasm.

The primordial germ cells may already at an early embryonic stage become visible in the mesoderm bands. In *Sphaerium* there is one primordial gonocyte in each mesoderm band (Okada, 1936, 1939) (Fig. 65a). They arise from the primary mesoblasts M_l and M_r, after each of the latter has split off three small mesodermal elements (Woods, 1931). They are characterized, in addition to the above-mentioned particulars, by the possession of a mitochondrial cloud around the nucleus. This is

originally derived from the oocyte. During cleavage it passes by differential divisions into the mesodermal teloblasts (cf. above, p. 84), then
in a similar way into the primordial germ cells. WOODS considers this
mitochondrial cloud as a 'Keimbahn determinant', not in the sense of
causal factors, but as marker of the sequence of cells leading to the germ

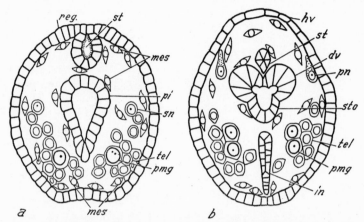

Fig. 65. Frontal sections through successive larval stages of *Sphaerium japonicum*,
showing primordial germ cells in mesoderm bands. *dv*, primordium of larval
liver; *hv*, head vesicle; *in*, hindgut; *mes*, mesenchyme cells; *pi*, gut; *pmg*, primordial germ cells; *pn*, anlage of protonephridium; *reg*, rudiment of cerebral
ganglion; *sn*, nephroblast; *st*, stomodaeum; *sto*, stomach; *tel*, teloblastic cell
mass of mesoderm. After OKADA, 1936.

cells. He supposes that it consists of reserve food substances, not consumed in the cells having a low metabolism (WOODS, 1932). Each of the
two primordial gonocytes divides once (Fig. 65b), but then they remain
inactive for a long time. During further development they come to lie
in the ventral wall of the lower pericardial cavity. Then division re-
commences. The mitochondria are now distributed among the germ
cells, and disappear, so that eventually each germ cell has only a few
scattered mitochondria. The two groups of germ cells come to lie near
the median plane. Each now forms a gonad primordium, which is solid
at first, but later develops a cavity in its centre.

In *Cyclas* the primordial germ cells differentiate from the common
cell masses on either side of the hindgut, which give rise to heart and
kidney too (MEISENHEIMER, 1901b). They multiply rapidly, and form
paired cell groups ventrally to the pericardium, which then unite to an
unpaired cell mass.

When the primordial germ cells differentiate still later, they split off from the wall of the pericardium. For instance, in *Dreissensia* (MEISEN-HEIMER, 1901a) a local thickening of the wall of the pericardium occurs, posteriorly in the median plane between the nephrostomes. It becomes detached from the pericardium, and a rapid multiplication of cells occurs. It extends laterally and cranially, then divides in two halves. In *Anodonta* (HERBERS, 1913) the reproductive organs likewise arise from the wall of the pericardium, in front of the nephrostomes. On either side a tubular outgrowth, with one-layered epithelial wall, appears, which grows downwards into the foot. Here it branches repeatedly, and gives rise to the gonad. Primordial germ cells differentiate at the ends of the ramifications; later the sex cells are formed in these places. The gonads of *Mya* also grow ventrally as branched tubes from a pair of primordia situated ventrally to the pericardium (COE and TURNER, 1938). The rudiments of the two sides are connected by a transverse strand behind. The tip of each ramification forms a syncytium containing two kinds of nuclei; the larger give rise to germ cells, the smaller to follicle cells. The latter have a nutritive function. They have a large central vacuole; later an accumulation of lipid and protein granules occurs in the cytoplasm, being somewhat different in the two sexes. The germ cells lie scattered along the periphery of the tubes; local accumulations of these cells may form new centres for the outgrowth of side-branches.

In *Sphaerium* the anterior part of the gonad gives rise to the *male sex gland*. The region behind it narrows, and forms the *efferent duct* of the sperm, debouching into the posterior *female gland*, from which the *hermaphroditic duct* runs to the cloaca. This duct is formed by the lumen of the gonad extending backwards through movement apart of the cells; it breaks through into the cloacal cavity near the nephric pore (WOODS, 1931). In *Mya* the gonads open into the suprabranchial cavities at the position of the original primordia. A large central lumen appears in each gonad by the moving apart of the follicle cells, beginning at the orifice and extending forwards; the transverse connection becomes hollow in the same way (COE and TURNER, 1938). In *Anodonta* the outgrowing gonad applies itself laterally against the ectoderm of the side of the foot; here the genital pore breaks through. The connection of the gonad with the pericardium is lost, but its proximal end remains as a closed gonopericardial duct. This duct, and the efferent duct of the gonad are lined with long cilia (HERBERS, 1913).

The primordial germ cells of the Gastropoda exhibit the same characteristics as those of the Lamellibranchiata: a large clear vesicular nucleus with big nucleolus, the chromatin arranged along the nuclear membrane; a clear not very basophil cytoplasm, which is poor in ribonucleic acid.

The gonad may also in this group become recognizable as such at very different stages.

In *Paludina* the *gonad* originates as a proliferation of the wall of the pericardium on the left side next to the rudimentary left kidney (VON ERLANGER, 1891; DRUMMOND, 1902; OTTO and TÖNNIGES, 1906). It grows out into a cell strand below the liver. At its end a club-shaped thickening is formed, in which a lumen appears by a moving apart of the cells. In *Littorina* the gonad arises likewise from a proliferation of the pericardium wall turned towards the liver. Initially a solid mass of cells with heavily stained nuclei is formed. Then a central lumen appears in this mass (DELSMAN, 1912). In other cases the gonad becomes first recognizable as an isolated mesodermal cell mass in the body cavity, e.g. in *Crepidula* (MORITZ, 1939), *Limnaea* (FRASER, 1946), *Oncidium* (JOYEUX-LAFFUIE, 1882), *Helix* (ANCEL, 1903) and *Arion* (PABST, 1914) (Fig. 66, a–b). This cell mass is at first solid, but then a lumen appears by separation of the cells. It is lined by a single-layered germinal epithelium. In some cases the gonad primordium is only recognizable as such, after it has come into connection with the inner end of the ectodermal anlage of the gonoduct, e.g. in *Limax* (HOFFMANN, 1922) and *Arion* (LAVIOLETTE, 1954).

Mesodermal cells form at an early stage a connective tissue envelope round the gonad. Later the gonad becomes lobate by local evaginations of its surface. Secondary evaginations may give rise to acini, in which eventually the ovo- and spermatogenesis take place.

The gonad of *Paludina* remains from the beginning in close connection with the rudimentary left kidney. Its lumen opens eventually into the latter close to the renopericardial opening. This communication between the left kidney and the pericardium gets lost. The rest of the kidney becomes the initial part of the *primary gonoduct* (DRUMMOND, 1902; OTTO and TÖNNIGES, 1906). The left horn of the mantle cavity elongates greatly, and becomes a tubular channel, that forms the rest of the primary gonoduct (OTTO and TÖNNIGES; JOHANSSON, 1951). In the female, the gonoduct grows considerably in length, and begins to coil. The *albumen gland* develops at a very late stage from the original blind end of the horn of the mantle cavity, near the mouth of the left kidney. This part elongates and forms from eight to twelve tubular evaginations, that give rise to the gland. The remaining part of the gonoduct develops into the *oviduct, receptaculum seminis, uterus* and *vagina*. In the male, the primary gonoduct gives rise to the proximal part of the *vas deferens* only. Its distal part develops from a furrow in the floor of the mantle cavity, which closes into a tube and is constricted off from the epithelium. It then grows out independently forward towards the right tentacle, which it traverses along its entire length, to open at its tip. Near the orifice the rudiment of the *penis sac* is formed as a groove. The secondary gonoduct is enveloped by muscle fibres at this place, forming the *ductus ejaculatorius*. Hence, the gonoducts of *Paludina* are ectodermal in both sexes, apart from a short proximal part which is derived from the left kidney. This part is not ciliated, in contrast to the ectodermal portions.

In *Crepidula* the penis develops as a small outgrowth at the head behind the right tentacle. At its lower side there is a shallow ciliated furrow which continues on the right side of the neck region towards the edge of the mantle, where it is continuous with a tubular gonoduct. This is supposed to arise from an outgrowth of the gonad, growing forwards to the posterior end of the ciliated furrow, into which it opens (MORITZ, 1939).

Very complicated is the course of morphogenesis of the gonoducts in the Pulmonata. It has extensively been studied, e.g. in *Limnaea* (FRASER, 1946), *Bulinus* (DE LARAMBERGUE, 1933, 1939), *Arion* (PABST, 1914; LAVIOLETTE, 1954) and *Limax* (HOFFMANN, 1922).

The efferent part of the reproductive organs is derived in *Limnaea* and *Bulinus* from two completely separated primordia: (1) the rudiment of the primary gonoduct, as an ectodermal invagination from the mantle cavity, (2) the anlage of the copulatory organs and the distal part of the vas deferens, as an ectodermal invagination behind the right (in *Bulinus* the left) tentacle. In *Arion* and *Limax*, on the contrary, these organs arise from a common primordium.

The rudiment of the *primary gonoduct* occurs in all species mentioned at an early stage as an ectodermal invagination in the posterior part of the mantle cavity, close behind the efferent duct of the kidney (Fig. 66, a–b). It is directed backwards. It grows in, and connects at an early stage with the rudiment of the gonad. In *Limnaea* a secondary outgrowth forms at the base of the primary invagination; it is directed anteriorly. In the meantime the original invagination is displaced towards the left in consequence of the rotation of the visceral sac. From this point both tubes are now directed to the right, forming an acute angle with each other (Fig. 66d). The opening of the original invagination loses its connection with the mantle cavity proper (a small separate part of this cavity remaining connected with the gonoduct, however). The anterior limb of the gonoduct now grows towards the right side of the body, and reaches the body wall at the place of the future ♀ genital pore, which breaks through only much later, however. In *Bulinus* the rudiment of the gonoduct likewise loses its connection with the surface, and the ♀ genital pore is secondarily formed by a side-branch from the primary gonoduct opening at the surface.

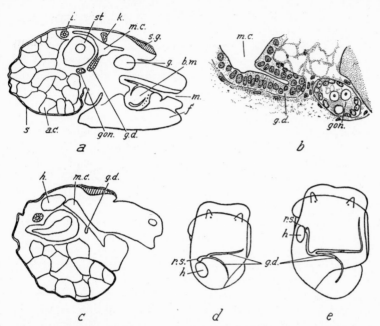

Fig. 66. Development of the reproductive tract in *Limnaea stagnalis appressa*. (a) Mediosagittal section through 6-day old embryo (cf. Pl. XII A), indicating positions of the reproductive tract primordia. (b) Reproductive tract primordia at higher magnification. (c) Oblique section through 8-day embryo. The posterior part of the mantle cavity, from a point just anterior to the primary invagination of the genital duct anlage, will become the seminal receptacle and part of its duct. (d) Diagram of reproductive tract in 10-day old embryo. (e) The same in 14-day old embryo. *a.c.*, albumen cells; *b.m.*, buccal mass; *f*, foot; *g*, ganglion; *g.d.*, genital duct; *gon.*, gonad; *h*, heart; *i*, hindgut; *k*, kidney; *m*, mouth; *m.c.*, mantle cavity; *r.s.*, receptaculum seminis; *s*, shell; *s.g.*, mantle fold; *st*, stomach. After FRASER, 1946.

In *Limax* the original opening of the invagination is first displaced ventrally, so that it comes to lie outside the mantle cavity. Then it shifts forwards during the outgrowth of the head region, ultimately reaching its definitive place on the right side of the head behind the tentacle. A swelling near the orifice forms the rudiment of the copulatory organs (in *Arion* this gives rise to the so-called 'upper atrium').

The proximal part of the gonoduct, near the gonad, remains thin, and gives rise to the *hermaphroditic duct*. In *Arion* its proximal part arises from the gonad, according to PABST. Later its epithelium is thrown into folds. Evaginations of the hermaphroditic duct give rise to the *vesiculae seminales* in *Limnaea*. The distal end of this part may expand into a *fertilization chamber*.

The following part of the gonoduct widens considerably. Proximally, a blind pouch occurs, from which tubular lateral evaginations grow out. They form secondary outgrowths, and become glandular, together forming the *albumen gland*.

The rest of the gonoduct divides into a male and female duct. First the lumen is divided by folds from the wall, then a longitudinal splitting may occur. In the Basommatophora this division is complete. It begins in *Bulinus* at the distal end; in *Limnaea* it progresses from both ends at the same time. In *Limax* the division is proximally incomplete, a longitudinal fold extending into the lumen; distally this fold fuses with the opposite wall, so that two separate channels are formed. In *Arion* no division takes place at all.

The female duct may then differentiate further into various parts with different structure. Accessory glands (e.g. the *glandula nidamentaria accessoria* in *Limnaea*) may arise by lateral outgrowth. From a part of the male duct the *prostata* is formed by widening of the lumen, folding of the wall, and the formation of finger-like evaginations.

The *receptaculum seminis* is formed in *Arion* and *Limax* from the gonoduct by constriction. At first the lumen is divided in two parts by folds arising from the opposite walls; then the receptaculum is constricted off, beginning at its proximal end and progressing towards the genital orifice. In *Limnaea* only the distal part of the duct of the receptaculum originates in this way. The proximal part, and the receptaculum proper, arise, according to FRASER, from the deeper part of the mantle cavity, which is constricted off from the rest of the cavity at an early stage, and remains in connection with the gonoduct by the original invagination opening (Fig. 66, c–e).

In *Limnaea* and *Bulinus*, a solid strand of cells grows forward from the place of the ♀ genital pore, in the direction of the copulatory organs (Fig. 66e). This strand becomes hollow, and thereby gives rise to the middle part of the *ductus deferens* (the proximal part arising by splitting from the gonoduct, the distal part from the primordium of the copulatory organs). In *Arion* and *Agriolimax* the vas deferens originates as an outgrowth from the upper atrium, which connects proximally with the gonoduct. In *Limax* it arises by constriction from the penis and the distal part of the primary gonoduct.

The primordium of the *copulatory organs* (penis and preputium) originates in *Limnaea* and *Bulinus* as an ectodermal invagination behind the base of the right (in *Bulinus* the left) tentacle, surrounded by a small group of mesenchyme cells. In *Limax* the penis is formed as a lateral bud of the swollen distal part of the gonoduct. In *Arion* no true penis occurs.

The invagination in *Limnaea* and *Bulinus* soon becomes deeper, and tubular. Its one end remains in connection with the surface (with the gonoduct in *Limax*), and becomes the ♂ genital pore. The other end bulges into the body cavity. Its wall thickens, and a differentiation into *penis* and *preputium* takes place. In *Bulinus* this occurs by a process of delamination, the central part becoming separated as the penis from the enveloping sheath. Hence the penis has a lumen from the beginning, and remains connected with the preputium both proximally and distally. In *Limnaea*, on the contrary, the penis forms as a papilla at the inner end of the cavity of the preputium, which is pierced by the distal part of the vas deferens. The latter is formed here by the outgrowth of a narrow duct from the inner end of the preputium, which connects secondarily with the middle part of the vas deferens. In *Limax* the vas deferens arises by constriction from the penis primordium, beginning at the connection of the latter with the gonoduct, and progressing in proximal direction along the penis, without however extending to its proximal end, so that a caecum is formed in this place. First the lumen is divided by folds, then external constriction follows, which extends even some distance along the distal part of the gonoduct. A penis retractor is formed from muscle cells, running from the blind end of the penis towards the opposite body wall.

In the Cephalopoda the primordial germ cells may become visible at an early stage. According to FAUSSEK (1901) they are found in *Loligo* in the posterior part of the blastoderm between the first rudiments of the gills, as very large cells with large bean-shaped nuclei and abundant cytoplasm, lying between the mesoderm and the perivitelline membrane. According to TEICHMANN (1903) these cells have arisen by proliferation from the superficial layer of the blastoderm. At a later stage, the primordium of the gonad is found as an unpaired median cell group ventrally against the sinus posterior. When the two pericardial rudiments unite in the midline, this occurs ventrally to the gonad primordium, so that this comes to lie at first in the dorsal mesocardium, and later forms a protruding ridge in the mediodorsal wall of the pericardial cavity.

The *gonoducts* take rise from the walls of the pericardium, as furrows which close to a tube. The formation of the female reproductive organs in *Sepia* was extensively studied by DÖRING (1908). The rudiment of the *oviduct* originates as a short, deep evagination of the coelomic epithelium, which closes to a tube, progressing in anterio-posterior direction. In this way, by continuous formation and closure of a furrow, it extends to the ovary. Its wall exhibits longitudinal folds at an early stage;

s

later secondary folds appear. Its distal part comes into connection with the rudiment of the *oviduct gland*. This arises from an epithelial thickening in the ectoderm of the mantle cavity, which is originally paired. Both thickenings sink in, forming grooves, which then close to a channel from their hind end. The right one now begins to degenerate; the left constricts from the surface and gives rise to a pouch with single-layered wall, still connected with the surface by a narrow cleft. This pouch now surrounds the anterior end of the oviduct rudiment, which eventually breaks through into the pouch upon a papilla. Epithelial lamellae, with a connective tissue core, form in the wall of the oviduct gland. The epithelium differentiates into gland cells with basal nuclei, and intervening ciliary cells with apical nuclei. Later accessory lamellae are formed. The *nidamental glands* arise likewise from ectodermal thickenings of the visceral sac, ventrally to the posterior ends of the kidneys. They sink in, and close from their hind end into short pouches. Lamellae are formed as in the oviduct gland, especially from their outer wall. The *accessory nidamental glands* are the latest to appear, as paired circular ectodermal thickenings on the ventral side of the visceral sac, a short distance in front of the nidamental glands. Then epithelial ridges are formed, running almost radially, somewhat curved, and branched in their peripheral parts. These ridges thicken at their free margins, and fuse with each other, leaving rows of pores which lead into flask-like grooves. These grooves are the rudiments of the tubuli. Connective tissue partitions grow in between the tubuli. The latter grow inwards, and branch at their inner ends. From these parts the true glandular tubes take rise, possessing a tall columnar epithelium. The left and right gland unite. Secondarily their fields of discharge are reduced by subepithelial musculature, intruding from all sides; at the same time they grow out forwards. The gonoducts and accessory glands in *Loligo* and *Sepiola* develop in a similar way.

CHAPTER VII

Conclusions

In this chapter we shall try to sketch out the principal traits of molluscan development, as they emerge from the causal analysis developed in previous chapters.

The central problem, underlying every investigation in developmental physiology, can be formulated as follows: How does the ordered spatial multiplicity of the adult organism arise in the course of development from the relatively simple structure of the initial stages?

The 'outfit', which the embryo is provided with at the beginning of its career, consists in the main of three components: (1) its genotypical constitution, located in the genes in the chromosomes, and which is, in the fertilized egg, derived half from the mother and half from the father; (2) a certain assortment of substances in the egg cytoplasm, and (3) a cortical field.

We have seen in chapter I that the cytoplasmic substances are accumulated in the egg during oogenesis. The growing oocyte derives a regular supply of substances from its surroundings, among which the nurse cells or follicle cells presumably are especially important. The ingested substances may be partly laid down as such in the cell. In general, however, they will be used as raw materials in synthetic processes, by which the specific ooplasmic substances, characteristic of the full-grown oocyte as a reproductive cell, are produced.

An important centre of this synthetic activity is found in the nucleolus. In view of the close topographical and genetical relationships between nucleolus and chromosomes, it appears probable that the chemical transformations taking place in the nucleolus are under the control of the genes of the diploid oocyte nucleus. The synthesized substances, among which are presumably basic and other polypeptides and ribonucleoproteins, are passed on to the cytoplasm for further elaboration. With the aid of cytoplasmic microsomes and Golgi bodies further synthetic processes are accomplished, until the egg has attained its final size and species-specific composition.

This species-specificity may in part be due to the presence of proteins or of other high-molecular substances of unique composition or steric structure, such as are detected in immunological reactions. It must be emphasized, however, that it is not strictly necessary to admit the exis-

263

tence of such compounds; differences in relative proportions of common substances may, at least at this early stage, suffice to account for species-specificity.

The ooplasmic substances of the full-grown oocyte are in general rather uniformly distributed throughout the egg. Distinct localizations of these substances are at this stage scarcely encountered. Hence, the various parts of the inner egg cytoplasm are alike in their chemical composition and physical state; the spatial multiplicity of the egg is of a very low order.

On the other hand, it is hardly conceivable that the ordered pattern of events which manifests itself as soon as development gets going, should not have its starting-point in the structure of the unfertilized egg. In looking for the prodromes of the future spatial pattern in the unfertilized egg, it is natural to turn to the egg cortex. We have seen the important role played by the cortex from the very beginning of development. It is the seat of polarity and dorsiventrality. The cortical field provides the co-ordinates, to which all developmental processes are related. Apparently, this field is present as soon as development begins. We must assume that it is built up in some way or other during oogenesis. As a matter of fact, there are indications that it is present and has already come into operation in the oocyte (cf. p. 63).

We have come to the conclusion that the cortical field has not only a polar structure, but is also organized in dorsoventral and transverse directions (p. 194). Its two-dimensional pattern may be based on local differences in colloid or submicroscopic structure of the cortex. How can we imagine that such a pattern is established during oogenesis?

There are two possibilities that must be taken into consideration. On the one hand, the cortical field may be built up from within, as an automatic patterning process under the control e.g. of the oocyte nucleus. On the other hand, it is conceivable that the pattern of the cortical field is, so to speak, imprinted upon the egg from the outside. Although at first sight the first alternative may appear the most likely one, in my opinion there are strong arguments in favour of the second. In the first place, it is hard to understand in what way the oocyte nucleus could induce a two-dimensional pattern in the cortex, unless one assumes that the nucleus has a similar structure itself, and can send out directional 'messages' towards the periphery. But, moreover, we know that the polarity of the egg is indeed determined by its position in the ovary, the side from which the food stream reaches the growing oocyte becoming the vegetative end of the main axis of the egg in molluscs. As regards left-right asymmetry, according to STURTEVANT's hypothesis this is laid down in the immature, diploid egg during oogenesis (cf. p. 104). Though

STURTEVANT may have thought in the first place of the diploid oocyte nucleus as the controlling agent of asymmetry, his explanation also holds good if we assume that the surrounding (diploid) cells of the ovary are responsible.

With respect to dorsiventrality, matters are more difficult. We have found some indications that the early molluscan egg has no fixed dorsiventrality, and that the position of the plane of symmetry is only determined secondarily, e.g. by the penetration of the fertilizing sperm (*Cumingia*), or by the fusion of the polar lobe with one of the first two blastomeres. However, in the case of *Cumingia* (p. 92) it appears that, besides the sperm entrance point, there must be another factor, located in the egg, which decides whether the first cleavage furrow deviates to the left or to the right. Moreover, in most molluscan eggs, especially those without a polar lobe, nothing is known about epigenetic factors determining the plane of bilateral symmetry. Perhaps, the relationships are similar to those e.g. in the Amphibia, where a more or less labile determination of bilateral symmetry takes place in the ovary, which may easily be overthrown by epigenetic factors leading to the establishment of a new plane of symmetry.

However this may be, for the moment it appears the most likely hypothesis that the cortical field is built up during oogenesis by the action of the surrounding nurse cells or follicle. One may expect, then, that these cells would not lie in a haphazard way around the oocyte but are arranged according to a regular pattern. This is a consequence which lends itself to empirical verification. If it holds true, this may mean that the prodromes of pattern are passed down from the preceding generation to the next, which would represent an interesting modern version of the age-old idea of preformation.

As soon as development starts, an ordered sequence of processes is set going, in which the three components distinguished above: nucleus, cytoplasm with its substances, and cortex, interact. The cytoplasmic substances, starting from a state of roughly uniform distribution, begin to concentrate in certain regions of the egg, under the influence of attractive and repulsive forces emanating from the cortex. At the same time the nuclear cycle of maturation, amphimixis and cleavage takes its prescribed course, in which the positions and directions of nuclei and spindles are controlled by the cortical field too. The time relations and normal concatenation between these processes are regulated by an autonomous process in the cytoplasm, a kind of 'inner clock', set in motion either at the moment of fertilization or at the breakdown of the germinal vesicle, which follows its course independently of the nuclear cycle, and by which the various partial processes are called forth at the right moment. The result of this ordered sequence of events is the normal course of cleavage, and the differential distribution of the cytoplasmic substances among the cleavage cells.

Further complexity may now occur in various ways, of which especially two may be considered here. In the first place, the concentration of cytoplasmic substances in certain cells may create favourable conditions for the occurrence of chemical reactions or synthetic activities, in which new substances are produced. The activation of previously inhibited cell enzymes may play an important part here. The newly-formed substances may in their turn in subsequent divisions be unequally distributed among the cells.

Secondly, the primary chemo-differentiation may create the prerequisite conditions for the intervention of the nuclear genes in the developmental process. The genotypically identical cleavage nuclei become located in cells showing differences in physical and chemical properties of their cytoplasm. The interactions between nuclei and cytoplasm will result in differences among the reactions that are set going in the various parts of the germ. Nuclear genes, which have so far remained inactive, can begin to unfold their activity once they have found a suitable substrate on which to act. Therefore, in different parts of the germ different genes will be activated. Though no clear examples of the existence of this mechanism in the early development of molluscs are known up to the present, we may presume in analogy with other groups that it begins to play a part from a certain stage of development.

We saw that the primary chemo-differentiation, under the influence of the cortical field, forms the sufficient cause of larval differentiations, and lays down the general pattern of the embryo in broad outline (p. 197). Moreover, it conditions the local changes in cell shape and cell affinity, which bring about the morphogenetic movements leading to gastrulation and formation of the germ layers. However, the organogenesis and histogenesis of the adult organs require the intervention of new causal factors, which only appear during gastrulation consequent on the attainment of new topographical relationships between the cells. As regards the nature of the interactions thereby established, our knowledge is still very restricted. We only know that it has the character of an induction process in the case of the shell gland of the Gastropoda. Although there are a few indications of similar relationships in other cases (e.g. eye and optic ganglion in Cephalopoda), much work remains to be done in this field.

If we now look back on this brief survey of molluscan development, one or two things are very striking. In the first place, it is surprising how little has remained of the classical picture of the molluscan egg as a paradigm of mosaic development. The old, more or less static representation of development in this group has more and more given way to a dynamic picture, in which the spatial multiplicity of the adult animal is gradually built up by a system of directed movements.

The second observation that can be made is that this summary of molluscan development is, with little modification, applicable to almost any group of the animal kingdom. As a matter of fact, in my opinion the results of the last decennia point more and more to the fundamental unity of the main trends of development in various groups. It is not my intention to expound this view here in great detail. For this I may refer to my previous book *An Outline of Developmental Physiology* (1954).

Of course, there are important differences between the groups. In some, the differential distribution of cytoplasmic substances cannot be followed as easily as in the development of molluscs. This may in part be due to the fact that cytochemical methods have been employed to a lesser extent in those cases. It is probable, however, that there are real differences in this respect between the so-called 'mosaic' and 'regulation' eggs of older authors, at least as concerns the stage at which the germinal localizations occur.

VON UBISCH has, in a series of recent publications, defended the view that the germinal localizations are of little importance for determination. Cellular differentiation is governed, according to this author, by a system of gradients in combination with the genotypical constitution of the nuclei. Between those two there is a relationship such that particular genes are activated at certain levels of the gradients. The latter are based on differences in colloidal state of the cytoplasm. The cytoplasmic substances act only secondarily through their influence on the colloidal state of the cytoplasm.

In my opinion, VON UBISCH is here going too far in his rejection of the cytoplasmic substances as important causal agents in development. It is true that their importance has been greatly exaggerated in the classical theory of 'mosaic development'. But it can hardly be denied that the cytochemical composition of the cells in some way or other conditions their differentiation. Moreover, the view that the activation of the genes is, in a way, a biochemical process, depending on the chemical nature of the cytoplasmic components, for the moment affords a much more promising point of attack for future research than VON UBISCH's rather abstract 'Zuordnungs'–hypothesis. Finally, it seems to me that VON UBISCH has not sufficiently taken into account the evidence that the gradient-systems of the egg are, at least for the greater part, bound to the cortex.

It is self-evident that the picture of molluscan development drawn above has only a tentative character, and that much more research will be needed in order to fill this rough draft with a concrete content. Its main merit is that it enables us to map out the lines of future research.

In the first place, this will have to be directed towards an elucidation of the physical nature of the cortical field, and of the forces that it exerts upon the various components of the cells. Secondly, a characterization in biochemical terms of the various substances playing a part in morphogenesis, of the chemical reactions taking place between them, and of the synthetic processes preceding and accompanying differentiation, will be necessary. A knowledge of the submicroscopic structure of the cells, especially of the intracellular localization of various enzymes, may, in conjunction with the above-mentioned data, provide a clearer picture of the intracellular pattern of differentiation processes. It will then perhaps be possible to get a clearer understanding of the interactions between the nuclear genes and the cytoplasm, through which the genotypical constitution becomes actualized in development.

More and more we begin to see that the exploration of the prodigy of animal development, which began hardly seventy years ago, is still in its initial phase. The task still lying before us is immense. Our rate of progress will depend on choosing the right points of attack. If this book may help in defining them, it has fulfilled its purpose.

References

AHTING, K. (1902): Untersuchungen über die Entwickelung des Bojanus'schen Organs und des Herzens der Lamellibranchier. *Jen. Z. Naturwiss.* **36**, 181.

ALLEN, R. D. (1953): Fertilization and artificial activation in the egg of the surf-clam, *Spisula solidissima. Biol. Bull.* **105**, 213.

ANCEL, P. (1903): Histogénèse et structure de la glande hermaphrodite d'*Helix pomatia* (Linn.). *Arch. Biol.* **19**, 389.

ARENDSEN DE WOLFF-EXALTO, E. (1947): Some investigations on the embryonic development of *Limnaea stagnalis* L. *Proc. Kon. Ned. Akad. v. Wetensch., Amsterdam.* **50**, 315.

ARVY, L. (1949): Particularités de l'évolution nucléolaire au cours de l'ovogénèse chez *Limnaea stagnalis* L. *C.R. Ac. Sci. Paris* **228**, 1983.

—— (1950a): Données histologiques sur l'ovogénèse chez *Dentalium entale* Deshayes. *Arch. Biol.* **61**, 187.

—— (1950b): Activité nucléolaire et vitellogénèse chez *Eolis papillosa* L. *Bull. Soc. Zool. France* **75**, 159

ATTARDO, C. (1955a): Localizzazione della citocromo-ossidasi e dei lipidi nell' uovo di *Bithynia codiella. Ric. Scient.* **25**, 2797.

—— (1955b): Effetti dell' azide sodico sulle uova di *Bithynia codiella. Rend. Accad. Naz. Lincei, Cl. Sci.* (8) **19**, 83.

AVEL, M. (1925): Sur les propriétés physiques de l'appareil de Golgi des éléments génitaux des Pulmonés. *C.R. Soc. Biol.* **93**, 26.

BABA, K. (1938): The later development of a solenogastre, *Epimenia verrucosa* (Nierstrasz). *J. Dept. Agric. Kyusyu Imp. Univ.* **6**, 21.

BALDWIN, E. (1935): The energy sources in ontogenesis. VIII. The respiratory quotient of developing gastropod eggs. *J. exp. Biol.* **12**, 27.

BALLENTINE, R. (1940): Analysis of the changes in respiratory activity accompanying the fertilization of marine eggs. *J. Cell. Comp. Physiol.* **15**, 217.

BECK, K. (1912): Anatomie deutscher *Buliminus*-Arten. *Jen. Z. Naturwiss.* **48**, 187.

BERG, W. E. (1950): Lytic effects of sperm extracts on the eggs of *Mytilus edulis. Biol. Bull.* **98**, 128.

—— (1954a): Peptidases in isolated blastomeres of *Mytilus edulis. Proc. Soc. exp. Biol. Med.* **85**, 606.

—— (1954b): Investigations of cytoplasmic determination in mosaic eggs. Cellular biology: *Proc. 15th Ann. Biol. Colloquium*, 30.

BERG, W. E. and P. B. KUTSKY (1951): Physiological studies of differentiation in *Mytilus edulis*. I. The oxygen consumption of isolated blastomeres and polar lobes. *Biol. Bull.* **101**, 47.

BERTHIER, J. (1948): Le fer dans l'ovogénèse chez *Planorbis corneus*. *Bull. biol. Fr. Belg.* **82**, 61.

BEVELANDER, G. and P. BENZER (1948): Calcification in marine molluscs. *Biol. Bull.* **94**, 176.

BLOCH, I. (1896): Die embryonale Entwickelung der Radula von *Paludina vivipara*. *Jen. Z. Naturwiss.* **30**, 350.

BLOCH, S. (1938): Beitrag zur Kenntnis der Ontogenese von Süsswasser-pulmonaten, mit besonderer Berücksichtigung der Mitteldarmdrüse. *Rev. suisse Zool.* **45**, 157.

BLOCHMANN, F. (1882): Ueber die Entwicklung der *Neritina fluviatilis* Müll. *Z. wiss. Zool.* **36**, 125.

—— (1883): Beiträge zur Kenntnis der Entwicklung der Gastropoden. *Z. wiss. Zool.* **38**, 392.

BLUMRICH, J. (1891): Das Integument der Chitonen. *Z. wiss. Zool.* **52**, 404.

BOLOGNARI, A. (1954): Aspetti dell' ovogenesi di *Aplysia depilans* L. (Moll. Gast. Opis.). *Boll. Zool.* **21**, 185.

—— (1956): Particolari manifestazioni del nucleolo degli ovociti in accrescimento di *Haliotis lamellosa* Lam. (Moll. Gast. Pros.) e di *Aplysia depilans* L. (Moll. Gast. Opis.). *Acta histochem.* **2**, 229.

BOUTAN, L. (1899): La cause principale de l'asymétrie des Mollusques Gastéropodes. *Arch. Zool. exp. gén.* (III) **7**, 203.

—— (1902): La détorsion chez les Gastéropodes. *Arch. Zool. exp. gén.* (III) **10**, 241.

BOYCOTT, A. E. and C. DIVER (1923): On the inheritance of sinistrality in *Limnaea peregra*. *Proc. Roy. Soc. London* **B 95**, 207.

——, C. DIVER, S. L. GARSTANG and F. M. TURNER (1931): The inheritance of sinistrality in *Limnaea peregra* (Mollusca, Pulmonata). *Philos. Trans. Roy. Soc. London* **B 219**, 51.

BRACHET, J. (1929): Recherches sur le comportement de l'acide thymo-nucléique au cours de l'oogénèse chez diverses espèces animales. *Arch. Biol.* **39**, 677.

BRAMBELL, F. W. R. (1924): The nature and origin of yolk. Experimental studies of the oocytes of *Helix aspersa* and *Patella vulgata*. *Brit. J. exp. Biol.* **1**, 501.

BRETSCHNEIDER, L. H. (1948): Insemination in *Limnaea stagnalis* L. *Proc. Kon. Ned. Akad. v. Wetensch., Amsterdam* **51**, 358.

—— and G. C. HIRSCH (1937): Kernwachstum und Nukleolengrösse bei den Eiern von *Lima hians* (Lamell.). Ein Beitrag zur Frage der partiellen Systeme. *Cytologia* **8**, 128.

—— and CHR. P. RAVEN (1951): Structural and topochemical changes in the egg cells of *Limnaea stagnalis* L. during oogenesis. *Arch. Néerl. Zool.* **10**, 1.

BROEK, E.v.D. and CHR. P. RAVEN (1951): Cytological and morphogenetic effects of lithium chloride solutions on the uncleaved eggs of *Limnaea stagnalis. Proc. Kon. Ned. Akad. v. Wetensch., Amsterdam* C **54**, 226.

BROWNE, E. N. (1910): Effects of pressure on *Cumingia* eggs. *Arch. Entw. mech.* **29**, 243.

BUGLIA, G. (1908): Sullo scambio gassoso delle uova di *Aplysia limacina* nei vari periodi dello sviluppo. *Arch. di Fisiol.* **5**, 455.

BURESCH, I. (1911): Untersuchungen über die Zwitterdrüse der Pulmonaten. I. Die Differenzierung der Keimzellen bei *Helix arbustorum. Arch. f. Zellforschg.* **7**, 314.

BUTCHER, E. O. (1929): The formation, regeneration, and transplantation of eyes in *Pecten gibbus borealis. Anat. Rec.* **44**, 261.

BYRNES, E. F. (1900): The maturation and fertilization of the egg of *Limax agrestis* (Linné). *J. Morph.* **16**, 201.

CARAZZI, D. (1905-6): L'embriologia dell' *Aplysia* e i problemi fondamentali dell' embriologia comparata. *Arch. Ital. Anat. Embriol.* **4**, 231, 459; **5**, 667.

CARRICK, R. (1939): The life-history and development of *Agriolimax agrestis* L., the gray field slug. *Trans. Roy. Soc. Edinburgh* **59**, 563.

CARRIKER, M. R. (1943): Variability, developmental changes, and denticle-replacement in the radula of *Limnaea stagnalis apressa* Say. *The Nautilus* **57**, 52.

CARTER, G. S. (1928): On the structure of the cells bearing the velar cilia in the nudibranch veliger. *Brit. J. exp. Biol.* **6**, 97.

CASTEEL, D. B. (1904): The cell-lineage and early larval development of *Fiona marina*, a nudibranch mollusc. *Proc. Acad. Nat. Sci. Philadelphia* **56**, 325.

CHUN, C. (1902): Ueber die Natur und die Entwicklung der Chromatophoren bei den Cephalopoden. *Verh. D. Zool. Ges.* **12**, 162.

CLELAND, K. W. (1950): Respiration and cell division in developing oyster eggs. *Proc. Linn. Soc. N.S. Wales* **75**, 282.

—— (1951): The enzymatic architecture of the unfertilized oyster egg. *Austral. J. exp. Biol. Med. Sci.* **29**, 35.

CLEMENT, A. C. (1935): The formation of giant polar bodies in centrifuged eggs of *Ilyanassa. Biol. Bull.* **69**, 403.

—— (1938): The structure and development of centrifuged eggs and egg fragments of *Physa heterostropha. J. exp. Zool.* **79**, 435.

—— (1952): Experimental studies on germinal localization in *Ilyanassa*. I. The role of the polar lobe in determination of the cleavage pattern and its influence in later development. *J. exp. Zool.* **121**, 593.

—— (1956): Experimental studies on germinal localization in *Ilyanassa*. II. The development of isolated blastomeres. *J. exp. Zool.* **132**, 427.

—— and F. E. LEHMANN (1956): Ueber das Verteilungsmuster von Mitochondrien und Lipoidtropfen während der Furchung des Eies von *Ilyanassa obsoleta* (Mollusca, Prosobranchia). *Die Naturwiss.* **43**, 478.

COE, W. R. and H. J. TURNER (1938): Development of the gonad and gametes in the soft-shell clam (*Mya arenaria*). *J. Morph.* **62**, 91.

COLE, H. A. (1938): The fate of the larval organs in the metamorphosis of *Ostrea edulis*. *J. Mar. Biol. Assoc. U.K.* **22**, 469.

COLLIER, J. R. (1954): The intracellular localization of the alanylglycine dipeptidase activity in the egg of *Ilyanassa obsoleta*. *Biol. Bull.* **107**, 324.

COMANDON, J. and P. DE FONBRUNE (1935): Recherches effectuées aux premiers stades du développement d'oeufs de Gastéropodes et d'un ver à l'aide de la cinématographie. *Arch. Anat. Micr.* **31**, 79.

CONKLIN, E. G. (1897): The embryology of *Crepidula*. *J. Morph.* **13**, 1.

—— (1901): Centrosome and sphere in the maturation, fertilization and cleavage of *Crepidula*. *Anat. Anz.* **19**, 280.

—— (1904): Experiments on the origin of the cleavage centrosomes. *Biol. Bull.* **7**, 221.

—— (1907): The embryology of *Fulgur*. A study of the influence of yolk on development. *Proc. Acad. Nat. Sci. Philadelphia* **1907**, 320.

—— (1910): The effects of centrifugal force upon the organization and development of the eggs of fresh water pulmonates. *J. exp. Zool.* **9**, 417.

—— (1912a): Experimental studies in nuclear and cell division in the eggs of *Crepidula plana*. *J. Acad. Nat. Sci. Philadelphia* **15**, 501.

—— (1912b): Cell size and nuclear size. *J. exp. Zool.* **12**, 1.

—— (1917): Effects of centrifugal force on the structure and development of the eggs of *Crepidula*. *J. exp. Zool.* **22**, 311.

—— (1938): Disorientations of development in *Crepidula plana* produced by low temperatures. *Proc. Amer. Philos. Soc.* **79**, 179.

COSTELLO, D. P. (1934): The hyaline zone of the centrifuged egg of *Cumingia*. *Biol. Bull.* **66**, 257.

—— (1939a): The volumes occupied by the formed cytoplasmic components in marine eggs. *Physiol. Zool.* **12**, 13.

—— (1939b): Some effects of centrifuging the eggs of nudibranchs. *J. exp. Zool.* **80**, 473.

—— (1945): Segregation of ooplasmic constituents. *J. Elisha Mitchell Sci. Soc.* **61**, 277.

CRABB, E. D. (1927): The fertilization process in the snail, *Lymnaea stagnalis appressa* Say. *Biol. Bull.* **53**, 67.

CRAMPTON, H. E. (1894): Reversal of cleavage in a sinistral gastropod. *Ann. N.Y. Acad. Sci.* **8**, 167.

—— (1896): Experimental studies on gasteropod development. *Arch. Entw. mech.* **3**, 1.

CREEK, G. A. (1951): The reproductive system and embryology of the snail *Pomatias elegans* (Müller). *Proc. Zool. Soc. London* **121**, 599.

CROFTS, D. R. (1938): The development of *Haliotis tuberculata*, with special reference to organogenesis during torsion. *Phil. Trans. Roy. Soc. London* **B 228**, 219.

CROFTS, D. R. (1955): Muscle morphogenesis in primitive gastropods and its relation to torsion. *Proc. Zool. Soc. London* **125**, 711.

DAKIN, W. J. (1928): The eyes of *Pecten, Spondylus, Amussium* and allied lamellibranchs, with a short discussion on their evolution. *Proc. Roy. Soc. London* **B 103**, 355.

DALCQ, A. (1928): Le rôle du calcium et du potassium dans l'entrée en maturation de l'oeuf de Pholade (*Barnea candida*). *Protoplasma* **4**, 18.

DAN, K., S. ITO and D. MAZIA (1952): Study of the course of formation of the mitotic apparatus in *Arbacia* and *Mactra* by isolation techniques. *Biol. Bull.* **103**, 292.

DAUTERT, E. (1929): Die Bildung der Keimblätter von *Paludina vivipara*. *Zool. Jahrb., Anat.* **50**, 433.

DELAGE, Y. (1899): Etudes sur la mérogonie. *Arch. Zool. exp. gén.* (III) **7**, 383.

DELSMAN, H. C. (1912): Ontwikkelingsgeschiedenis van *Littorina obtusata*. Diss. Amsterdam 1912.—Cf. Entwicklungsgeschichte von *Littorina obtusata*. *Tijdschr. Ned. Dierk. Ver.* (2) **13**, 170 (1914).

DISTASO, A. (1908): Studii sull' embrione di Seppia. *Zool. Jahrb., Anat.* **26**, 565.

DIVER, C. (1925): The inheritance of inverse symmetry in *Limnaea peregra*. *J. Genet.* **15**, 113.

—— and I. ANDERSSON-KOTTÖ (1938): Sinistrality in *Limnaea peregra* (Mollusca, Pulmonata). The problem of mixed broods. *J. Genet.* **35**, 447.

DÖRING, W. (1908): Ueber Bau und Entwicklung des weiblichen Geschlechtsapparates bei myopsiden Cephalopoden. *Z. wiss. Zool.* **91**, 112.

DREW, G. A. (1899): Some observations on the habits, anatomy and embryology of members of the Protobranchia. *Anat. Anz.* **15**, 493.

—— (1901): The life-history of *Nucula delphinodonta* (Mighels). *Quart. J. Micr. Sci.* **44**, 313.

—— (1906): The habits, anatomy, and embryology of the giant scallop (*Pecten tenuicostatus*, Mighels). *Univ. of Maine Studies* **6**, 1.

DRUMMOND, I. M. (1902): Notes on the development of *Paludina vivipara*, with special reference to the urino-genital organs and theories of gasteropod torsion. *Quart. J. Micr. Sci.* **46**, 97.

ECKARDT, E. (1914): Beiträge zur Kenntnis der einheimischen Vitrinen. *Jen. Z. Naturwiss.* **51**, 213.

ELBERS, P. F. (1952): On the influence of potassium ions on the lithium effect in *Limnaea stagnalis*. *Proc. Kon. Ned. Akad. v. Wetensch., Amsterdam* **C 55**, 74.

—— (1957): Electronmicroscopy of protein crystals in ultrathin sections of the egg of *Limnaea stagnalis*. *Proc. Kon. Ned. Akad. v. Wetensch., Amsterdam* **C 60**, 96.

ERLANGER, R. v. (1891): Zur Entwicklung von *Paludina vivipara*. *Morph. Jahrb.* **17**, 337, 636.

ERLANGER, R. V. (1892): Beiträge zur Entwicklungsgeschichte der Gasteropoden. *Mitth. Zool. Stat. Neapel* **10**, 376.

FABER, J. (1950): Induced rotation of cleavage spindles in *Limnaea stagnalis* L. *Proc. Kon. Ned. Akad. v. Wetensch., Amsterdam* **53**, 1490.

FAHMY, O. G. (1949): Oogenesis in the desert snail *Eremina desertorum* with special reference to vitellogenesis. *Quart. J. Micr. Sci.* **90**, 159.

FAURÉ FREMIET, E. and H. MUGARD (1948): Ségrégation d'un matériel cortical au cours de la segmentation chez l'oeuf de *Teredo norvegica*. *C.R. Acad. Sci. Paris* **227**, 1409.

—— and J. THAUREAUX (1949): Effet de quelques détergents sur l'oeuf de *Teredo norvegica*. *Biochim. Biophys. Acta* **3**, 536.

FAUSSEK, V. (1901): Untersuchungen über die Entwicklung der Cephalopoden. *Mitth. Zool. Stat. Neapel* **14**, 83.

FERNANDO, W. (1931a): The origin and development of the pericardium and kidneys in *Ostrea*. *Proc. Roy. Soc. London* **B 107**, 391.

—— (1931b): The development of the kidney in *Ampullaria* (*Pila*) *gigas*. *Proc. Zool. Soc. London* **1931**, 745.

—— (1931c): The origin of the mesoderm in the gastropod *Viviparus* (=*Paludina*). *Proc. Roy. Soc. London* **B 107**, 381.

FISCHER, P. H. (1940): Structure et évolution de l'épithelium de l'opercule chez *Purpura lapillus* L. *Bull. Soc. Zool. France* **65**, 199.

FOL, H. (1875): Etudes sur le développement des Mollusques. I. Sur le développement des Ptéropodes. *Arch Zool. exp. gén.* **4**, 1.

—— (1880): Etudes sur le développement des Mollusques. III. Sur le développement des Gastéropodes pulmonés. *Arch. Zool. exp. gén.* **8**, 103.

FRANC, A. (1940): Recherches sur le développement d'*Ocinebra aciculata*, Lamarck (Mollusque gastéropode). *Bull. biol. France Belg.* **74**, 327.

—— (1950): Présence d'acide thymonucléique diffus dans le nucléoplasme des ovocytes chez certains Gastéropodes Prosobranches. *C.R. Acad. Sci. Paris* **231**, 1562.

—— (1951): Ovogénèse et évolution nucléolaire chez les Gastéropodes Prosobranches. *Ann. Sci. Nat.* (11) **13**, 135.

FRASER, L. A. (1946): The embryology of the reproductive tract of *Lymnaea stagnalis appressa* Say. *Trans. Amer. Micr. Soc.* **65**, 279.

FRY, H. J. and M. E. PARKS (1934): Studies of the mitotic figure. IV. Mitotic changes and viscosity changes in eggs of *Arbacia, Cumingia*, and *Nereis*. *Protoplasma* **21**, 473.

GABE, M. and M. PRENANT (1949): Contribution à l'histologie de l'ovogénèse chez les Polyplacophores. *La Cellule* **53**, 99.

—— and M. PRENANT (1952): Sur le rôle des odontoblastes dans l'élaboration des dents radulaires. *C.R. Acad. Sci. Paris* **235**, 1050.

GARNAULT, P. (1888-89): Sur les phénomènes de la fécondation chez l'*Helix aspersa* et l'*Arion empiricorum*. *Zool. Anz.* **11**, 731; **12**, 10, 33.

GATENBY, J. B. (1919): The cytoplasmic inclusions of the germ cells. V. The gametogenesis and early development of *Limnaea stagnalis* L.

with special reference to the Golgi apparatus and the mitochondria. *Quart. J. Micr. Sci.* **63**, 445.

GEILENKIRCHEN, W. L. M. (1952a): Differences in lithium effects in *Limnaea* after treatment of whole egg-masses and isolated egg capsules. *Proc. Kon. Ned. Akad. v. Wetensch., Amsterdam* **C 55**, 192.

—— (1952b): The action of lithium chloride on the eggs of *Limnaea stagnalis* at different oxygen pressures. *Proc. Kon. Ned. Akad. v. Wetensch., Amsterdam* **C 55**, 311.

GRASVELD, M. S. (1949): On the influence of various chlorides on maturation and cleavage of the egg of *Limnaea stagnalis* L. *Proc. Kon. Ned. Akad. v. Wetensch., Amsterdam* **52**, 284.

GRIFFIN, B. B. (1899): Studies on the maturation, fertilization and cleavage of *Thalassema* and *Zirphaea*. *J. Morph.* **15**, 583.

GROOT, A. P. DE (1948): The influence of higher concentrations of lithium chloride on maturation and first cleavages of the egg of *Limnaea stagnalis*. *Proc. Kon. Ned. Akad. v. Wetensch., Amsterdam* **51**, 588.

HAMMARSTEN, O. D. and J. RUNNSTRÖM (1925): Zur Embryologie von *Acanthochiton discrepans* Brown. *Zool. Jahrb., Anat.* **47**, 261.

HARMS, W. (1909): Postembryonale Entwicklungsgeschichte der Unioniden. *Zool. Jahrb., Anat.* **28**, 325.

HARTUNG, E. W. (1947): Cytological and experimental studies on the oocytes of fresh water pulmonates. *Biol. Bull.* **92**, 10.

HARVEY, E. N. (1931): The tension at the surface of marine eggs, especially those of the sea urchin, *Arbacia*. *Biol. Bull.* **61**, 273.

HAYE, S. C. A. and CHR. P. RAVEN (1953): The influence of cyanide on the lithium effect in the development of *Limnaea stagnalis*. *Proc. Kon. Ned. Akad. v. Wetensch., Amsterdam* **C 56**, 326.

HEATH, H. (1899): The development of *Ischnochiton*. *Zool. Jahrb., Anat.* **12**, 567.

—— (1904): The larval eye of Chitons. *Proc. Acad. Nat. Sci. Philadelphia* **56**, 257.

HEIKENS, M. C. (1947): Viscosity changes during cleavage in the eggs of *Limnaea stagnalis*. *Proc. Kon. Ned. Akad. v. Wetensch., Amsterdam* **50**, 789.

HEILBRUNN, L. V. (1920): Studies in artificial parthenogenesis. III. Cortical change and the initiation of maturation in the egg of *Cumingia*. *Biol. Bull.* **38**, 317.

—— (1925): Studies in artificial parthenogenesis. IV. Heat parthenogenesis. *J. exp. Zool.* **41**, 243.

—— (1926): The absolute viscosity of protoplasm. *J. exp. Zool.* **44**, 255.

HERBERS, K. (1913): Entwicklungsgeschichte von *Anodonta cellensis* Schröt. *Z. wiss. Zool.* **108**, 1.

HESS, O. (1956a): Die Entwicklung von Halbkeimen bei dem Süsswasser-Prosobranchier *Bithynia tentaculata* L. *Roux' Arch. Entw. mech.* **148**, 336.

HESS, O. (1956b): Die Entwicklung von Exogastrulakeimen bei dem Süss-wasser-Prosobranchier *Bithynia tentaculata* L. *Roux' Arch. Entw. mech.* **148**, 474.

HEYDER, P. (1909): Zur Entwicklung der Lungenhöhle bei *Arion*. Nebst Bemerkungen über die Entwicklung der Urniere und Niere, des Pericards und Herzens. *Z. wiss. Zool.* **93**, 90.

HEYMONS, R. (1893): Zur Entwicklungsgeschichte von *Umbrella mediter-ranea* Lam. *Z. wiss. Zool.* **56**, 245.

HIRATA, A. A. (1953): Studies on shell formation. II. A mantle-shell preparation for *in vitro* studies. *Biol. Bull.* **104**, 394.

HIRSCHLER, J. (1918): Ueber den Golgischen Apparat embryonaler Zellen. Untersuchungen an Embryonen von *Limnaeus stagnalis* L., Mollusca. *Arch. mikr. Amat.* **91**, 140.

HOADLEY, L. (1930): Polocyte formation and the cleavage of the polar body in *Loligo* and *Chaetopterus*. *Biol. Bull.* **58**, 256.

HOFFMANN, H. (1922): Ueber die Entwicklung der Geschlechtsorgane bei *Limax maximus* L. *Z. wiss. Zool.* **119**, 493.

—— (1932): Ueber die Radulabildung bei *Lymnaea stagnalis*. *Jen. Z. Naturwiss.* **67**, 535.

HOFFMANN, R. W. (1902): Ueber die Ernährung der Embryonen von *Nassa mutabilis* Lam. Ein Beitrag zur Morphologie und Physiologie des Nucleus und Nucleolus. *Z. wiss. Zool.* **72**, 657.

HOLLINGSWORTH, J. (1941): Activation of *Cumingia* and *Arbacia* eggs by bivalent cations. *Biol. Bull.* **81**, 261.

HOLMES, S. J. (1900): The early development of *Planorbis*. *J. Morph.* **16**, 369.

HORSTMANN, H. J. (1955): Untersuchungen zur Physiologie der Begat-tung und Befruchtung der Schlammschnecke *Lymnaea stagnalis* L. *Z. Morph. Ökol. Tiere* **44**, 222.

HUDIG, O. (1946): The vitelline membrane of *Limnaea stagnalis*. *Proc. Kon. Ned. Akad. v. Wetensch., Amsterdam* **49**, 554.

IKEDA, K. (1930): The fertilization cones of the land snail, *Eulota (Eulo-tella) similaris stimpsoni* Pfeiffer. *Jap. J. Zool.* **3**, 89.

INABA, F. (1936): Studies on the artificial parthenogenesis of *Ostrea gigas* Thunberg. *J. Sci. Hirosima Univ.* (B 1) **5**, 29.

ITO, S. and C. LEUCHTENBERGER (1955): The possible role of the DNA content of spermatozoa for the activation process of the egg of the clam, *Spisula solidissima*. *Chromosoma* **7**, 328.

JODREY, L. H. (1953): Studies on shell formation. III. Measurement of calcium deposition in shell and calcium turnover in mantle tissue using the mantle-shell preparation and Ca[45]. *Biol. Bull.* **104**, 398.

JOHANSSON, J. (1951): On the embryology of *Viviparus* and its significance for the phylogeny of the Gastropoda. *Ark. Zool., Andra Ser.* **1**, 173.

JORDAN, H. E. (1910): A cytological study of the egg of *Cumingia* with special reference to the history of the chromosomes and the centro-some. *Arch. Zellforschg.* **4**, 243.

JOYEUX-LAFFUIE, J. (1882): Organisation et développement de l'Oncidie, *Oncidium celticum* Cuv. *Arch. Zool. exp. gén.* **10**, 225.

KOFOID, C. A. (1895): On the early development of *Limax. Bull. Mus. Comp. Zool. Harvard Coll.* **27**, 35.

KONOPACKI, M. (1933): Histophysiologie du développement de *Loligo vulgaris. Bull. intern. Acad. polon. Sci. Lettr., Cl. Sci.* **B II**, 51.

KORSCHELT, E. and K. HEIDER (1902): Lehrbuch der vergleichenden Entwicklungsgeschichte der wirbellosen Thiere. *Allgemeiner Theil* I. Jena, Gustav Fischer.

KOSTANECKI, K. (1902): Ueber künstliche Befruchtung und künstliche parthenogenetische Furchung bei *Mactra. Bull. intern. Acad. Sci. Cracovie, Cl. Sci.* **1902**, 363.

—— (1904): Cytologische Studien an künstlich parthenogenetisch sich entwickelnden Eiern von *Mactra. Arch. Mikr. Anat.* **64**, 1.

—— (1908): Zur Morphologie der künstlichen parthenogenetischen Entwicklung bei *Mactra.* Zugleich ein Beitrag zur Kenntnis der vielpoligen Mitose. *Arch. Mikr. Anat.* **72**, 327.

—— and A. WIERZEJSKI (1896): Ueber das Verhalten der sogen. achromatischen Substanzen im befruchteten Ei. Nach Beobachtungen an *Physa fontinalis. Arch. Mikr. Anat.* **47**, 309.

KOWALEWSKY, A. (1883a): Embryogénie du *Chiton polii* (Philippi). *Ann. Mus. Hist. Nat. Marseille* **1**, no. 5.

—— (1883b): Etude sur l'embryogénie du Dentale. *Ann. Mus. Hist. Nat. Marseille* **1**, no. 7.

KRAUSS, M. (1950): Lytic agents of the sperm of some marine animals. I. The egg membrane lysin from sperm of the giant keyhole limpet *Megathura crenulata. J. exp. Zool.* **114**, 239.

LABBÉ, A. (1933): La génèse des yeux dorsaux chez les Oncidiadés. *C.R. Soc. Biol.* **114**, 1002.

LAMS, H. (1910): Recherches sur l'oeuf d'*Arion empiricorum* (Fér.). (Accroissement, maturation, fécondation, segmentation.) *Mém. Acad. roy. Belg., Cl. Sci.* (in 4°) (II) **2**.

LARAMBERGUE, M. DE (1933): Développement de l'appareil génital dans les deux formes (A et B) de *Bullinus contortus* Mich. *C.R. Ac. Sci. Paris* **197**, 190.

—— (1939): Etude de l'autofécondation chez les Gastéropodes Pulmonés. Recherches sur l'aphallie et la fécondation chez *Bulinus (Isidora) contortus* Michaud. *Bull. biol. Fr. Belg.* **73**, 21.

LAVIOLETTE, P. (1954): Etude cytologique et expérimentale de la régénération germinale après castration chez *Arion rufus* L. (Gastéropode pulmoné). *Ann. Sci. nat., Zool.* **11**, 427.

LILLIE, F. R. (1895): The embryology of the Unionidae. *J. Morph.* **10**, 1.

—— (1901): The organization of the egg of *Unio*, based on a study of its maturation, fertilization, and cleavage. *J. Morph.* **17**, 227.

LINVILLE, H. R. (1900): Maturation and fertilization in pulmonate gasteropods. *Bull. Mus. Comp. Zool. Harvard Coll.* **35**, 213.

T

LUCKÉ, B. and R. A. RICCA (1941): Osmotic properties of the egg cells of the oyster (Ostrea virginica). J. gen. Physiol. 25, 215.

LUDFORD, R. J. (1928): Studies in the microchemistry of the cell. I. The chromatin content of normal and malignant cells, as demonstrated by Feulgen's 'Nucleal-reaction'. Proc. Roy. Soc. London B 102, 397.

MANCUSO, V. (1953): Ricerche di topografia chimica nell' uovo di Gasteropodi Polmonati. Rend. Ist. Super. Sanita Roma 16, 367.

—— (1954): La G-nadi ossidasi nell' uovo di Physa rivularis Ph. Ric. Scient. 24, 1886.

—— (1955a): L'azione dell' azide sodico sullo sviluppo dell' uovo di Physa rivularis Ph. Riv. di Biol. (N.S.) 47, 203.

—— (1955b): Sostanze Nadi positive nello sviluppo di Physa rivularis Ph. Ric. Scient. 25, 2843.

—— (1955c): Azione del cianuro di potassio sullo sviluppo di Physa rivularis Ph. Rend. Accad. Naz. Lincei, Cl. Sci. (VIII) 19, 71.

MAY, F. and H. WEINLAND (1953): Ueber Glykogenbildung in den galaktogenhaltigen Eiern der Weinbergschnecke (Helix pomatia) im Verlaufe der Embryonalentwicklung. Z. f. Biol. 105, 339.

MAZZARELLI, G. (1898): Bemerkungen über die Analniere der freilebenden Larven der Opisthobranchier. Biol. Centralbl. 18, 767.

McFARLAND, F. M. (1897): Celluläre Studien an Mollusken-Eiern. Zool. Jahrb., Anat. 10, 227.

MEDEM, F. GRAF v. (1942): Beiträge zur Frage der Befruchtungsstoffe bei marinen Mollusken. Biol. Zentralbl. 62, 431.

—— (1945): Untersuchungen über die Ei- und Spermawirkstoffe bei marinen Mollusken. Zool. Jahrb., allg. Zool. 61, 1.

MEISENHEIMER, J. (1896): Entwicklungsgeschichte von Limax maximus L. I. Furchung und Keimblätterbildung. Z. wiss. Zool. 62, 415.

—— (1898): Entwicklungsgeschichte von Limax maximus L. II. Die Larvenperiode. Z. wiss. Zool. 63, 573.

—— (1899): Zur Morphologie der Urniere der Pulmonaten. Z. wiss. Zool. 65, 709.

—— (1901a): Entwicklungsgeschichte von Dreissensia polymorpha Pall. Z. wiss. Zool. 69, 1.

—— (1901b): Die Entwicklung von Herz, Perikard, Niere und Genitalzellen bei Cyclas im Verhältnis zu den übrigen Mollusken. Z. wiss. Zool. 69, 417.

METZ, CH. B. and J. E. DONOVAN (1949): Fertilizin from the eggs of the clam, Mactra solidissima. Biol. Bull. 97, 257.

MEVES, F. (1915): Ueber den Befruchtungsvorgang bei der Miesmuschel (Mytilus edulis L.). Arch. mikr. Anat., Abt. II 87, 47.

MEYERHOF, O. (1911): Untersuchungen über die Wärmetönung der vitalen Oxydationsvorgänge in Eiern. I. Biochem. Z. 35, 246.

MINGANTI, A. (1950): Acidi nucleici e fosfatasi nello sviluppo della Limnaea. Riv. di Biol. 42, 295.

MORGAN, T. H. (1910): Cytological studies of centrifuged eggs. *J. exp. Zool.* **9**, 593.

—— (1933): The formation of the antipolar lobe in *Ilyanassa*. *J. exp. Zool.* **64**, 433.

—— (1935a): Centrifuging the eggs of *Ilyanassa* in reverse. *Biol. Bull.* **68**, 268.

—— (1935b): The separation of the egg of *Ilyanassa* into two parts by centrifuging. *Biol. Bull.* **68**, 280.

—— (1935c): The rhythmic changes in form of the isolated antipolar lobe of *Ilyanassa*. *Biol. Bull.* **68**, 296.

—— (1936): Further experiments on the formation of the antipolar lobe of *Ilyanassa*. *J. exp. Zool.* **74**, 381.

—— (1937): The behavior of the maturation spindles in polar fragments of *Ilyanassa* obtained by centrifuging. *Biol. Bull.* **72**, 88.

—— and A. TYLER (1930): The point of entrance of the spermatozoön in relation to the orientation of the embryo in eggs with spiral cleavage. *Biol. Bull.* **58**, 59.

—— and A. TYLER (1938): The relation between entrance point of the spermatozoön and bilaterality of the egg of *Chaetopterus*. *Biol. Bull.* **74**, 401.

MORITZ, C. E. (1939): Organogenesis in the gasteropod *Crepidula adunca* Sowerby. *Univ. Calif. Publ. Zool.* **43**, 217.

MORRIS, M. (1917): A cytological study of artificial parthenogenesis in *Cumingia*. *J. exp. Zool.* **22**, 1.

MOTOMURA, I. (1954): Parthenogenetic activation with potassium permanganate in the eggs of the bivalve and the sea urchin. *Sci. Rep. Tôhoku Univ.* (IV) **20**, 213.

NAEF, A. (1909): Die Organogenese des Cölomsystems und der zentralen Blutgefässe von *Loligo*. *Jen. Z. Naturwiss.* **45**, 221.

—— (1928): Die Cephalopoden. *Fauna e Flora del Golfo di Napoli* **35**.

NIJENHUIS, E. D. (1951): Cytological and morphogenetic effects of lithium chloride solutions on eggs of *Limnaea stagnalis* treated during second cleavage. *Proc. Kon. Ned. Akad. v. Wetensch., Amsterdam* C **54**, 537.

OBST, P. (1899): Untersuchungen über das Verhalten der Nucleolen bei der Eibildung einiger Mollusken und Arachnoiden. *Z. wiss. Zool.* **66**, 161.

OKADA, K. (1936): Some notes on *Sphaerium japonicum biwaense* Mori, a freshwater bivalve. IV. Gastrula and fetal larva. *Sci. Rep. Tôhoku Imp. Univ.* (IV) **11**, 49.

—— (1939): The development of the primary mesoderm in *Sphaerium japonicum biwaense* Mori. *Sci. Rep. Tôhoku Imp. Univ.* (IV) **14**, 25.

OTTO, H. and C. TÖNNIGES (1906): Untersuchungen über die Entwicklung von *Paludina vivipara*. *Z. wiss. Zool.* **80**, 411.

PABST, H. (1914): Entwicklung des Genitalapparats von *Arion empiricorum* Fér. *Zool. Jahrb., Anat.* **38**, 465.

PARAT, M. (1928): Contribution à l'étude morphologique et physiologique du cytoplasme. Chondriome, vacuome (appareil de Golgi), enclaves, etc. pH, oxydases, peroxydases, rH de la cellule animale. *Arch. Anat. micr.* **24**, 73.

PARIS, A. J. (1953): Histological investigations on exogastrulae of *Limnaea stagnalis* obtained by centrifuging the eggs. *Proc. Kon. Ned. Akad. v. Wetensch., Amsterdam* **C 56**, 406.

PASTEELS, J. (1930): Les effets de la rupture de la balance des chlorures de l'eau de mer sur l'oeuf de Pholade, *Barnea candida. Arch. Biol.* **40**, 247.

—— (1931): Recherches sur le déterminisme du mode de segmentation des Mollusques Lamellibranches (actions des rayons ultra-violets sur l'oeuf de *Barnea cand.*). *Arch. Biol.* **42**, 389.

—— (1934): Recherches sur la morphogénèse et le déterminisme des segmentations inégales chez les Spiralia. *Arch. Anat. micr.* **30**, 161.

—— (1935): Recherches sur le déterminisme de l'entrée en maturation de l'oeuf chez divers Invertébrés marins. *Arch. Biol.* **46**, 229.

—— (1938a): Le role du calcium dans l'activation de l'oeuf de pholade. *Trav. Stat. Zool. Wimereux* **13**, 515.

—— (1938b): Sensibilisateurs et réalisateur dans l'activation de l'oeuf de *Barnea candida. Bull. Acad. roy. Belgique, Cl. Sci.* (5) **24**, 721.

—— (1950): Mouvements localisés et rythmiques de la membrane de fécondation chez des oeufs fécondés ou activés (*Chaetopterus, Mactra, Nereis*). *Arch. Biol.* **61**, 197.

PEASE, D. C. (1940): The influence of centrifugal force on the bilateral determination and the polar axis of *Cumingia* and *Chaetopterus* eggs. *J. exp. Zool.* **84**, 387.

PELLUET, D. and A. H. G. WATTS (1951): The cytosome of differentiating cells in the ovotestis of slugs. *Quart. J. Micr. Sci.* **92**, 453.

PELSENEER, P. (1900): Les yeux céphaliques chez les Lamellibranches. *Arch. Biol.* **16**, 97.

PELTRERA, A. (1940): La capacità regolative dell' uovo di *Aplysia limacina* L. studiate con la centrifugazione e con le reazioni vitali. *Pubbl. Staz. Zool. Napoli* **18**, 20.

PLATNER, G. (1886): Zur Bildung der Geschlechtsprodukte bei den Pulmonaten. *Arch. mikr. Anat.* **26**, 599.

PÖTZSCH, O. (1904): Ueber die Entwicklung von Niere, Pericard und Herz bei *Planorbis corneus. Zool. Jahrb., Anat.* **20**, 409.

PORTMANN, A. (1925): Der Einfluss der Nähreier auf die Larvenentwicklung von *Buccinum* und *Purpura. Z. Morph. Ökol. Tiere* **3**, 526.

—— (1926): Der embryonale Blutkreislauf und die Dotterresorption bei *Loligo vulgaris. Z. Morph. Ökol. Tiere* **5**, 406.

—— (1930): Die Larvennieren von *Buccinum undatum* L. *Z. Zellforschg. mikr. Anat.* **10**, 401.

—— (1955): La métamorphose 'abritée' de *Fusus* (Gast. Prosobranches). *Rev. Suisse Zool.* **62** Suppl., 236.

PORTMANN, A. and A. M. BIDDER (1928): Yolk-absorption in *Loligo* and the function of the embryonic liver and pancreas. *Quart. J. Micr. Sci.* **72**, 301.

PRENANT, M. (1924): Etudes histologiques sur les peroxydases animales. *Arch. Morph. gén. exp.* **21**.

PRUVOT, G. (1890): Sur le développement d'un Solénogastre. *C.R. Ac. Sci. Paris.* **111**, 689.

—— (1892): Sur l'embryogénie d'une *Proneomenia*. *C.R. Ac. Sci. Paris* **114**, 1211.

PRUVOT-FOL, A. (1925): Morphogénèse des odontoblastes chez les Mollusques. *Arch. Zool. exp. gén.* **64**, 1.

—— (1926): Le bulbe buccal et la symmétrie des Mollusques. I. La radula. *Arch. Zool. exp. gén.* **65**, 209.

RABL, C. (1879): Ueber die Entwicklung der Tellerschnecke. *Morph. Jahrb.* **5**, 562.

RANZI, S. (1928a): Suscettibilità differenziale nello sviluppo dei Cefalopodi (Analisi sperimentale dell' embriogenesi). *Pubbl. Staz. Zool. Napoli* **9**, 81.

—— (1928b): Correlazioni tra organi di senso e centri nervosi in via di sviluppo (Ricerche di morfologia sperimentale nei Cefalopodi). *Roux' Arch. Entw. mech.* **114**, 364.

—— (1930): Condizioni determinanti lo sviluppo delle branchie (Ricerche di embriologia sperimentale sui Cefalopodi). *Rend. R. Accad. Naz. Lincei, Cl. Sci.* (VI) **12**, 468.

—— (1931a): Sviluppo di parti isolate di embrioni di Cefalopodi (Analisi sperimentale dell' embriogenesi). *Pubbl. Staz. Zool. Napoli* **11**, 104.

—— (1931b): Resultati di ricerche di embriologia sperimentale sui Cefalopodi. *Arch. Zool. ital.* **16**, 403.

RANZOLI, F. (1953): Osservazioni citometriche e citochimiche sul comportamento dei nucleoli nell' ovogenesi di *Patella coerulea* L. *Caryologia* **5**, 137.

RATTENBURY, J. C. and W. E. BERG (1954): Embryonic segregation during early development of *Mytilus edulis*. *J. Morph.* **95**, 393.

RAVEN, CHR. P. (1938): Experimentelle Untersuchungen über die 'bipolare Differenzierung' des Polychaeten- und Molluskeneies. *Acta Neerl. Morph.* **1**, 337.

—— (1942): The influence of lithium upon the development of the pond snail, *Limnaea stagnalis* L. *Proc. Ned. Akad. v. Wetensch., Amsterdam* **45**, 856.

—— (1943): Sur les notions de 'gradient' et 'champ' dans l'embryologie causale. *Acta Biotheor.* **7**, 135.

—— (1945): The development of the egg of *Limnaea stagnalis* L. from oviposition till first cleavage. *Arch. Néerl. Zool.* **7**, 91.

—— (1946a): Development of *Limnaea stagnalis* L. In: M. W. WOERDEMAN and CHR. P. RAVEN, *Experimental embryology in the Nether-*

lands 1940-1945. Elsevier Publishing Cy., New York-Amsterdam, 1946.

—— (1946b): The development of the egg of *Limnaea stagnalis* L. from the first cleavage till the trochophore stage, with special reference to its 'chemical embryology'. *Arch. Néerl. Zool.* **7**, 353.

—— (1946c): The distribution of substances in eggs of *Limnaea stagnalis* L. centrifuged immediately before cleavage. *Arch. Néerl. Zool.* **7**, 496.

—— (1948): The influence of an electric field on the eggs of *Limnaea stagnalis* L. *Proc. Kon. Ned. Akad. v. Wetensch., Amsterdam* **51**, 1077.

—— (1949a): On the structure of cyclopic, synophthalmic and anophthalmic embryos, obtained by the action of lithium in *Limnaea stagnalis*. *Arch. Néerl. Zool.* **8**, 323.

—— (1949b): On maturation in the eggs of *Limnaea stagnalis* L. *Bijdr. t. d. Dierk.*, **28**, 372.

—— (1952): Morphogenesis in *Limnaea stagnalis* and its disturbance by lithium. *J. exp. Zool.* **121**, 1.

—— (1954): *An outline of developmental physiology*. Pergamon Press Ltd, London—McGraw-Hill Book Co., Inc., New York.

—— (1956) (in collaboration with A. C. DRINKWAARD, J. HAECK, N. H. VERDONK and L. A. VERHOEVEN): Effects of monovalent cations on the eggs of *Limnaea. Pubbl. Staz. Zool. Napoli* **28**, 136.

—— and A. M. TH. BEENAKKERS (1955): On the nature of head malformations obtained by centrifuging the eggs of *Limnaea stagnalis. J. Embr. exp. Morph.* **3**, 286.

—— , J. J. BEZEM and J. F. M. GEELEN (1953): The effect of chilling and cyanide on the osmotic equilibrium of the *Limnaea* egg. *Proc. Kon. Ned. Akad. v. Wetensch., Amsterdam* C **56**, 409.

—— , J. J. BEZEM and J. ISINGS (1952): Changes in the size relations between macromeres and micromeres of *Limnaea stagnalis* under the influence of lithium. *Proc. Kon. Ned. Akad. v. Wetensch., Amsterdam* C **55**, 248.

—— and L. H. BRETSCHNEIDER (1942): The effect of centrifugal force upon the eggs of *Limnaea stagnalis* L. *Arch. Néerl. Zool.* **6**, 255.

—— and F. BRUNNEKREEFT (1951): The formation of the animal pole plasm in centrifuged eggs of *Limnaea stagnalis* L. *Proc. Kon. Ned. Akad. v. Wetensch., Amsterdam* C **54**, 440.

—— and A. C. J. BURGERS (1952): The influence of temperature on the lithium effect in *Limnaea stagnalis*. *Proc. Kon. Ned. Akad. v. Wetensch., Amsterdam* C **55**, 554.

—— and S. DUDOK DE WIT (1949): On the influence of lithium chloride on the eggs of *Limnaea stagnalis* at the 24-cell stage. *Proc. Kon. Ned. Akad. v. Wetensch., Amsterdam* **52**, 28.

—— and M. TH. C. VAN EGMOND (1951): Centrifuging the eggs of *Limnaea* round about the third cleavage. *Proc. Kon. Ned. Akad. v. Wetensch., Amsterdam* C **54**, 325.

RAVEN, CHR. P. and G. A. VAN ERKEL (1955): The influence of calcium on the effects of a heat shock in *Limnaea stagnalis*. *Exp. Cell Res., Suppl.* **3**, 294.

—— and W. HUPKENS VAN DER ELST (1950): The influence of hypertonicity on the eggs of *Limnaea stagnalis*. *Proc. Kon. Ned. Akad. v. Wetensch., Amsterdam* **53**, 1005.

——, J. C. KLOEK, E. J. KUIPER and D. J. DE JONG (1947): The influence of concentration, duration of treatment and stage of development in the lithium-effect upon the development of *Limnaea stagnalis*. *Proc. Kon. Ned. Akad. v. Wetensch., Amsterdam* **50**, 584.

—— and H. KLOMP (1946): The osmotic properties of the egg of *Limnaea stagnalis* L. *Proc. Kon. Ned. Akad. v. Wetensch., Amsterdam* **49**, 101.

—— and TH. C. M. KOEVOETS (1952): Combined effects of lithium and centrifuging on the eggs of *Limnaea*. *Proc. Kon. Ned. Akad. v. Wetensch, Amsterdam* C **55**, 697.

—— and J. C. A. MIGHORST (1946): The influence of high concentrations of $CaCl_2$ on maturation in the egg of *Limnaea stagnalis*. *Proc. Kon. Ned. Akad. v. Wetensch., Amsterdam* **49**, 1003.

—— and H. W. MOOY (1954): The influence of calcium and cyanide on the morphogenetic effects of reduced partial oxygen pressure in the development of *Limnaea stagnalis*. *Proc. Kon. Ned. Akad. v. Wetensch., Amsterdam* C **57**, 424.

—— and F. VAN RIJCKEVORSEL (1953): The influence of anaerobiosis on the eggs of *Limnaea stagnalis*. *Proc. Kon. Ned. Akad. v. Wetensch., Amsterdam* C **56**, 1.

—— and A. H. G. C. RIJVEN (1948): Induction of head malformations in *Limnaea stagnalis* L. by lithium treatment in advanced cleavage stages. *Proc. Kon. Ned. Akad. v. Wetensch., Amsterdam.* **51**, 427.

—— and J. R. ROBORGH (1949): Direct effects of isotonic and hypotonic lithium chloride solutions on unsegmented eggs of *Limnaea stagnalis*. *Proc. Kon. Ned. Akad. v. Wetensch., Amsterdam* **52**, 614, 773.

——, A. C. DE ROON and A. M. STADHOUDERS (1955): Morphogenetic effects of a heat shock on the eggs of *Limnaea stagnalis*. *J. Embryol. exp. Morph.* **3**, 142.

—— and M. A. SIMONS (1948): On the specificity of the lithium effect on the development of *Limnaea stagnalis*. *Proc. Kon. Ned. Akad. v. Wetensch., Amsterdam* **51**, 1232.

—— and N. SPRONK (1952): The action of beryllium on the development of *Limnaea stagnalis*. *Proc. Kon. Ned. Akad. v. Wetensch., Amsterdam* C **55**, 541.

—— and W. VAN ZEIST (1950): On the influence of distilled water and lithium chloride upon the eggs of *Limnaea stagnalis* L. at the 2-cell stage. *Proc. Kon. Ned. Akad. v. Wetensch., Amsterdam* **53**, 601.

RIES, E. (1937): Die Verteilung von Vitamin C, Glutathion, Benzidin-Peroxydase, Phenolase (Indophenolblau-Oxydase) und Leuko-methylenblau-Oxydoredukase während der frühen Embryonalent-wicklung verschiedener wirbelloser Tiere. *Pubbl. Staz. Zool. Napoli* **16**, 363.

—— (1938): Histochemische Untersuchungen über frühembryonale Sonderungsprozesse in zentrifugierten Eiern von *Aplysia. Bio-dynamica* **40**, 1.

—— (1939): Histochemische Sonderungsprozesse während der frühen Embryonalentwicklung verschiedener wirbelloser Tiere. *Arch. exp. Zellforschg.* **22**, 569.

—— and M. GERSCH (1936): Die Zelldifferenzierung und Zellspeciali-sierung während der Embryonalentwicklung von *Aplysia limacina* L. Zugleich ein Beitrag zu Problemen der vitalen Färbung. *Pubbl. Staz. Zool. Napoli* **15**, 223.

ROBERT, A. (1902): Recherches sur le développement des Troques. *Arch. Zool. exp. gén.* (3) **10**, 269.

RÖSSLER, R. (1885): Die Bildung der Radula bei den cephalophoren Mollusken. *Z. wiss. Zool.* **41**, 447.

ROTTMANN, G. (1901): Ueber die Embryonalentwicklung der Radula bei den Mollusken. I. Die Entwicklung der Radula bei den Cephalo-poden. *Z. wiss. Zool.* **70**, 236.

RUGH, R. (1953): The X-irradiation of marine gametes. A study of the effects of X-irradiation at different levels on the germ cells of the clam, *Spisula* (formerly *Mactra*). *Biol. Bull.* **104**, 197.

SACARRAO, G. F. (1943): Observations sur les dernières phases de la vie embryonnaire de l'*Eledone. Arq. Mus. Bocage* **14**, 25.

—— (1945): Etudes embryologiques sur les Céphalopodes. *Arq. Mus. Bocage* **16**, 33.

—— (1949): Sobre as primeiras fases da ontogenese de '*Tremoctopus violaceus*' Delle Chiaje. *Arq. Mus. Bocage* **20**, 1.

—— (1952a): Remarks on gastrulation in Cephalopoda. *Arq. Mus. Bocage* **23**, 43.

—— (1952b): Le complexe entodermique des Mollusques à oeufs riches en vitellus. *Arq. Mus. Bocage* **23**, 121.

—— (1952c): Notice on the shell gland of *Argonauta. Arq. Mus. Bocage* **23**, 35.

—— (1953): Sur la formation des feuillets germinatifs des Céphalo-podes et les incertitudes de leur interprétation. *Arq. Mus. Bocage* **24**, 21.

—— (1954a): Sur la génèse des chromatophores de *Tremoctopus. Rev. Fac. Ci. Lisboa* (II C) **4**, 295.

—— (1954b): Quelques aspects sur l'origine et le développement du type d'oeil des Céphalopodes. *Rev. Fac. Ci. Lisboa* (II C) **4**, 123.

SALENSKY, W. (1887): Etude sur le développement du Vermet. *Arch. Biol.* **6**, 655.

SANDERSON, A. R. (1940): Maturation in the parthenogenetic snail, *Potamopyrgus jenkinsi* Smith, and in the snail *Peringia ulvae* (Pennant). *Proc. Zool. Soc. London* **A 110**, 11.

SAUNDERS, A. M. C. and M. POOLE (1910): The development of *Aplysia punctata*. *Quart. J. Micr. Sci.* **55**, 497.

SAWADA, N. (1952): Experimental studies on the maturation division of eggs in *Mactra veneriformis*. I. Inhibitory effect of the body fluid. *Mem. Ehime Univ.* (II) **1**, 231.

—— (1954a): Experimental studies on the maturation division of eggs in *Mactra veneriformis*. IV. On the effect of certain polysaccharides. *Mem. Ehime Univ.* (II) **B 2**, 89.

—— (1954b): Experimental studies on the maturation division of eggs in *Mactra veneriformis*. V. On the activation by periodate. *Mem. Ehime Univ.* (II) **B 2**, 93.

SCHLEIP, W. (1925): Die Furchung dispermer *Dentalium*-eier. *Arch. Entw. mech.* **106**, 86.

SCHNABEL, H. (1903): Ueber die Embryonalentwicklung der Radula bei den Mollusken. II. Die Entwicklung der Radula bei den Gastropoden. *Z. wiss. Zool.* **74**, 616.

SCLUFER, E. (1955): The respiration of *Spisula* eggs. *Biol. Bull.* **109**, 113.

SERRA, J. A. and A. QUEIROZ LOPES (1945): Données pour une cytophysiologie du nucléole. I. L'activité nucléolaire pendant la croissance de l'oocyte chez les Helicidae. *Portug. Acta Biol.* **1**, 51.

SMITH, F. G. W. (1935): The development of *Patella vulgata*. *Phil. Trans. Roy. Soc. London* **B 225**, 95.

SOBELS, F. H. (1948): The influence of thiourea on the development of *Limnaea stagnalis* L. *Proc. Kon. Ned. Akad. v. Wetensch., Amsterdam* **51**, 900.

SOLLAS, I. B. J. (1907): The molluscan radula; its chemical composition, and some points in its development. *Quart. J. Micr. Sci.* **51**, 115.

SOUTHWICK, W. E. (1939): The 'agglutination' phenomenon with spermatozoa of *Chiton tuberculatus*. *Biol. Bull.* **77**, 157.

SPEK, J. (1921): Beiträge zur Kenntnis der chemischen Zusammensetzung und Entwicklung der Radula der Gastropoden. *Z. wiss. Zool.* **118**, 313.

—— (1934): Die bipolare Differenzierung des Cephalopoden- und des Prosobranchiereies. *Roux' Arch. Entw. mech.* **131**, 362.

STALFOORT, TH. G. J. (1952): On the influence of Na-oxalate and Na-citrate on maturation and cleavage of the egg of *Limnaea stagnalis* L. *Proc. Kon. Ned. Akad. v. Wetensch., Amsterdam* **C 55**, 184.

STAUFFACHER, H. (1894): Eibildung und Furchung bei *Cyclas cornea* L. *Jen. Z. Naturwiss.* **28**, 196.

—— (1897): Die Urniere bei *Cyclas cornea* (Lam.). *Z. wiss. Zool.* **63**, 43.

STEMPELL, W. (1900): Ueber die Bildungsweise und das Wachstum der Muschel- und Schneckenschalen. *Biol. Centralbl.* **20**, 595, 637, 655, 698, 731.

STRELIN, G. (1939a): Experimental study on the development of molluscs in connection with the problem of physiological gradient. *C.R. (Doklady) Acad. Sci. U.R.S.S.* **24**, 942.

—— (1939b): Determination and physiological characteristics of the rudiment of the conch-gland and the flittering field of *Anodonta anatina* L. *C.R. (Doklady) Acad. Sci. U.R.S.S.* **24**, 945.

STURTEVANT, A. H. (1923): Inheritance of direction of coiling in *Limnaea*. *Science* **58**, 269.

TCHAKHOTINE, S. (1935): La parthénogénèse artificielle de l'oeuf de la Pholade, par micropuncture ultraviolette. *C.R. Soc. Biol.* **119**, 1394.

TEICHMANN, E. (1903): Die frühe Entwicklung der Cephalopoden. *Verh. D. Zool. Ges.* **13**, 42.

TÖNNIGES, C. (1896): Die Bildung des Mesoderms bei *Paludina vivipara*. *Z. wiss. Zool.* **61**, 541.

TRUEMAN, E. R. (1951): The structure, development, and operation of the hinge ligament of *Ostrea edulis*. *Quart. J. Micr. Sci.* **92**, 129.

TYLER, A. (1930): Experimental production of double embryos in annelids and molluscs. *J. exp. Zool.* **57**, 347.

—— (1939): Extraction of an egg membrane-lysin from sperm of the giant keyhole limpet (*Megathura crenulata*). *Proc. Nat. Acad. Sci.* **25**, 317.

—— (1940): Sperm agglutination in the keyhole limpet, *Megathura crenulata*. *Biol. Bull.* **78**, 159.

—— (1949a): Fertilization and immunity. *Physiol. Rev.* **28**, 180.

—— (1949b): Properties of fertilizin and related substances of eggs and sperm of marine animals. *Amer. Natural.* **83**, 195.

—— and S. W. Fox (1939): Sperm agglutination in the keyhole limpet and the sea urchin. *Science* **90**, 516.

—— and S. W. Fox (1940): Evidence for the protein nature of the sperm agglutinins of the keyhole limpet and the sea-urchin. *Biol. Bull.* **79**, 153.

—— and B. T. SCHEER (1937): Inhibition of fertilization in eggs of marine animals by means of acid. *J. exp. Zool.* **75**, 179.

USSOW, M. (1881): Untersuchungen über die Entwickelung der Cephalopoden. *Arch. Biol.*, **2**, 553.

VIALLETON, M. L. (1888): Recherches sur les premières phases du développement de la seiche (*Sepia officinalis*). *Ann. Sci. Nat., Zool.* (7) **6**, 165.

VISSCHEDIJK, A. H. J. (1953): The effect of a heat shock on morphogenesis in *Limnaea stagnalis*. *Proc. Kon. Ned. Akad. v. Wetensch., Amsterdam* C **56**, 590.

VITAGLIANO, G. (1950): Osservazioni sul comportamento delle cellule follicolari nella gametogenesi di *Cavolinia tridentata* Forskal (Moll. Pterop.). *Pubbl. Staz. Zool. Napoli* **22**, 367.

VRIES, L. G. DE (1953): The antagonistic action of calcium with respect to the effects of lithium on the development of *Limnaea stagnalis*. *Proc. Kon. Ned. Akad. v. Wetensch., Amsterdam* **C 56**, 584.

WASSERLOOS, E. (1911): Die Entwicklung der Kiemen bei *Cyclas cornea* und andern Acephalen des süssen Wassers. *Zool. Jahrb., Anat.* **31**, 171.

WATASE, S. (1891): Studies on Cephalopods. I. Cleavage of the ovum. *J. Morph.* **4**, 247.

WEIGMANN, R. (1928): Ueber das Vorkommen von Spiralastern in den Richtungsspindeln von *Physa fontinalis* L. und *Limnaea stagnalis* L. *Z. wiss. Zool.* **131**, 255.

WERNER, B. (1939): Ueber die Entwicklung und Artunterscheidung von Muschellarven des Nordseeplanktons, unter besonderer Berücksichtigung der Schalenentwicklung. *Zool. Jahrb., Anat.* **66**, 1.

—— (1955): Ueber die Anatomie, die Entwicklung und Biologie des Veligers und der Veliconcha von *Crepidula fornicata* L. (Gastropoda Prosobranchia). *Helgol. wissensch. Meeresunters.* **5**, 169.

WHITAKER, D. M. (1933): On the rate of oxygen consumption by fertilised and unfertilised eggs. *J. gen. Physiol.* **16**, 475, 497.

WIERZEJSKI, A. (1905): Embryologie von *Physa fontinalis* L. *Z. wiss. Zool.* **83**, 502.

WILSON, E. B. (1904a): Experimental studies on germinal localization. I. The germ-regions in the egg of *Dentalium*. *J. exp. Zool.* **1**, 1.

—— (1904b): Experimental studies on germinal localization. II. Experiments on the cleavage-mosaic in *Patella* and *Dentalium*. *J. exp. Zool.* **1**, 197.

WOLFSON, A. (1880): Embryologie de *Lymnaeus stagnalis*. *Bull. Acad. Imp. Sci. St. Petersbourg* **26**, 79.

WOODS, F. H. (1931): History of the germ cells in *Sphaerium striatinum* (Lam.). *J. Morph.* **51**, 545.

—— (1932): Keimbahn determinants and continuity of the germ cells in *Sphaerium striatinum* (Lam.). *J. Morph.* **53**, 345.

WORLEY, L. G. (1944): Studies of the vitally stained Golgi apparatus. II. Yolk formation and pigment concentration in the mussel *Mytilus californianus* Conrad. *J. Morph.* **75**, 77.

—— and E. K. WORLEY (1943): Studies of the supravitally stained Golgi apparatus. I. Its cycle in the tectibranch Mollusc, *Navanax inermis* (Cooper). *J. Morph.* **73**, 365.

YASUGI, R. (1938): On the mode of cleavage of the eggs of the oysters *Ostrea spinosa* and *O. gigas* under experimental conditions (a preliminary note). *Annot. Zool. japon.* **17**, 295.

Author Index

U

Taxonomic Index

294

Subject Index

Abortive eggs   132, 162
Acephaly   189, 191
Achromatic apparatus   23
Acidophily   7, 13
Acrosome   28, 52, 53
Action spectrum   193
Activation of eggs   53, 54, 105
— of enzymes   48, 266
— of genes   266, 267
— of sperm   52
Adductor   135, 242
— , larval   134, 135, 169, 171, 242
Aesthetes   227
Affinity   123, 266
Agglutination, sperm   52
Agglutinin   52
Albumen   80, 85, 142, 155, 157, 158, 162, 163, 238
— cells   156, 163, 186, 187, 196, 197, 229, 238, 259
— gland   257, 260
— vacuoles   80, 85, 102, 103, 120, 121, 139, 140, 141, 143, 145, 158, 160, 163, 186, 187, 196
Amino acids   20
Amitosis   200
Amoebocytes   167
Amoeboid motility   4, 24, 27, 33, 34, 46, 56, 60, 90, 103
Amphiaster   30, 31, 54, 79
Amphimixis   265
Amphinucleolus   6, 7, 16, 76
Amylase   42
Anabolism   188
Anaerobiosis   46, 125, 192
Anal cells   114, 128, 155, 160, 171
— plate   115, 116
Anastral spindle   54, 76
Androgamones   52
Anophthalmia   189
Antagonism   48, 124, 192, 193
Anterior end   68, 116, 127
Antifertilizin   52
Anus   114, 128, 130, 131, 132, 134, 155, 160, 171, 172, 173, 176, 178, 227, 240
Aorta   240, 248
— anterior   246, 250

Aorta cephalica   248, 250
— posterior   246, 250
Aperture cell   164, 165, 166
Apical flagellae   127, 128
— plate   113, 129, 133, 134, 142, 143 et seq., 156, 182, 189, 190, 193, 194, 196, 213, 228
— sense organ,   129, 138, 144, 216
— tuft   127, 129, 132, 142, 143, 144, 179, 181, 182, 184
Apocrine secretion   162, 196
Apophyses   150
Apposition   204, 234
Apyrase   42
Aragonite   202
Archenteron   103, 110, 111, 113, 115 et seq., 118, 120, 121, 123, 134, 148, 156, 159, 172, 181, 197, 198
Archoplasm   9
Areolae   4, 13
Argentea   223
Arginine   17, 20
Arms   175 et seq., 201
Arterial system   248
Arteries   246, 250
— , cephalic   246
— , pedal   246
— , visceral   246
Articulamenta   150, 227
Ascorbic acid   18, 20, 21
Ash content   206
Aster   22 et seq., 28, 29, 32, 36, 37, 38, 42, 44, 59, 66, 75, 76, 80, 83, 106
— , sperm   25, 27, 28, 29 et seq., 33, 34, 37, 52, 55, 56, 83
Astral rays   22 et seq., 29, 31, 32, 38, 44
Asymmetry   104, 106, 131, 150, 171 et seq., 195, 264
— , inverse   186
Atrioventricular septum   247
— valves   245
Atrium   244 et seq.
Attraction   60, 101, 188, 194, 265
— field   102
Axes of egg   1, 92, 106, 113, 264
— of embryo   68, 96